JOURNAL OF CHROMATOGRAPHY LIBRARY – volume 22A

chromatography

fundamentals and applications of chromatographic and electrophoretic methods

part A: fundamentals and techniques

JOURNAL OF CHROMATOGRAPHY LIBRARY

JOURNAL OF CHROMATOGRAPHY\LIBRARY - volume 22A

chromatography

fundamentals and applications of chromatographic and electrophoretic methods

part A: fundamentals and techniques

edited by
E. Heftmann

Western Regional Research Center, U.S. Department of Agriculture, Berkeley, CA 94710

ELSEVIER SCIENTIFIC PUBLISHING COMPANY
Amsterdam — Oxford — New York   1983

ELSEVIER SCIENTIFIC PUBLISHING COMPANY
Molenwerf 1
P.O. Box 211, 1000 AE Amsterdam, The Netherlands

Distributors for the United States and Canada:

ELSEVIER SCIENCE PUBLISHING COMPANY INC.
52, Vanderbilt Avenue
New York, NY 10017

ISBN 0-444-42043-6 (Vol. 22 part A)
ISBN 0-444-41616-1 (Series)
ISBN 0-444-42045-2 (Set)

Printed in The Netherlands

TO BRIGITTE

Contents

List of authors and coauthors (*)

Mr. Edward R. Adlard, Shell Research Ltd., Thornton Research Centre, P.O. Box 1, Chester CH1 3SH, Great Britain (Part B)

Dr. Robert P. Bywater, Pharmacia Fine Chemicals, Box 175, S-751 04 Uppsala, Sweden (Part A)

Dr. Nicholas Catsimpoolas, Biochemical Research Laboratories, Department of Biobehavioral Sciences, Boston University Medical Center, Boston, MA 02118, USA (Part B)

Dr. Shirley C. Churms, Department of Organic Chemistry, University of Cape Town, Rondebosch 7700, South Africa (Part B)

Dr. Graham J. Cowling, formerly Department of Biophysics, University of London, King's College, School of Biological Sciences, London WC2B 5RL, Great Britain. Present address: Searle Research & Development, G.D. Searle & Co., Ltd., P.O. Box 53, High Wycombe, Bucks HP12 4HI, Great Britain (Part B)

Dr. Carl A. Cramers, Laboratorium voor Instrumentele Analyse, Technische Hogeschool, P.O. Box 513, 5600 MB Eindhoven, The Netherlands (Part A)

Dr. Rodney Croteau, Institute of Biological Chemistry, Washington State University, Pullman, WA 99164, USA (Part B)

Dr. David H. Dolphin, Department of Chemistry, University of British Columbia, Vancouver, B.C., Canada V6T 1W5 (Part B)

Dr. Frans M. Everaerts, Laboratorium voor Instrumentele Analyse, Technische Hogeschool, Postbus 513, 5600 MB Eindhoven, The Netherlands (Part A)

Dr. Lawrence Fishbein, National Center for Toxicological Research, Food & Drug Administration, Department of Human Health Services, Jefferson, AR 72079, USA (Part B)

Dr. Jeffrey B. Harborne, Department of Botany, Plant Science Laboratories, University of Reading, Reading RG6 2AS, Great Britain (Part B)

Dr. Erich Heftmann, Western Regional Research Center, U.S. Department of Agriculture, Berkeley, CA 94710, USA. Home address: 108 Cañon Dr., P.O. Box 928, Orinda, CA 94563, USA (Parts A and B)

Dr. Csaba Horváth, Department of Chemical Engineering, Mason Laboratory, Yale University, P.O. Box 2159, New Haven, CT 06520, USA (Part A)

Dr. Jaroslav Janák, Institute of Analytical Chemistry, 662 28 Brno, Czechoslovakia (Part B)

Dr. Arnis Kuksis, Banting & Best Department of Medical Research, University of Toronto, Toronto, Ont., Canada M5G 1L6 (Part B)

Dr. Thomas Kuster, Med.-chem. Laboratorium, Kinderspital Zürich, 8032 Zürich, Switzerland (Part B)

Dr. Michael Lederer, Institut de chimie minérale et analytique, Faculté des Sciences, Collège propédeutique, Dorigny, CH-1015 Lausanne, Switzerland (Part B)

Dr. Karel Macek, Institute of Physiology, Czechoslovak Academy of Sciences, 142 20 Prague, Czechoslovakia (Part A)

* Dr. Harold M. McNair, Department of Chemistry, Virginia Polytechnic Institute and State University, Blacksburg, VA 24061, USA (Part A)

* Dr. Nigel V.B. Marsden, Institutionen för Fysiologi och Medicinsk Fysik, Uppsala Universitets Biomedicinska Centrum, Box 572, S-751 23 Uppsala, Sweden (Part A)

* Dr. Wayne R. Melander, Department of Chemical Engineering, Mason Laboratory, Yale University, P.O. Box 2159, New Haven, CT 06520, USA (Part A)

* Dr. F.E.P. Mikkers, Laboratorium voor Instrumentele Analyse, Technische Hogeschool, Postbus 513, 5600 MB Eindhoven, The Netherlands (Part A)

* Dr. Alois Niederwieser, Med.-chem. Laboratorium, Kinderspital Zürich, 8032 Zürich, Switzerland (Part B)

* Dr. Robert C. Ronald, Institute of Biological Chemistry, Washington State University, Pullman, WA 99164, USA (Part B)

Dr. Raymond P.W. Scott, Instrument Division, Perkin-Elmer Corporation, Norwalk, CT 06856, USA (Part A)

* Dr. J. Vacík, Department of Physical Chemistry, Charles University, 501 65 Hradec Králové, Czechoslovakia (Part A)

* Dr. Th.P.E.M. Verheggen, Laboratorium voor Instrumentele Analyse, Technische Hogeschool, Postbus 513, 5600 MB Eindhoven, The Netherlands (Part A)

Dr. Gerald H. Wagman, Microbiological Strain Laboratory, Schering-Plough Corporation, Kenilworth, NJ 07033, USA (Part B)

Dr. Harold F. Walton, Department of Chemistry, University of Colorado, Campus Box 215, Boulder, CO 80309, USA (Part A)

* Dr. Marvin J. Weinstein, formerly Microbiological Strain Laboratory, Schering-Plough Corporation, Kenilworth, NJ 07033, USA (Part B)

List of abbreviations

A	ampere (Amp)
Å	ångström $= 10^{-8}$ cm
AC	alternating current
AE	aminoethyl
AFID	alkali flame-ionization detector
AGR	anhydroglucose residue
ANB	2-amino-5-nitrobenzophenone
ASTM	American Society for Testing and Materials
atm	atmosphere $= 760$ Torr
BD-cellulose	benzoylated DEAE-cellulose
t-BDMS	*t*-butyl dimethylsilyl
BHT	(2,6)-di-*t*-butyl-*p*-cresol (butylated hydroxytoluene)
b.p.	boiling point
b.r.	boiling range
BSA	N,O-bis(trimethylsilyl)acetamide
BSTFA	bis(trimethylsilyl)trifluoroacetamide
BTT	3-benzyl-1-*p*-tolyltriazine
C	centigrade, celsius
CA	cycloamyloses
CAM	cellulose acetate membrane (electrophoresis)
cc	cubic centimeter (cm^3)
CC	column chromatography
CCD	countercurrent distribution
CDD	chlorinated dibenzo-*p*-dioxins
CECD	Coulson electrolytic conductivity detector
Chap.	chapter
CI	chemical ionization
CLU	crosslinked unit structure
CM	carboxymethyl
cm	centimeter
conc.	concentrated
cpm	counts per minute
C.V.	coefficient of variation
CZE	continuous zone electrophoresis
DBM	diazobenzyloxymethyl
DC	direct current
DCC	droplet countercurrent chromatography
DEAE	diethylaminoethyl
DMSO	dimethylsulfoxide
DP	degree of polymerization
DTT	dithiothreitol

DP	degree of polymerization
DTT	dithiothreitol
DVS	divinylsulfone
ECD	electron-capture detector
ECL	effective chain length
ECTEOLA	epichlorohydrintriethanolamine
ED	electrochemical detector
EDTA	ethylenediaminetetraacetic acid
EHV	effective hydrodynamic volume
EI	electron impact
ELS	electrophoretic light scattering
EMIT	enzyme multiplied immunoassay technique
eqn.	equation
eV	electron-volt
FD	field desorption
FFF	field-flow fractionation
fg	femtogram = 10^{-15} g
FIA	fluorescent indicator analysis
FID	flame-ionization detector
fmole	femtomole = 10^{-15} mole
ft	feet
FTIR	Fourier transform infrared
g	gram
GC	gas chromatography
GC^2	glass capillary gas chromatography
GLC	gas–liquid chromatography
GPC	gel-permeation chromatography
GSC	gas–solid chromatography
h	hour
HETP	height equivalent to a theoretical plate
HFB	heptafluorobutyryl
HI	hydrophobic interaction
HIC	hydrophobic interaction chromatography
HIE	hydrogen isotope exchange
HPLC	high-performance liquid chromatography (high-pressure liquid chromatography)
HPTLC	high-performance thin-layer chromatography
hR_F	$R_F \times 100$
HVE	high-voltage electrophoresis
IC	Ion Chromatography
ID	inside diameter
IF	isoelectric focusing
in.	inches
IP	Institute of Petroleum
IR	infrared

ITLC	Instant Thin-Layer Chromatography
ITP	isotachophoresis
kV	kilovolt = 10^3 V
l	liter
LC	liquid chromatography
LCC	liquid column chromatography
LC–EC	liquid chromatography electrochemical detector
LFER	linear free energy relations
LLC	liquid–liquid chromatography
LSC	liquid–solid chromatography
M	molar
m	meter
mA	milliampere = 10^{-3} A
μA	microampere = 10^{-6} A
MBE	moving-boundary electrophoresis
m.d.q.	minimum detectable quantity
ME	mercaptoethanol
meq	milliequivalents = 10^{-3} equivalents
μeq	microequivalents = 10^{-6} equivalents
MF	mass fragmentography
mg	milligram = 10^{-3} g
μg	microgram = 10^{-6} g
MID	multiple-ion detection
min	minutes
ml	milliliter = 10^{-3} l
μl	microliter = 10^{-6} l
mM	millimolar = 10^{-3} M
mm	millimeter = 10^{-3} m
μm	micrometer = 10^{-6} m
mmole	millimole = 10^{-3} mole
μmole	micromole = 10^{-6} mole
MO	methyl oxime
mol.	molecular
mp	melting point
MS	mass spectrometry
MSA	N-methyl-N-trimethylsilylacetamide
msec	milliseconds = 10^{-3} sec
MSTFA	N-methyl-N-trimethylsilyltrifluoroacetamide
MTH	methylthiohydantoin
MTX	methotrexate
MU	methylene unit
mV	millivolt = 10^{-3} V
MW	molecular weight
MZE	multiphasic zone electrophoresis
N	normal

ng	nanogram $= 10^{-9}$ g
nm	nanometer $= 10^{-9}$ m
nmole	nanomole $= 10^{-9}$ mole
NMR	nuclear magnetic resonance
NPD	nitrogen–phosphorus detector
OD	outside diameter
ODS	octadecylsilane or octadecylsilyl
OPA	o-phthalaldehyde
PAGE	polyacrylamide gel electrophoresis
PC	paper chromatography
PCA	polycyclic aromatic hydrocarbons
PCB	polychlorinated biphenyls
P-cellulose	phosphate cellulose
PCN	polychloronaphthalene
PCP	pentachlorophenol
PDM	programed multiple development
PE	paper electrophoresis
PEG	polyethylene glycol
PEI	polyethyleneimine
PEO	polyethylene oxides
PFB	pentafluorobenzyl
pg	picogram $= 10^{-12}$ g
PGE	pore-limit gel electrophoresis
pI	isoelectric point
PLC	preparative layer chromatography
PLOT	porous-layer open tubular (columns)
pmole	picomole $= 10^{-12}$ mole
ppb	parts per billion $= 10^{-9}$ parts
ppm	parts per million $= 10^{-6}$ parts
ppt	parts per trillion $= 10^{-12}$ parts
psi	pounds/sq.in. $= 51.77$ torr
PTFE	polytetrafluoroethylene (Teflon)
PTH	phenylthiohydantoin
RI	refractive index
R.I.	Retention Index
RIA	radioimmunoassay
RRT	relative retention time
RT	retention time
SBF	separation by flow
SCOT	support-coated open tubular (columns)
S.D.	standard deviation
SDS	sodium dodecyl sulfate
SEC	size- (or steric) exclusion chromatography
sec	seconds
SFC	supercritical-fluid chromatography

SIM	selected-ion monitoring
SM	sulfomethyl
SP	sulfopropyl
sq.	square
SSS	steady state stacking
t	tertiary
TAS	thermomicro-transfer-application-separation (technique)
TCA	trichloroacetic acid
TCD	thermal conductivity detector
TCDD	tetrachlorodibenzodioxins
TCP	tetrachlorophenol
TD	thermionic detector
TEA	thermal energy analyzer
TEAB	triethylammonium bicarbonate
TEAE	tetraethylaminoethyl
temp.	temperature
TFA	trifluoroacetyl
TFG	thermofractography
THF	tetrahydrofuran
TLC	thin-layer chromatography
TLE	thin-layer electrophoresis
TLG	thin-layer gel chromatography
TMAH	trimethylanilinium hydroxide
TMCS	trimethylchlorosilane
TMS	trimethylsilyl
TMSDE	trimethylsilyldiethylamine
Tris	tris(hydroxymethyl)aminomethane
UV	ultraviolet
V	volt
vol.	volume
v/v	vol./vol.
WCOT	wall-coated open tubular (columns)
wt.	weight
w/w	wt./wt.

Foreword

This is the fourth edition of the classic work on *Chromatography* edited by Erich Heftmann. The first edition appeared 20 years ago, and each of the three preceding editions has an authoritative Foreword written by a leading investigator in the field. I do not so qualify, although I have enjoyed some encounters with chromatography.

I recall first meeting László Zechmeister, one of the initial giants in this area of investigation, about 1940 during one of his early visits to Berkeley (perhaps his first visit). I had just completed my period of service with Gilbert Newton Lewis as his research assistant. Lewis introduced me to Zechmeister, expressing unusual admiration for the chromatographic method of separation which he told me had been invented many years before by a fellow named Tsvet. (A name like that is easy to remember.) Lewis and I, a year or two earlier, had been trying to develop a method for separating neighboring rare earth elements from each other and thus we had an unusual interest in what Zechmeister told us about chromatography.

My next encounter with chromatography came only a couple of years later. Working at the wartime Metallurgical Laboratory at the University of Chicago, I had the responsibility of developing an industrial-scale method, suitable for operation by remote control, for separating small quantities of the then new element plutonium from large amounts of uranium and intensely radioactive fission products. Recalling my talks with Zechmeister, I included column chromatography (using inorganic adsorbents) among the various separation methods to be investigated by the group of chemists working with me. In the competition among the various alternatives this method lost out to the at that time better understood co-precipitation approach.

However, only a few years later, we turned again to the chromatographic method, this time with extraordinary success. We used column chromatography, with organic ion-exchange adsorbents, to separate the predominantly tri-positive transplutonium elements from each other and from the rare earth elements. And of particular significance to me was the application of this technique to demonstrate, even to those who were initially disbelievers, the validity of the actinide concept for placing the transuranium elements in the periodic table.

My account here, of course, represents a parochial view of chromatography. This aspect represents today only a tiny part of a field that has grown by leaps and bounds, a field that is so well covered in this new (fourth) edition of Heftmann's book. The present range of individual methods and techniques, and the extent of applications to the various branches of chemistry, biochemistry, biology and other fields, are too broad to summarize in this Foreword — some idea of this breadth can be gleaned by looking at the table of contents. Authoritative coverage has been insured by having experts cover each of these diverse aspects.

This up-dated edition of *Chromatography* should be welcomed by investigators whose research employs some aspects of these broad and versatile techniques and for use as a reference work by an even broader span of readers.

Berkeley, California
July 1982

GLENN T. SEABORG

Preface

Since 1954, when I began to teach a course in chromatography for professionals in the Washington area under the sponsorship of the U.S. Department of Agriculture Graduate School, it has been my aim to present the art and science of chromatography and electrophoresis to a larger audience in definitive form. Realizing that no single individual can select the most important aspects of the vast literature in this field, I have gathered some of the best-known authorities in each of the specialized areas of chromatographic and electrophoretic methods and their applications, and I organized the first multi-authored book on "Chromatography" in 1961. The rapid growth of the literature and the eager acceptance of the First Edition prompted me to bring out a Second Edition in 1967. After the Reinhold Publishing Corporation, which had published the first two editions, merged with Van Nostrand, I again revised "Chromatography" in 1975.

Again, the time has come for taking stock of the actual status of our field, but because so much has happened in chromatography and electrophoresis since 1975 and because "Chromatography" is now published by Elsevier Scientific Publishing Company, I want it to be a new book rather than a revised edition. Keeping the successful format of previous editions but only a few of my previous coauthors, I have attempted to feature the most recent and most significant techniques and applications and to relegate established or obsolete methods to the older books. The new group of authors has succeeded, I believe, in presenting their specialties in a new light.

My functions in this cooperative enterprise have been to establish the framework for this book, to invite some of the world's most outstanding teachers and research workers for each topic, to advise them on areas to be included or omitted, and then to produce the extent of uniformity expected of a textbook without destroying the individuality of each expert's point of view. On the whole, I feel that I have done the best I could with people who are by nature highly individualistic and justifiably proud of their own accomplishments. I owe thanks to my coauthors, not only for their own contributions, but also for helping me in editorial decisions.

Orinda, California   ERICH HEFTMANN

Chapter 1

Survey of chromatography and electrophoresis

ERICH HEFTMANN

CONTENTS

1.1. CLASSIFICATIONS

Chromatography and electrophoresis are the most important members of the class of differential migration methods [1–3].

Most chemical operations, including chemical analysis, involve the separation of mixtures into individual components. Familiar examples are: filtration, extraction, distillation, and electrolysis. The object of differential migration methods is to separate mixtures by causing their components to move to different locations.

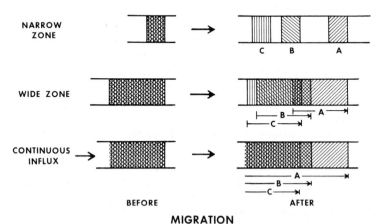

MIGRATION

Fig. 1.1. Differential migration of three components of a mixture. When the sample zone is narrow (top), its components are completely separated, but there is overlap when it is wide (middle). Continuous influx of sample (bottom) can yield only a fraction of the fastest migrant (A) in pure form.

References on p. A16

Fig. 1.1 is a schematic representation of the spatial separation of a sample mixture of 3 components (A, B, and C), initially confined to a rectangular zone, by migration to the right. If the migration distance is large compared to the width of the original sample zone (top), the fastest-moving component (A) will be completely separated from the slower-moving component (B), which also separates from the slowest component (C). However, if the initial sample zone is wide in comparison with the migration distance (middle), only a portion of the fastest and slowest components (A and C), respectively, will be separated from the mixtures, and B will not be isolated at all. Similarly, if a larger amount of sample mixture is allowed to flow into the system continuously from the left (bottom), only a small portion of A can be obtained in pure form, and neither B nor C can be isolated.

This illustrates three types of differential migration methods. For isolation purposes, migration from narrow zones (top of Fig. 1.1) is the method of choice, but for analytical purposes, migration from wide zones (middle of Fig. 1.1) (frontal analysis) or even from a continuous stream (bottom of Fig. 1.1) (break-through analysis) may be acceptable [4]. The analysis of serum proteins by the moving boundary method of electrophoresis is an example of differential migration from a wide zone, and the break-through analysis for dissolved salts in water by ion exchange is an example of continuous influx. Both of these analytical applications of differential migration are now obsolete, and we will concern ourselves only with the zonal methods, i.e. differential migration from narrow zones. Among the zonal methods, we shall disregard such examples as zone refining and zonal ultracentrifugation, and we shall concentrate on modern chromatography and zone electrophoresis.

In order to produce differential migration from a narrow zone we need a driving force. In chromatography the driving force is the flow of a liquid or a gas, and it is practical to divide chromatographic methods, accordingly, into two classes: liquid chromatography (LC) and gas chromatography (GC). In electrophoresis the electric field provides the driving force. The migrants are driven through a medium of some sort, which in electrophoresis generally is a stabilized electrolyte solution. Chromatographic media are either liquids or solids. Thus, chromatography takes place in a two-phase system, where one phase (either a liquid or a solid) remains stationary, while the other phase (either a liquid or a gas) is mobile. According to the nature of the mobile and stationary phases, we may thus distinguish the following subclasses of chromatography: liquid–liquid (LLC), liquid–solid (LSC), gas–liquid (GLC), and gas–solid chromatography (GSC).

The stationary phase exerts a more or less selective force on the migrants, which counteracts the driving force of the mobile phase and tends to retard the migration of individual components of the sample mixture. The resistive force may sometimes be difficult to define, and it is usefully designated by the vague term "sorption" and the stationary phase is referred to as "sorbent". During chromatography, migrant molecules repeatedly undergo sorption, which selectively retards them, and desorption, which allows them to be carried along with the mobile phase. This continuous distribution process forms the basis of chromatographic separations. The plate theory (Chap. 6.3.4.2) treats this process like a fractional distillation, and its efficiency is also measured in terms of height equivalent to a theoretical plate (HETP).

The term chemisorption is used by some authors to describe specific migrant/sorbent interactions, such as ion exchange, oxidation/reduction, complex formation, etc. Thus, argentation chromatography, which is based on the formation of complexes between olefins and a stationary phase containing silver nitrate, is an example of chemisorption.

Solid stationary phases retard the migration of sample components by adsorption, absorption, and various other processes; liquid stationary phases sorb them mainly by acting as solvents. In electrophoresis, as well as in many types of chromatography, liquids are held stationary, usually by sorption on an inert solid, the so-called support. In GC and LC the migrants will then partition themselves between the mobile phase and the stationary liquid. A conventional classification scheme of chromatographic processes, based on resistive forces, distinguishes adsorption, partition, ion-exchange, exclusion, affinity, and other types of chromatography, although usually more than one of these processes is involved.

Practical designations of chromatographic and electrophoretic methods refer to materials and techniques, rather than to the underlying mechanisms. Novices are often confused by taking such terminology literally, and there is much discussion about the use of more descriptive names. However, since most well-intentioned efforts to curb the use of popular names have failed, it is better to define them than to introduce new terminology [5]. After all, the name chromatography itself is inappropriate, because the separation methods it denotes have nothing to do with writing in colors.

1.2. COLUMN CHROMATOGRAPHY

It could be argued that column chromatography (CC) should more properly be called liquid column chromatography (LCC), because gas chromatography is also carried out in columns. However, since there is no other way to perform gas chromatography, the term column chromatography has become restricted to column chromatography in which the mobile phase is a liquid. The stationary phase is a more or less finely divided solid, which is "packed" into a tube of some sort. The sample is applied to one end of the column, and the chromatogram is developed by passing a solvent through it from that end. Under optimal conditions, the mobile phase (eluent) will carry the sample components along at different rates, depending on their relative affinity for the stationary and mobile phases, as shown in Fig. 1.2.

If the chromatographic tube is transparent and the sample components are colored, chromatographic zones or bands may be observed as they progress along the column (Fig. 1.2, bottom). Earlier experimenters would now extrude the packing material and recover individual components by sectioning the developed chromatogram, sometimes after inspecting it in ultraviolet (UV) light or after appropriate staining of the column. This procedure has survived in the form of so-called "dry columns", which are sausage-like sorbent columns in thin-walled plastic tubes,

References on p. A16

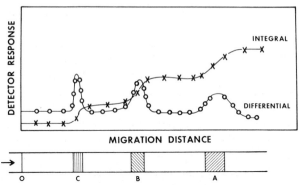

Fig. 1.2. Representations of a chromatogram or electropherogram. The mobile phase or the flow of electric current, moving from left to right past the sample at the origin (O), has carried the components A, B, and C of a mixture to different locations. The physical arrangement of zones (bands) constitutes a chromatogram or electropherogram (bottom). A scanner passing over it would produce the differential detector response recorded (top), which consists of a series of peaks. In elution chromatography or in gas chromatography the recording of a suitable property of the components in the effluent, plotted against eluate volume or elapsed time constitutes the chromatogram. A plot of the total amount of components eluted vs. time, volume, or distance gives a step pattern (integral chromatogram), whereas a plot of their concentration in the eluate at any time vs. time, volume, or distance shows a series of peaks (differential chromatogram).

suitable for slicing after the chromatogram is developed. Generally, the length of the chromatographic column determines its resolving power, whereas the width determines its capacity. A forgotten preparative technique is the coupling of column sections with successively smaller inside diameter (composite column).

In contemporary column chromatography (elution chromatography), the mobile phase (eluent, developer) passes out of the other end of the chromatographic tube, carrying the individual zones into the column effluent (eluate). They can be detected by suitable methods, producing an elution pattern or elution curve (Fig. 1.2, top), or they may be collected separately in fractions, either by means of an automatic fraction collector or manually.

The width of each band, the sharpness of each peak (see Fig. 1.2, legend), the smallness of effluent volume containing one component—in other words, the resolving power of the chromatographic procedure—depends on various factors. Some of them, collectively called diffusion, tend to make the chromatographic zones spread out and overlap. Diffusion is minimized and efficiency is improved by the use of very small and uniform particles of sorbents. However, pressure is required to force eluents through tubes packed with fine particles of sorbents. This type of high-performance chromatography is therefore also known as high-pressure liquid chromatography (HPLC) [6–13].

The sorbent may be in the form of minute porous and irregular particles (usually silica [14]) or spherical beads, coated with a sorbent layer by adsorption or, preferably, by some chemical reaction (bonded phase [15]). Columns packed with such surface-coated (porous-layer, "pellicular") beads are more efficient, but have a lower capacity than columns of porous particles. Occasionally, improved efficiency is obtained by a continuous change in flowrate (flow program, pressure program). Solutes in the effluent are detected and estimated by means of some detector (cf. Fig. 1.2) [16]. Among the detectors used for HPLC, only the differential refractometer [refractive index (RI) detector] and the transport detectors, which provide for carrying the solutes to some GC detector, are universally applicable. The UV and infrared (IR) spectrophotometers respond to specific chromophores in the solute molecules that must be absent from the eluent.

In chromatography—and to some extent also in electrophoresis—it is often practical to subject the sample to some preliminary chemical manipulations. The purpose of these manipulations may be to simplify the mixture, to make it more soluble, more or less volatile, or to improve the separability or detectability of its components, e.g. by converting them to fluorescent derivatives [17]. Derivatization should be quantitative, yield only a single product, and avoid excessive contamination by reagents. Another procedure, used in automatic CC analyzers, is post-column

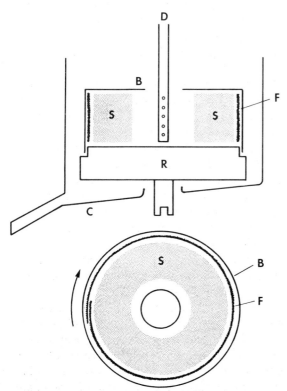

Fig. 1.3. Chromatofuge. The apparatus for radial column chromatography, shown in cross section (top), consists of a perforated basket (B), lined with a filter (F) and filled with a sorbent (S). A plan view of this is shown at the bottom. The eluent issues from the holes in a delivery tube (D), passes through the column, which spins around its axis on a rotor (R), and is collected by a stationary cup (C). (Reproduced from *J. Chromatogr.*, 66 (1972) 365, with permission [18].)

derivatization. This means that the column effluent is subjected to some chemical treatment which produces colored or fluorescent derivatives.

Centrifugal column chromatography [18] relies on centrifugal force instead of pressure to drive the eluent through the sorbent. In this method the column is formed in a basket centrifuge (chromatofuge) and the chromatogram is developed from a hollow core in the center of the column to its periphery, rather than from one end to the other (Fig. 1.3). The chromatographic zones are cylinders, which expand during development and finally emerge from the surface of the column. This is not to be confused with a technique in which solvents are forced through small columns, lying in a centrifuge (Centri-chrom).

In displacement analysis the eluent is a solvent that is more strongly adsorbed than the sample, causing the sample to be displaced from the adsorbent. The sample components then move along the column, displacing each other and ultimately emerging in the effluent in order of increasing adsorption. Because the components follow each other in close succession, "carriers" may be added to the sample. Carriers are more strongly adsorbed than some sample components and less strongly than others. They thus act as spacers between them (carrier displacement analysis).

In elution chromatography, the same eluent may be used throughout (isocratic elution) or the eluent may be changed during the experiment to solvents of increasing eluting power (solvent strength). This change not only speeds up the experiment, but also tends to sharpen zones that are trailing ("tailing") or fronting (have a diffuse front end). It may be carried out stepwise (solvent program) or gradually (gradient elution). Partially separated substances may often be completely separated by recycling chromatography, i.e. by passing the effluent repeatedly through the column and thereby, in effect, increasing its length.

In partition chromatography, two partially miscible solvents are used. Normally, the more polar of the two solvents forms the stationary phase, but in reversed-phase partition chromatography the mobile phase is more polar. In that case, it is actually unnecessary to coat the support with a nonpolar solvent, provided its surface is nonpolar. Reversed-phase partition often separates relatively nonpolar substances which may not be separable by the normal partition process. In countercurrent distribution, the partition between two partially miscible solvents occurs in stages rather than continuously. Its modern version, called (droplet) countercurrent chromatography (DCC) [19,20], is a continuous process, differing from partition chromatography by the absence of a solid support for the stationary phase.

Whereas the adsorbents and the supports for partition systems must be packed tightly into the chromatographic tubes in order to prevent the mobile phase from bypassing them ("channeling"), ion exchangers and hydrophilic gels, which swell and shrink in operation, are used in loose columns or "beds". Structurally, ion exchangers are ionized sponge-like polymers with exchangeable cations and anions (Chap. 7.2) [21,22]. They bind ions of opposite charge reversibly and thereby retard their elution. Whereas earlier ion exchangers were natural or semisynthetic materials, synthetic resins are now widely used, especially in inorganic analysis (Chap. 7.6) [23]. Like other acids and bases, they may be strongly or weakly ionized: resins carrying sulfonic acid groups are strong cation exchangers, carboxylic acids are weak cation exchangers, quaternary ammonium groups are strong anion exchangers, and amines are weak anion exchangers. Cellulose, modified by attachment of ionized groups, has been used as ion-exchange material, particularly in protein chromatography (Chap. 11.2.2). Examples are: carboxymethyl (CM), diethylaminoethyl (DEAE) and epichlorohydrintriethanolamine (ECTEOLA) cellulose.

Eluents used in ion-exchange chromatography are usually buffers, varying in pH, ionic strength, and complexing ability. In ligand-exchange chromatography an ion, say a metal cation held stationary on a cation-exchange column, reversibly forms complexes with sample components, which emerge from the column in inverse order of the strength of ligand binding. Ion-pair chromatography is a method in which ionic samples are neutralized by oppositely charged counterions to produce a hydrophobic pair suitable for reversed-phase partition chromatography. The addition of cyclodextrins, surfactants, or other micellar solutes to an aqueous mobile phase potentially allows water-insoluble compounds to be chromatographed in the presence of water-soluble materials ("pseudophase" LC). Soaps and similar counterions may also coat the hydrophobic stationary phase to confer ion-exchange properties upon it (soap chromatography). Ion Chromatography (IC) (Chap. 22.6) is a proprietary name given to an ion-exchange technique in which the effluent from a pellicular resin column passes through another ion exchanger (suppressor column) to remove buffer before it enters a conductivity detector. The name is confusing and, to make it even more confusing, it has also been used to denote the technique of single-ion detection in GC–mass spectrometry (MS) (Chap. 1.4).

A new method for separating proteins according to their isoelectric points (pI) is called chromatofocusing. When a protein on a column of agarose ion exchanger is eluted with a composite ("poly-") buffer of a pH below its pI, a linear pH gradient will form in the column and the protein will be concentrated in a region where the pH is equal to its pI, as in isoelectric focusing (see Chap. 1.5). As elution progresses, the focused bands of individual proteins will be eluted in the order of their pI values.

Salting-out chromatography is an obsolete technique for isolating proteins by causing them to precipitate on ion exchangers. Ion-retardation resins contain both cations and anions in so-called "snake cage" structures and retard all electrolytes. Ion-exclusion resins, on the other hand, adsorb non-ionized materials and allow ionic compounds to pass.

The gels used for size or steric exclusion chromatography (SEC) are non-ionic polymers which tend to retard those solute molecules that are small enough to fit into their pores. To name this technique gel filtration or molecular-sieve chromatography is especially confusing, because this gives the impression that the larger molecules are retained in preference to the smaller ones. Gel permeation chromatography (GPC) would be a more descriptive term, but for some reason it has been restricted to the chromatography with hydrophobic polymers as sorbents and organic solvent as eluents. Fortunately, the use of the noncommittal name gel chromatography is increasing (Chap. 8) [24,26].

The hydrophilic gels are crosslinked (dextran) or linear (agarose) polysaccharides or synthetic polymers (e.g., polyacrylamide) with a known porosity and fractionation range for water-soluble molecules. Hydrophobic gels for the fractionation of materials soluble in organic solvents are hydrocarbon polymers (e.g., polystyrene). In addition to their chromatographic applications, both types are useful in the determination of the molecular weight distribution of polydisperse mixtures. Porous glass or silica has also been used in the chromatography of hydrophobic as well as hydrophilic materials. In contrast to the polysaccharides, such packing material is also suitable for HPLC. Hydrophilic as well as hydrophobic dextran derivatives are available which sorb solutes by a range of mechanisms, including partition and hydrophobic interaction. Ion-exchanging groups, such as the strongly acidic sulfopropyl (SP), the weakly acidic carboxymethyl (CM), the strongly basic diethyl-(2-hydroxypropyl)aminoethyl (QAE), and the weakly basic DEAE group, have also been attached to gels.

Affinity chromatography (Chap. 8.9) [27–31] is one of the most specific methods of isolating reactive molecules, such as enzymes, and even larger aggregates, such as viruses. The sorbent is a gel, such as agarose, which has been coupled with a suitable ligand, e.g. an enzyme substrate. When a solution containing the material to be isolated (in this case an enzyme) is passed through a column containing the specially prepared sorbent, the specific reversible interaction between the sorbent and that material (in our case, between the enzyme and its substrate) retards it so that it may be eluted in concentrated form. In an application of this technology which is not strictly chromatographic, an enzyme immobilized on a gel column may be used as a reactor which transforms a dissolved substrate as it passes through. Affinity chromatography is applicable to various specific interactions, such as the enzyme–inhibitor, hormone–receptor, and antigen–antibody reactions and the hybridization of polynucleotides. Even whole cells have been isolated by affinity chromatography.

1.3. PLANAR CHROMATOGRAPHY

Sorbents in the form of a sheet or film serve as the migration medium in one plane. This is best described as planar chromatography (Chap. 5) [32–36]. The name flat-bed chromatography is to be avoided, because in many instances the sheet or film is not flat but planar, i.e. two-dimensional. Sheets of filter paper have been used extensively for paper chromatography (PC), but layers of finely powdered sorbents give more compact zones in a shorter time. Originally, the powders were spread loosely on a nearly horizontal glass plate (spread-layer or loose-layer chromatography). Both of these methods have by now been largely supplanted by thin-layer chromatography (TLC), in which a sorbent layer (most commonly a layer of silica gel, 250 μm thick) is firmly bound (usually with gypsum) to a support of glass, plastic, or aluminum foil. Sintered layers on glass plates have the advantage of being reusable [37]. Layers bound to fiber glass paper are marketed under the trade name Instant Thin-Layer Chromatography (ITLC). In thin-layer gel (TLG) chromatography, where no binder is used, the thin-layer plates must be held only slightly inclined to let the mobile phase flow downward. Adherent layers are usually held in vertical position and the mobile phase is allowed to ascend by capillary action.

In cases where the layers consist of polysaccharides (paper, dextran gel, etc.) the stationary phase is actually bound water. It forms a partition system with mobile phases consisting of a partially miscible organic solvent. Rectangular layers with sorptive properties that show a gradation from one edge to the other (gradient layers) are occasionally used in TLC. Similar schemes have been advocated for PC (e.g., pH gradients).

For analytical purposes, samples are applied in the form of spots at a point (origin) near one edge of a rectangular sheet or plate. In preparative work, the samples are streaked, often by means of a special device (applicator, streaker) on a line parallel to that edge. It is also possible to condense effluent fractions from a gas chromatograph or heated sample cartridge at the origin of a thin-layer plate (thermofractography). The chromatograms are developed in a closed vessel (chamber) by allowing the edge of the rectangular sheet or plate to dip into the mobile phase, which then advances past the sample to a paralled line (solvent front) near the opposite edge. Filter paper may be shaped into a cylinder or coil, and sorbent layers may cover a rod (Chromarod, chromatobar) or the inside of a tube. Even filaments of sorbents (e.g., silk) have been used for planar chromatography.

One of the advantageous features of planar chromatography is that several samples can be chromatographed side-by-side, thus saving time and providing a direct comparison. It is also possible to increase resolution by allowing the mobile phase to pass through the sorbent without stopping at the end of the sheet (continuous development) or to make several passes through the sorbent [(programed) multiple development (PMD)]. A sample spotted near the corner of a square sheet may also be successively chromatographed in two directions, perpendicular to each other, to produce a two-dimensional chromatogram.

Radial development occurs when the mobile phase is allowed to spread from a central spot on the sorbent sheet. Samples, applied in an arc or circle around that spot, will then produce concentric arcs or circles of chromatographic zones. If the development of a planar chromatogram is analogous to classical CC, continuous development is analogous to CC by elution, multiple development to recycling chromatography, and radial development to centrifugal CC. Incidentally, radial development in planar chromatography may also be accelerated by centrifugal force in a phonograph-like instrument.

A narrow vapor space above the thin layer makes for faster, sharper, and more reproducible chromatograms ["sandwich" chamber, Brenner-Niederwieser (BN) chamber]. High-performance thin-layer chromatography (HPTLC) [38] is said to offer increased speed, sensitivity, efficiency, and reproducibility by providing for precise control of the flowrate of the mobile phase and of the composition of the stationary phase and vapor phase. Vapor-programed TLC operates on the basis of exposing various regions of the thin-layer plate to different solvent vapors.

Colorless substances may be visualized in paper or thin-layer chromatograms by nondestructive methods (e.g., exposure to iodine vapors or examination in UV light) or by spraying or otherwise treating the chromatogram with more or less specific detection reagents. For isolation work or quantitative analysis, zones may be individually eluted, either before or after staining.

References on p. A16

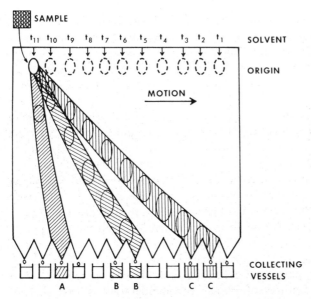

Fig. 1.4. Resolution of a continuous sample stream. Sample was continuously applied to a stationary spot near the top of a slowly rotating paper cylinder, which was irrigated by a downward flow of eluent. When the cylinder is opened, it is seen that the individual components have formed streaks. The position of zones would be as shown (spots), if the sample had been chromatographed on a stationary sheet at times t_1 to t_{11}. In actual operation, the run-off from the sheet is collected in stationary collecting vessels.

A chromatogram containing light-absorbing or fluorescent zones may be auto-matically assayed by densitometry [39], which yields a recording like the one shown in Fig. 1.2. Similarly, a radiochromatogram scanner will automatically reveal and assay radioactive zones in a chromatogram. Another detection method for radioac-tive material is radioautography. A photographic film, pressed against the chromato-gram, will produce a record of the radioactive zones. Similarly, biologically active substances, e.g., antibiotics, may be detected on the chromatogram by placing it in contact with responsive microorganisms (bioautography). The sorbent layer on a rod or in a tube may also be passed through a ring oven to produce vapors which may be detected by GC detectors.

LC usually separates samples in batches, but a continuous stream of sample solution can be resolved into component streaks by applying it to a stationary spot near the top of a slowly rotating sheet [40]. Solvent, continuously supplied to the top edge of the sheet, continuously drips off the bottom of the sheet into stationary collecting vessels. Fig. 1.4 shows the helical paths of the components, which are the resultants of two vectors, the horizontal circular movement of the sheet (shown after the cylinder has been opened) and the vertical migration of the chromatographic zones.

1.4. GAS CHROMATOGRAPHY

For the chromatographic separation of volatile or volatilized samples, an inert carrier gas (usually nitrogen or helium) is made to sweep past them and to pass through a long and narrow tube, containing a sorbent and kept at appropriate temperatures. The sample is introduced at one end of the tube, and the effluent gas, emerging at the other end, passes through a detector (Chap. 6.3.6) [41–44]. The detector response, recorded on a strip chart and referred to as the gas chromatogram, consists of a series of peaks (Fig. 1.2). The position of a peak in the chromatogram (retention time) may be used for the identification of sample components, and the size of the peaks may be used for estimating their amounts.

Many substances which tend to decompose at the operating temperature of the gas chromatograph can nevertheless be chromatographed in the form of stable and volatile derivatives. Derivatization may be carried out prior to sample injection or in specialized inlets (heater, reaction chamber, pyrolyzer, etc.). The samples are either injected with a syringe through a septum or switched into the carrier gas stream by means of a sampling valve. To reduce the size of samples for capillary GC (see below), sample splitters admit only an aliquot to the column.

For GLC, the support of the stationary phase is diatomaceous earth or some other finely divided refractory solid, which is often "deactivated", i.e. washed with acid or base or silanized, to eliminate adsorption phenomena. The stationary phase is a high-boiling liquid, usually a synthetic polymer, which coats the support. Support and "phase" form the column packing, used to fill the glass or metal tubes ("packed columns") characteristically bent or coiled to fit the column oven.

During operation, the temperature of the column may be held constant (isothermal) or it may be gradually raised (temperature programing) to promote the elution of slower migrants. This is analogous to isocratic development and gradient elution, respectively, in LC. Suitable packings will show no "bleed", i.e. they will be thermally stabile at the operating temperatures, which may be up to 400°C. For GSC, the packings are natural, synthetic, or semisynthetic adsorbents, often used at low temperatures.

When empty ("open") capillary tubes with a sorbent-coated inside wall (open tubular columns) are used instead of packed columns, the efficiency of separation is greatly increased. Metal or glass capillaries may be simply coated with a high-boiling liquid [wall-coated open tubular (WCOT) columns] or their walls may be provided with an adherent porous support, which is coated with a stationary phase [support-coated open tubular (SCOT) columns]. SCOT columns have a greater sample capacity but lower efficiency than the corresponding WCOT columns. Packed capillary columns may be highly efficient, but require high gas pressures.

Integral detectors (see Fig. 1.2), such as Janák's eudiometer for measuring the volume of eluted gases, are now obsolete. The universally applicable flame-ionization detector (FID), and the thermal conductivity detector (TCD, katharometer) are most commonly used. The electron-capture detector (ECD) responds specifically to halogens and other electron-capturing atoms, and the thermionic detector (TD) is used for the selective analysis of organophosphorus compounds.

References on p. A16

When the gas chromatograph is "interfaced" with a mass spectrometer (GC–MS), a most powerful combination of separating and identifying capability is obtained. The mass spectrometer can also be employed as a selective and sensitive detector for GC by single-ion monitoring. In multiple-ion detection (MID) or mass fragmentography (MF) the mass spectrometer is focused on selected fragment ions. A computer may be programmed to produce a fragment-ion chromatogram (mass fragmentogram), i.e. an elution pattern for each of these ions, and to yield qualitative and quantitative information about sample components, even if they are not completely separated.

1.5. ELECTROPHORESIS

The migration of charged particles from a narrow zone in stabilized electrolytes has been named (zone) electrophoresis, ionophoresis, ionography, kataphoresis, electrochromatography, etc., to differentiate it from the older method of migration from a wide zone in free electrolyte solutions (moving boundary electrophoresis, MBE) (see Fig. 1.1, middle). However, because none of these names has been universally adopted and the older method is no longer used, we shall use the general term electrophoresis to cover a number of contemporary techniques (Chap. 9) [33,34,45–49].

In a vertical column, the electrolyte may be stabilized by providing for a progressively higher density in downward direction (density gradient electrophoresis), but usually electrolytes are held stationary by absorption in various natural or synthetic polymers. Accordingly, such names as paper electrophoresis (PE), cellulose acetate membrane (CAM), agar gel, starch gel, polyacrylamide gel electrophoresis (PAGE), etc., have come into use. Categories have also been set up according to the techniques or apparatus used [e.g., column and thin-layer electrophoresis (TLE)].

The migration medium counteracts diffusion to some extent. Application of relatively high voltages [high-voltage electrophoresis (HVE)] speeds up migration of relatively small molecules and also reduces their diffusion. Certain gels selectively retard electromigration by a sieve effect. Thus, the protein subunits, produced by sodium dodecyl sulfate (SDS) denaturation, separate in PAGE according to their size (SDS–PAGE). In gradient gel electrophoresis (pore-limit gel electrophoresis, PGE) the size of the gel decreases in the direction of migration, thus retarding smaller and smaller migrants.

Instead of using the same buffer throughout the electrophoretic system (continuous buffer), the sample may be sandwiched between two ion boundaries to produce a thin starting zone (discontinuous buffer, disc electrophoresis). By coincidence, the zones, separated in a polyacrylamide-filled tube, are disc-shaped. In isotachophoresis (ITP) [50], the migrants form adjacent zones (steady state stacking, SSS) between two ion boundaries, the leading and the terminating zone. The zones may be separated from each other by adding to the sample a spacer substance, having a mobility intermediate between two consecutive components. Thus, ITP is analogous to displacement analysis and the spacers are analogous to the carriers in carrier displacement analysis (Chap. 1.2). In electrofocusing (isoelectric focusing, IF), a mixture of ampholytes is added to the stabilized electrolyte, and when the current is applied, it generates a pH gradient. Proteins or other amphoteric substances will migrate in such a field until they reach the pH region corresponding with their isoelectric point and will form very narrow zones [51].

Planar electrophoresis has the same advantages over the column technique as planar chromatography, e.g., the simultaneous comparison of several samples in a single electropherogram. Two-dimensional separations, analogous to two-dimensional PC or TLC, may be obtained by electrophoresis in two dimensions e.g., at different pH values, or by applying an electric field first in one direction, say in an agarose strip, where the mobility depends on the net charge of migrants, and then in a perpendicular direction, say in a rectangular gradient gel slab, where the migrants separate according to size. The techniques for qualitative and quantitative analysis are also analogous to those in PC or TLC. For the specific detection of proteins, the precipitation with monospecific antibodies (immunofixation) may be used.

In immunoelectrophoresis the position of individual proteins, separated by electrophoretic migration from a point source, is revealed by a precipitin reaction with an antiserum, deposited alongside the path of migration. When a gel strip containing electrophoretically separated antigens is laid on a gel slab containing an antibody, they can be further resolved by electromigration in a second dimension (crossed immunoelectrophoresis). The retardation by the antibody produces a rocket-shaped

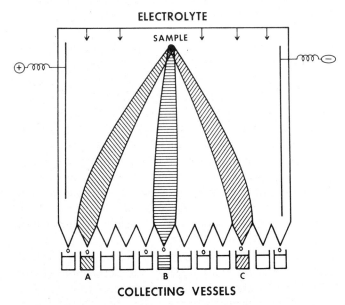

Fig. 1.5. Continuous electrophoresis. The sample, which is continuously applied to a spot near the top of a "hanging curtain" of filter paper, is laterally separated into three components by an electric field, while they are being washed down by the downward flow of electrolyte. The components form streaks that lead to the collecting vessels.

References on p. A16

zone, the length of which can be used to estimate the quantity of antigen (electroim-munoassay, rocket electrophoresis).

Two-dimensional separation by the use of PC in one direction and PE in the other direction also increases resolution by utilizing two different properties of migrant molecules. Continuous (free-flow) electrophoresis on filter paper or in gel slabs utilizes the flow of electrolyte to separate a stream of sample into streaks of individual components (Fig. 1.5).

1.6. CONCLUSIONS

Chromatography is probably the most versatile of all separation methods. It is applicable to all soluble or volatile mixtures. The choice of chromatographic methods depends on the nature and amount of sample, the objective of the separation, and the limitations of available time, equipment, and expertise.

The only chromatographic method applicable to fixed gases is GC, and GSC is often preferred to GLC (Chap. 23). Other vapors, such as hydrocarbons, are best separated by GLC. Compounds which are not volatile at the maximum operating temperature of the gas chromatograph may nevertheless be separated by GC, if they can be converted to volatile derivatives. However, the applicability of GC is also limited by their stability and quantity. Although gas chromatographs for large samples are available, GC is not an ideal preparative method. The chief advantages of GC are that it is relatively fast and capable of automation. Its chief disadvantage is the cost of equipment. The petroleum industry, which can stand the expense, has been its primary sponsor.

Theoretically, all soluble substances are separable by the application of the proper LC technique. Ion exchange and electrophoresis are applicable only to ionic or ionogenic materials, i.e. substances convertible to ionic species. Gel chromatography is limited to materials of relatively high molecular weight ($10^3 - 10^6$ daltons). Adsorption and partition chromatography apply to the middle range of molecular weights ($10^2 - 10^4$ daltons) and are therefore of greatest interest to the organic chemist. For small amounts, the planar methods are adequate. They have the advantage that several samples can be compared simultaneously and that they are cheap. They require a minimum of equipment, but some skill. Although preparative and quantitative versions of planar chromatography have been devised, they are not ideal. Modern CC has all the advantages of GC as well as the disadvantage of cost, but it is recommended for analytical and preparative work, especially in cases where material is sensitive to heat, light, or oxidation.

The mobility of organic molecules in chromatographic systems is obviously a function of their structure and of the interplay of sorption and desorption. Under specified chromatographic conditions, relationships between the structure and mobility of organic molecules can be established which help in their identification. However, no reliance can be placed on structure determination based on chromatographic evidence alone. Direct chromatographic comparison of an unknown compound with a suitable reference compound does furnish reliable evidence when the two compounds are not identical. However, identification by a single coincidence of chromatographic mobilities ("isoschmier") is risky, to say the least. This is not to say that chromatographic and electrophoretic methods cannot furnish much valuable information simply and quickly (e.g., the degree of polymerization by gel chromatography or the isoelectric point by IF).

For the novice, a number of introductory textbooks on the general topic of chromatography have become available in the past decade [52–55]. Review articles for advanced students appear periodically in a variety of books [56–58], and journals [59,60]. The bibliographies in *Analytical Chemistry* [59] and the *Journal of Chromatography* [60] and abstract journals are particularly valuable for research workers. Several symposium series [61,62] and journals specialize in chromatography [60,63–67] and electrophoresis [68].

Review articles on specific topics in chromatography are published at a satisfactory rate, but there are many fields which would benefit from additional exposure. Some subjects I would like to read about are listed below.

Systematic organic and inorganic analysis. The time is near to replace the analytical schemes for the identification of ions and molecules which we were taught and keep on teaching our students by a rational application of such chromatographic techniques as TLC.

Nomenclature of chromatography. A critical examination of the origin, meaning, and value of the terms used by authors in our specialty is needed. Some degree of uniformity may result from it [5,69].

History of chromatographic apparatus. There is an interesting evolution from articles intended for other uses, such as combs and hair dryers, which were pressed into the service of PC, to such complex instrumentation as fully automated TLC (Chromatape) and data processing equipment for GC–MS systems.

Applications of chromatography to various scientific objectives, such as clinical chemistry, forensic analysis, and remote testing (e.g., the monitoring of radioactive processes or extraterrestrial environments).

What lies ahead in chromatography? Great strides have been taken in making sorbents more specific since Pauling's original suggestion [70], but further extensions of affinity chromatography may be anticipated. *Preparative chromatography* (e.g., centrifugal chromatography [18], countercurrent chromatography [19,20], and "flip-flop" chromatography [71]) may also expect to see a "rapid development". If chromatography is to be used on a large scale (e.g., for the scavenging of trace contaminants or for the purification of drugs), more practical continuous processes will have to be devised. Other obvious directions for future technological improvements lie in the complete automation of the qualitative and quantitative analysis of column effluents (microprocessors). Several attempts at designing a universal detector for LC are already underway.

Supercritical fluid chromatography [72] and other methods that make the mobile phase in vapor chromatography also selective should further improve the capabilities of GC. For the separation of substances of very high molecular weight field-flow fractionation (FFF) appears to hold great promise. It is a process akin to chromatography, in which an external field provides the selective resistive force [73]. Of course,

References on p. A16

it is always possible that a new process will come along and replace chromatography and/or electrophoresis, but this is not likely in the foreseeable future.

REFERENCES

1 H.H. Strain, in E. Heftmann (Editor), *Chromatography*, Reinhold, New York, 1961, p. 11.
2 H.H. Strain, in E. Heftmann (Editor), *Chromatography*, Reinhold, New York, 2nd Edn., 1967, p. 11.
3 H.H. Strain and W.A. Svec, in E. Heftmann (Editor), *Chromatography*, Van Nostrand-Reinhold, New York, 3rd Edn., 1975, p. 14.
4 L. Hagdahl, in E. Heftmann (Editor), *Chromatography*, Reinhold, New York, 1961, p. 56.
5 International Union of Pure and Applied Chemistry, *Recommendations on Nomenclature for Chromatography*, IUPAC Secretariat, Oxford, 1972.
6 J.J. Kirkland (Editor), *Modern Practice of Liquid Chromatography*,Wiley, New York, 1971.
7 P.R. Brown, *High Pressure Liquid Chromatography. Biochemical and Biomedical Applications*, Academic Press, New York, 1973.
8 Z. Deyl, K. Macek and J. Janák (Editors), *Liquid Column Chromatography. A Survey of Modern Techniques and Applications*, J. Chromatogr. Library Series, Vol. 3, Elsevier, Amsterdam, 1975.
9 N.A. Parris, *Instrumental Liquid Chromatography. A Practical Manual on High-Performance Liquid Chromatographic Methods*, J. Chromatogr. Library Series, Vol. 5, Elsevier, Amsterdam, 1976.
10 R.P.W. Scott, *Contemporary Liquid Chromatography*, Wiley, New York, 1976.
11 J.F.K. Huber, *Instrumentation for High-Peformance Liquid Chromatography*, J. Chromatogr. Library Series, Vol. 13, Elsevier, Amsterdam, 1978.
12 L.R. Snyder and J.J. Kirkland, *Introduction to Modern Liquid Chromatography*, Wiley, New York, 2nd Edn., 1979.
13 H. Engelhardt, *High Performance Liquid Chromatography. Chemical Laboratory Practice*, Springer, New York, 1979.
14 K.K. Unger, *Porous Silica. Its Properties and Use as a Support in Column Liquid Chromatography*, J. Chromatogr. Library Series, Vol. 16, Elsevier, Amsterdam, 1979.
15 E. Grushka (Editor), *Bonded Stationary Phases in Chromatography*, Ann Arbor Sci. Publ., Ann Arbor, MI, 1974.
16 R.P.W. Scott, *Liquid Chromatography Detectors*, J. Chromatogr. Library Series, Vol. 11, Elsevier, Amsterdam, 1977.
17 J.F. Lawrence and R.W. Frei, *Chemical Derivatization in Liquid Chromatography*, J. Chromatogr. Library Series, Vol. 7, Elsevier, Amsterdam, 1976.
18 E. Heftmann, J.M. Krochta, D.F. Farkas and S. Schwimmer, *J. Chromatogr.*, 66 (1972) 365.
19 Y. Ito and R.L. Bowman, *J. Chromatogr.*, 147 (1978) 221.
20 K. Hostettmann, *Planta Med.*, 39 (1980) 1.
21 K. Dorfner, *Ion Exchangers. Properties and Applications*, Ann Arbor Sci. Publ., Ann Arbor, MI, 3rd Edn., 1972.
22 H.F. Walton, *Ion-Exchange Chromatography*, Halsted, Stroudsburg, PA, 1976.
23 J. Michal, *Inorganic Chromatographic Analysis*, Van Nostrand-Reinhold, New York, 1974.
24 H. Determann, *Gel Chromatography, Gel Filtration, Gel Permeation, Molecular Sieves*, Springer, New York, 2nd Edn., 1969.
25 L. Fischer, *An Introduction to Gel Chromatography*, North-Holland, Amsterdam, 1980.
26 W.W. Yau, J.J. Kirkland and D.D. Bly, *Modern Size-Exclusion Chromatography: Practice of Gel Permeation and Gel Filtration Chromatography*, Wiley, New York, 1979.
27 R.B. Dunlap (Editor), *Immobilized Biochemicals and Affinity Chromatography*, Plenum, New York, 1974.
28 W.B. Jakoby and M. Wilchek (Editors), *Affinity Techniques*, Methods in Enzymology Vol. 34, Academic Press, New York, 1974.
29 C.R. Lowe and P.D.G. Dean, *Affinity Chromatography*, Wiley, New York, 1974.

30 J. Turková, *Affinity chromatography*, J. Chromatogr. Library Series, Vol. 12, Elsevier, Amsterdam, 1978.

31 C.R. Lowe, *An Introduction to Affinity Chromatography*, North-Holland, Amsterdam, 1979.

32 A. Niederwieser and G. Pataki (Editors), *Progress in Thin-Layer Chromatography and Related Methods*, Ann Arbor Sci. Publ., Ann Arbor, MI, 1970–1972.

33 J. Sherma, G. Zweig and A. Bevenue, *Paper Chromatography and Electrophoresis*, Academic Press, New York, 1971.

34 I. Smith and J.G. Feinberg, *Paper and Thin-Layer Chromatography and Electrophoresis*, Longmans, London, 2nd Edn., 1972.

35 J. Gasparič and J. Churáček, *Laboratory Handbook of Thin-Layer Chromatography*, Horwood, Chichester, 1978.

36 J.W. Kirchner, *Thin-Layer Chromatography*, Wiley, New York, 2nd Edn., 1978.

37 T. Okumura, *J. Chromatogr.*, 184 (1980) 37.

38 A. Zlatkis and R.E. Kaiser (Editors), *HPTLC — High Performance Thin-Layer Chromatography*, J. Chromatogr. Library Series, Vol. 9, Elsevier, Amsterdam, 1977 .

39 J.C. Touchstone and J. Sherma (Editors), *Densitometry in Thin Layer Chromatography*, Wiley, New York, 1979.

40 J. Solms, *Helv. Chim. Acta*, 38 (1955) 1127.

41 D. Ambrose, *Gas Chromatography*, Butterworths, London, 2nd Edn., 1971.

42 P.G. Jeffery and P.J. Kipping, *Gas Analysis by Gas Chromatography*, Pergamon, Oxford, 2nd Edn., 1972.

43 H. Purnell, *New Developments in Gas Chromatography*, Advances in Analytical Chemistry, Vol. 11, Wiley, New York, 1973.

44 J. Ševčík, *Detectors in Gas Chromatography*, J. Chromatogr. Library Series, Vol. 4, Elsevier, Amsterdam, 1976.

45 S.T. Nerenberg, *Electrophoresis. A Practical Laboratory Manual*, Blackwell, Oxford, 2nd Edn., 1972.

46 J.R. Sargent and S.G. George, *Methods in Zone Electrophoresis*, BDH Chemicals, Poole, 3rd Edn., 1975.

47 P.G. Righetti, C.J. van Oss and J.W. Vanderhoff (Editors), *Electrokinetic Separation Methods*, Elsevier, Amsterdam, 1979.

48 Z. Deyl, F.M. Everaerts, Z. Prusík and P.J. Svendsen (Editors), *Electrophoresis. A Survey of Techniques and Applications*. J. Chromatogr. Library Series, Vol. 18, Elsevier, Amsterdam, 1979.

49 O. Gaal and L. Vereczkey, *Electrophoresis in the Separation of Biological Macromolecules*, Wiley, New York, 1980.

50 F.M. Everaerts, J.L. Beckers and T.P.E.M. Verheggen, *Isotachophoresis. Theory, Instrumentation and Applications*, J. Chromatogr. Library Series, Vol. 6, Elsevier, Amsterdam, 1976.

51 N. Catsimpoolas and J. Drysdale (Editors), *Biological and Biomedical Applications of Isoelectric Focusing*, Plenum, New York, 1977.

52 G. Zweig and J. Sherma (Editors), *Handbook of Chromatography*, Chem. Rubber Co., Cleveland, OH, 1972.

53 R. Stock and C.B.F. Rice, *Chromatographic Methods*, Halsted, New York, 3rd Edn., 1974.

54 E. Heftmann (Editor), *Chromatography. A Laboratory Handbook of Chromatographic and Electrophoretic Methods*, Van Nostrand-Reinhold, New York, 3rd Edn., 1975.

55 O. Mikeš, *Laboratory Handbook of Chromatographic and Allied Methods* Horwood, Chichester, 1979.

56 M. Lederer (Editor), *Chromatographic Reviews*, Elsevier, Amsterdam, since 1959.

57 J.C. Giddings and R.A. Keller (Editors) *Advances in Chromatography*, Dekker, New York, since 1965.

58 J. Cazes (Editor), *Chromatographic Science*, Dekker, New York, since 1965.

59 *Analytical Chemistry*, American Chemical Society, Washington, DC, since 1950.

60 *Journal of Chromatography*, Elsevier, Amsterdam, since 1958.

61 A. Frigerio and L. Renoz (Editors), *Recent Developments in Chromatography and Electrophoresis*, Chromatogr. Symposia Series, Vol. 1, Elsevier, Amsterdam, 1979.

62 N. Catsimpoolas (Editor), *Electrophoresis '78*, Proc. Inter. Conf., Elsevier, Amsterdam, 1978.

63 *Journal of Gas Chromatography*, Preston Tech. Abstr. Co., Evanston, IL, 1963–1968.

64 *Journal of Chromatographic Science*, Preston Tech. Abstr. Co., Evanston, IL, since 1968.

65 *Chromatographia*, Vieweg, Braunschweig, and Pergamon, Oxford, since 1968.

66 *Journal of High Resolution Chromatography and Chromatographic Communications*, Hüthig, Heidelberg, since 1978.

67 *Journal of Liquid Chromatography*, Dekker, New York, since 1978.

68 *Electrophoresis*, Verlag Chemie International, Deerfield Beach, FL, since 1980.

69 L.S. Ettre, *J. Chromatogr.*, 165 (1979) 235.

70 F.H. Dickey, *Proc. Nat. Acad. Sci. U.S.*, 35 (1949) 229.

71 A.J.P. Martin, I, Halász, H. Engelhardt and P. Sewell, *J. Chromatogr.*, 186 (1979) 15.

72 S.T. Sie, W. van Beersum and G.W.A. Rijnders, *Separ. Sci.*, 1 (1966) 459.

73 J.C. Giddings, *J. Chromatogr.*, 125 (1976) 3.

Chapter 2

History of chromatography and electrophoresis

ERICH HEFTMANN

CONTENTS

2.1. INTRODUCTION

Obviously, the history of chromatography has not changed since I last wrote about it [1], but there is a reason for including a brief chapter on it in this book. Historians and would-be historians of science continue to present the interesting story of how chromatographic and electrophoretic methods began and evolved in their own way, and newcomers to this field may wish to refer to some of their accounts. In some cases, they contain substantial new historical data, but novices should be warned that historians who are personally involved in the story are not always impartial and trustworthy witnesses. Thus, readers should be especially wary of autobiographies. A recent book entitled *75 Years of Chromatography—A Historical Dialogue* [2] is a case in point. It contains the autobiographies of 56 scientists, considered to be pioneers in chromatography by the editors of that book. While some of the first-hand accounts are undoubtedly valuable, they also contain the exaggerations and omissions one would expect on the basis of the individual authors' penchant for either egotism or modesty.

Armed with a healthy dose of skepticism, let us reexamine this bit of recent history of science in light of new data gathered by various authors. A relatively recent book on the history of analytical chemistry [3] contains a number of well-written chapters on various aspects of chromatography, but unfortunately references have to be ordered separately.

2.2. EARLY COLUMN CHROMATOGRAPHY

Sakodynskii [4] has recently published new data on Mikhail Semenovich Tsvet's *

---

* The official English transliteration of the Cyrillic spelling is used in this book. Other spellings, such as Tswett or Tsvett, have been used, e.g., in the German and French literature, by various authors, including Tsvet himself.

References on p. A25

life and work, together with some photographs never published before. In connection with chromatography, it is important to note that this undisputed pioneer of chromatography, having described the method in 1903 [5], gave a full account of it in German in 1906 [6]. Sakodynskii [4] quoted Ivanovsky, a prominent virologist at Warsaw University, as commenting on Tsvet's work in 1908: "He succeeded in establishing a highly original method for physical pigments, ensuring a desirable guarantee of their integrity, which is not an easy thing to do, due to their known extreme lability. I can say with confidence that, when a full explanation of the nature of photosynthetic pigments is finally made, this scientific success will be largely due to the work of Mr. Tsvet, who prepared the ground for a needed, but as yet unsuccessful, chemical investigation".

It is comforting to know that not all of Tsvet's contemporaries shared the scornful attitudes of Willstätter and other influential chemists, who could not grasp the significance of their contemporary's discovery and delayed its acceptance. Willstätter had a German translation of Tsvet's book [7] in manuscript form, which he passed on to his student, Kuhn. E. Lederer [8], who did his postdoctoral work under Kuhn, recognized the possibilities of chromatography and applied it to the separation of carotenes in carrots and xanthophylls in egg yolk in 1930. Although the method had been used sporadically in the period between 1910 and 1930 [9], it was not until that work was published [10] that chromatography came into general use.

In his article on Tsvet and the Nobel Prizes, Hais [11] relates that Dhéré, who used Tsvet's chromatographic technique for a study of the carotenoids in 1911, quoted a number of Nobel laureates on the significance of that method in their own research. The list of luminaries in Hais' article included Karrer, Ružička, Butenandt, Euler, Fischer, Kuhn, Wieland, Windaus, Tiselius (Fig. 2.1), Martin (Fig. 2.2), Synge (Fig. 2.3), Reichstein, Sanger, Calvin, Seaborg (Fig. 2.4), Moore (Fig. 2.5), Stein (Fig. 2.6), Anfinsen, du Vigneaud, Porter, Axelrod, and Leloir, but it could probably be extended. If Tsvet were rated according to the impact of his invention, he would undoubtedly rank among the foremost scientists of this century. However, gauged by other standards, the invention of chromatography cannot be considered to be among the greatest intellectual achievements of the Twentieth Century.

I have previously cited [1] the experiments of Way in England, who as early as 1850 experimented with ion exchange in columns of soil, the work by Reed in England in 1893 on the separation of inorganic and organic salts by passage through a kaolin column, and the work of Day in the United States in 1897 on petroleum fractionation by passage through columns of powdered limestone. There is some argument about assigning priority for the invention of chromatography on the basis of technical details and the experimenter's understanding of the process and the applicability of the principles. Chauvinistic feelings seem to color the opinions of some would-be historians, and readers who wish to become involved in such problems should delve into the references in my earlier chapter [1].

Fig. 2.1. Arne Tiselius (Reproduced from *75 Years of Chromatography – A Historical Dialogue*, Elsevier, Amsterdam, 1979, p. 494, with permission [2].)

Fig. 2.2. Archer J.P. Martin (Reproduced from *75 Years of Chromatography – A Historical Dialogue*, Elsevier, Amsterdam, 1979, p. 285, with permission [2].)

2.3. MIDDLE PERIOD OF LIQUID CHROMATOGRAPHY

Arguments also surround the significance of Nineteeth Century experiments by Runge, Schönbein, and Goppelsroeder, who observed the development of colored zones on materials in sheet form. As in the arguments about Tsvet's priority, it may be possible to cut through the murk by asking to what extent these early experiments conform to chromatographic practices:
a) Was the sample applied in a narrow zone?
b) Was fresh solvent used to developed the chromatogram?
c) Were ancillary methods of collecting or visualizing materials used?
d) Was the underlying principle and general applicability recognized?
I am afraid that the work of most of these forerunners of chromatography will be found wanting in one or several respects.

The first experimenters who consciously sought methods of what we now call planar chromatography were apparently Izmailov and Shraiber [12] in Russia and Brown [13] in the United States. However, PC as well as other chromatographic methods, such as GLC and HPLC, may be said to derive their strength from the classical work on the theory of partition chromatography of Martin and Synge [14], published in 1941. PC, which was introduced by Consden et al. [15] in 1944, was

References on p. A25

Fig. 2.3. Richard L.M. Synge (Reproduced from *75 Years of Chromatography – A Historical Dialogue*, Elsevier, Amsterdam, 1979, p. 447, with permission [2].)

Fig. 2.4. Glenn T. Seaborg (Reproduced from *75 Years of Chromatography – A Historical Dialogue*, Elsevier, Amsterdam, 1979, p. 405, with permission [2].)

exeedingly popular in the Fifties. Even substances which are obviously ill-suited for this approach, such as proteins, were chromatographed on paper. The reason for this immense popularity was that the method is ridiculously simple and requires only the most rudimental and inexpensive equipment. As a lecturer and judge of highschool science fairs, I have witnessed the speed with which this method is understood and the enthusiasm with which it is exploited.

While planar chromatography was establishing itself as an important branch of LC, progress was also made in CC [16]. During the Forties, the extrusion of column materials, exemplified by Zechmeister and von Cholnoky's work on carotenoids [9] made way for elution chromatography, then called "liquid chromatography" and exemplified by Reichstein and Shoppee's work on steroids [17]. Tiselius and his group [18,19] contributed many new concepts and devices during the Forties and Fifties, not only to electrophoresis (Chap. 2.6) but also to CC. He clarified the distinction between frontal, elution, and displacement analysis and introduced, among other techniques, carrier displacement [20] and gradient elution [21].

In the Sixties, PC was largely supplanted by TLC, which has many advantages, especially in adsorption chromatography. Scientists working in opulent laboratories, equipped with the latest electronic gear, tend to forget why their colleagues in poorly endowed laboratories cling to less efficient techniques. There are several advantages

Fig. 2.5. Stanford Moore (Reproduced from *75 Years of Chromatography – A Historical Dialogue*, Elsevier, Amsterdam, 1979, p. 297, with permission [2].)

Fig. 2.6. William H. Stein (Reproduced from *75 Years of Chromatography – A Historical Dialogue*, Elsevier, Amsterdam, 1979, p. 298, with permission [2].)

of PC and TLC ove GC and HPLC, but their main advantage is that they are within the reach of a small budget.

2.4. MODERN COLUMN CHROMATOGRAPHY

The highly efficient modern methods of CC are based on the invention of synthetic packing materials [22]. Ion-exchange chromatography did not begin its rise [23] until the sulfonated phenol–formaldehyde resins were synthesized in 1935 [24]. The momentous progress in ion exchange during the Second World War is recorded in a symposium issue of the American Chemical Society [25]. This work, which was aimed at the separation of lanthanide fission products, laid the foundation for the application of ion-exchange chromatography to the hydrolysis products of nucleic acids [26] and proteins [27]. The fertile fields of gel [28] and affinity chromatography [29] had their origin in the synthesis of crosslinked dextran gels in 1959 [30].

The idea of increasing the efficiency of LC by decreasing the particle size of the sorbent goes back at least to Martin and Synge [14], but instrumental problems delayed its realization. The first publication of practical apparatus for HPLC

References on p. A25

appeared in 1967 [31], although work in other laboratories had been reported at various meetings earlier. In addition to the column, fittings, and high-pressure pump, it required the adaptation of flow-through detectors and, most importantly, the preparation of column packing materials. These were initially adsorbents or ion exchangers of small particle size, which in some cases were coated with a stationary liquid phase. Reversed-phase partition chromatography actually goes back to 1950 [32], but because it is difficult to prevent "bleeding" of the stationary phase into the column effluent, it had fallen into disuse. Bonded stationary phases, originally produced for GLC, are now widely used in HPLC. Current research in CC is concerned with adapting it to large-scale or continuous operation and with eliminating the packing material by adopting countercurrent or WCOT (Chap. 2.5) principles.

Contemporary CC requires the purchase of ready-made packings or packed columns. Depending on the particle size, the purpose of the analysis, and the laboratory budget, additional purchases are required: fittings, pumps, detectors, recorders, injectors, fraction collectors, microprocessors, or complete liquid chromatographs. Automation and computerization have taken much of the tedium and some of the excitement out of chromatography. Ingenuity and craftsmanship have devolved from the chemist to the instrumentation specialists.

2.5. GAS CHROMATOGRAPHY

After much preliminary work on instrumentation for gas analysis, Hesse and his students [33] in Germany published the first account of their technique of separating vapors by the flow of gas through an adsorbent-filled tube in 1941. Although the authors called the process "adsorption distillation", the analogy with Tsvet's adsorption chromatography was clear to them. According to Ettre [34], the first modern gas chromatograph was built in Cremer's laboratory in Austria shortly after World War II [35]. Some of the other pioneers of GSC included Glueckauf in England, Claesson in Sweden, Janák in Czechoslovakia, Turkel'taub and Zhukhovitskii in Russia, and Hass in the United States.

The history of GLC has been told by one of its inventors, A.T. James [36]. In 1952, he and Martin [37] devised the first gas–liquid chromatograph. It was based on the theoretical considerations proferred by Martin and Synge in 1941 [14] and featured an automatic recording burette as a detector for the fatty acid vapors. Martin subsequently constructed a gas-density balance, but the catharometer, first used by Ray [38], the hydrogen flame detector [39], and still later the cross-section detector [40] constituted successive improvements in detection methods. This was followed by Lovelock's argon ionization detector [41], the ECD [42], and the FID [43,44], which are now widely used. While this was going on, improvements in column efficiency, based on new theoretical insights, continued to be made. Golay's studies [45] led him to propose the WCOT [46] and later the SCOT [47] columns. These, especially the glass capillary columns [48] are the present record holders in efficiency.

2.6. ELECTROPHORESIS

Electrophoresis is probably the oldest differential migration method, going back to the beginning of the Nineteenth Century. Michaelis [49], who coined the name electrophoresis, used it to determine the isoelectric points of proteins. Much of the subsequent work was done in Tiselius' laboratory, where the ingenious moving-boundary apparatus was perfected [19,50]. Although extremely useful for determining electromechanical properties of colloids, this apparatus is not designed to resolve mixtures.

Separation by electromigration from a narrow zone was first reported in 1937 by Koenig [51], who may be regarded as the inventor of paper electrophoresis. The preliminary report in Portugese was soon followed by a detailed article in German [52], but it was not until 1948 that this method was adopted by other research workers [53,54]. A floot of publications followed, exploring various theoretical and practical aspects of zone electrophoresis. Cellulose acetate film was introduced into analytical electrophoresis in 1957 [55].

Gel slabs, used in Martin's laboratory as early as 1946 [56], did not become popular as a migration medium until the advent of immunoelectrophoresis [57] and the demonstration by Smithies [58] that gels are superior to paper. Polyacrylamide, a gel of superior resolving power, was introduced by Ornstein [59] and Davis [60]. The principle of discontinuous electrophoresis was further developed into the technique now known as isotachophoresis [61]. The method underwent further refinement in the modification called isoelectric focusing. Electrophoretic methods, especially in combination with chromatography, are of immense value in the structural analysis of biological polymers.

REFERENCES

1 E. Heftmann, in E. Heftmann (Editor), *Chromatography. A Laboratory Handbook of Chromatographic and Electrophoretic Methods*, Van Nostrand-Reinhold, New York, 3rd Edn., 1975, p. 1.
2 L.S. Ettre and A. Zlatkis (Editors), *75 Years of Chromatography—A Historical Dialogue*, J. Chromatogr. Library Series, Vol. 17, Elsevier, Amsterdam, 1979.
3 H.A. Laitinen and G.W. Ewing (Editors), *A History of Analytical Chemistry*, Div. Anal. Chem., Amer. Chem. Soc., Washington, DC, 1977.
4 K.I. Sakodynskii, *J. Chromatogr.*, 220 (1981) 1.
5 M.S. Tsvet, *Proc. Warsaw Soc. Nat. Sci., Biol. Sec.*, 6 (1903) 14.
6 M.S. Tsvet, *Ber. Deut. Botan. Ges.*, 24 (1906) 316 and 384.
7 M.S. Tsvet, *Khromofilly v rastitel'nom i zhivotnom mire*, Tipogr. Varshavskago Uchebnago Okruga, Warsaw, 1910.
8 E. Lederer, *J. Chromatogr.*, 73 (1972) 361.
9 L. Zechmeister and L. von Cholnoky, *Die chromatographische Adsorptionsmethode*, Springer, Vienna, 1937.
10 R. Kuhn, A. Winterstein and E. Lederer, *Hoppe Seyler's Z. Physiol. Chem.*, 197 (1931) 141.
11 I.M. Hais, *J. Chromatogr.*, 86 (1973) 283.
12 N.A. Izmailov and M.S. Shraiber, *Farmatsiya*, 3 (1938) 1.
13 W.G. Brown, *Nature (London)* 143 (1939) 377.
14 A.J.P. Martin and R.L.M. Synge, *Biochem. J.*, 35 (1941) 91 and 1358.

15 R. Consden, A.H. Gordon and A.J.P. Martin, *Biochem. J.*, 38 (1944) 224.
16 R.L.M. Synge, *Biochem. Soc. Symp.*, 30 (1970) 175.
17 T. Reichstein and C.W. Shoppee, *Discuss. Faraday Soc.*, 7 (1949) 305.
18 A. Tiselius, *Kolloid Z.*, 105 (1943) 101.
19 A. Tiselius, *Angew. Chem.*, 67 (1955) 245.
20 A. Tiselius and L. Hagdahl, *Acta Chem. Scand.*, 4 (1950) 394.
21 R.S. Alm, R.J.P. Williams and A. Tiselius, *Acta Chem. Scand.*, 6 (1952) 826.
22 L.S. Ettre and C. Horváth, *Anal. Chem.*, 47 (1975) 422A.
23 R. Kunin, *Elements of Ion Exchange*, Reinhold, New York, 1960, p. 1.
24 B.A. Adams and E.L. Holmes, *J. Soc. Chem. Ind.*, 54 (1935) 1T.
25 Anon., *J. Amer. Chem. Soc.*, 69 (1947) 2769.
26 W.E. Cohn, *Science*, 109 (1949) 377.
27 S. Moore and W.H. Stein, *J. Biol. Chem.*, 192 (1951) 663.
28 A. Tiselius, J. Porath and P.A. Albertsson, *Science*, 141 (1963) 13.
29 P. Cuatrecasas and C.B. Anfinsen, *Annu. Rev. Biochem.*, 40 (1971) 259.
30 J. Porath and P. Flodin, *Nature (London)*, 183 (1959) 1657.
31 C.G. Horváth, B.A. Preiss and S.R. Lipsky, *Anal. Chem.*, 39 (1967) 1422.
32 G.A. Howard and A.J.P. Martin, *Biochem. J.*, 46 (1950) 532.
33 G. Hesse, H. Eilbrecht and F. Reicheneder, *Liebigs Ann. Chem.*, 546 (1941) 233.
34 L.S. Ettre, *J. Chromatogr.*, 112 (1975) 1.
35 E. Cremer and F. Prior, *Oesterr. Chem. Ztg.*, 50 (1949) 161.
36 A.T. James, *Biochem. Soc. Symp.*, 30 (1970) 199.
37 A.T. James and A.J.P. Martin, *Biochem. J.*, 50 (1952) 679.
38 N.H. Ray, *J. Appl. Chem.*, 4 (1954) 21 and 82.
39 R.P.W. Scott, *Nature (London)*, 165 (1955) 793.
40 H. Boer, in D.H. Desty (Editor), *Vapour Phase Chromatography*, Butterworths, London, 1956, p. 169.
41 J.E. Lovelock, *J. Chromatogr.*, 1 (1958) 35.
42 J.E. Lovelock and S.R. Lipsky, *J. Amer. Chem. Soc.*, 82 (1960) 431.
43 J. Harley, W. Nel and V. Pretorius, *Nature (London)*, 181 (1958) 177.
44 I.G. McWilliam and R.A. Dewar, *Nature (London)*, 181 (1958) 760.
45 M.J.E. Golay, *Anal. Chem.*, 29 (1957) 928.
46 M.J.E. Golay, in D.H. Desty (Editor), *Gas Chromatography 1958*, Butterworths, London, 1958, p. 36.
47 M.J.E. Golay, in R.P.W. Scott (Editor), *Gas Chromatography 1960*, Butterworths, London, 1960, p. 139.
48 D.H. Desty, J.N. Haresnape and B.H. Whyman, *Anal. Chem.*, 32 (1960) 302.
49 L. Michaelis, *Biochem. Z.*, 16 (1909) 81.
50 A. Tiselius, *Trans. Faraday Soc.*, 33 (1937) 524.
51 P. Koenig, *Actas III Congr. Sudam. Chim.*, 2 (1937) 334.
52 D. von Klobusitzky and P. Koenig, *Arch. Exp. Pathol. Pharmakol.*, 192 (1939) 271.
53 T. Wieland, *Angew. Chem.*, A60 (1948) 313.
54 G. Haugaard and T.D. Kroner, *J. Amer. Chem. Soc.*, 70 (1948) 2135.
55 J. Kohn, *Nature (London)*, 180 (1957) 986.
56 R. Consden, A.H. Gordon and A.J.P. Martin, *Biochem. J.*, 40 (1946) 33.
57 P. Grabar and C. Williams, *Biochim. Biophys. Acta*, 10 (1953) 193.
58 O. Smithies, *Biochem. J.*, 61 (1955) 629.
59 L. Ornstein, *Ann. N.Y. Acad. Sci.*, 121 (1964) 321.
60 B.J. Davis, *Ann. N.Y. Acad. Sci.*, 121 (1964) 404.
61 A.J.P. Martin and F.M. Everaerts, *Proc. Roy. Soc., Ser. A*, 316 (1970) 493.

Chapter 3

Theory of chromatography

CSABA HORVÁTH and WAYNE R. MELANDER

CONTENTS

References on p. A130

3.1. INTRODUCTION

No other analytical technique serves as many scientific disciplines as does chromatography. Gathering its technical and theoretical foundations from various scientific areas, chromatographic methods find applications in almost all branches of science and technology. The theory of chromatography draws on most areas of physical chemistry and has many roots in chemical engineering science. Two of these areas are of particular interest: the equilibrium distribution of a substance between two phases that is responsible for retention and selectivity, and the axial dispersion in the column that controls column efficiency. The aim of this chapter is to treat both phenomena in a concise yet comprehensive fashion at a level that is comfortable for most readers and to define the various terms encountered in chromatographic theory.

List of symbols on p. A122

Because it would be impossible to cover all of the theory of chromatography within the constraints of a book chapter, various optimization and design problems had to be omitted. The limitations of the various chromatographic techniques with regard to the speed of separation and number of resolvable components also had to be left out of the discussion. For further and more detailed treatment the reader is referred to some of the books that deal with particular areas of chromatographic theory [1–8]. Throughout this chapter we will concern ourselves mainly with linear elution chromatography, which has been the most popular and successful chromatographic mode. However, displacement chromatography, which is reappearing after a score of years in oblivion, is also described. In order to simplify this introduction to the theory of chromatography, our treatment is focused on GC and HPLC, the most advanced techniques, but it is understood that most of the conclusions drawn from a study of these two techniques are applicable, mutatis mutandis, to all of the other techniques, as the essentials of the chromatographic process proper are the same in all instances.

3.1.1. Elution chromatography

In elution chromatography, the efficiency with which the components of a mixture are separated is determined by two factors: (a) the differences in migration rates of the components and (b) the magnitude of the inevitable band spreading during chromatographic development. Constant but different migration velocities, i.e., isocratic elution, result in a disengagement by a distance ΔZ of the zone centers for two substances after the first has migrated a distance Z and

$$\Delta Z = \xi Z \qquad (3.1)$$

where ξ is a proportionality constant, determined by the relative magnitude of the two equilibrium constants for the distribution of the two components between the mobile and stationary phases. Consequently, the magnitude of ξ is controlled by the thermodynamics of such chromatographic systems.

In the course of the elution process, kinetic and flow phenomena cause inevitable spreading of the zones, resulting in more or less broad peaks, zones, or spots on the chromatogram. In linear chromatography, the concentration profile of the zones is given by a Gaussian (normal) distribution. The width of Gaussian peaks can be taken to be four standard deviations, $4\sigma_L$, measured in column length units, so that the resolution R_s obtained as a result of the differential migration process is conveniently defined as

$$R_s = \Delta Z / 4\sigma_L \qquad (3.2)$$

Unit resolution according to eqn. 3.2 represents an almost complete (98%) separation for Gaussian peaks.

As a result of the random band spreading process, the corresponding variance, σ_L^2, of the Gaussian concentration distribution is proportional to the migration distance

$$\sigma_L^2 = HZ \qquad (3.3)$$

References on p. A130

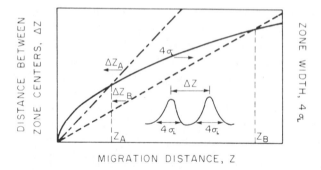

Fig. 3.1. Factors affecting separation in elution chromatography. The distance between the centers of gravity of two peaks increases linearly with the distance migrated, as shown by the lines ΔZ_A and ΔZ_B for two hypothetical pairs of migrants (broken lines). On the other hand, the width of the zones, as measured by $4\sigma_L$, increases with the square root of the migration distance (solid line). Unit resolution is obtained after the pair has migrated a distance given by the intersection of the ΔZ_A or ΔZ_B lines with the $4\sigma_L$ curve.

where H is the proportionality constant so that the peak width is

$$4\sigma_L = 4\sqrt{HZ} \tag{3.4}$$

The magnitude of H is determined by the dynamics of the chromatographic system, i.e., by the flow profile, the rate of mass transfer and sorption kinetics, as discussed later in this chapter.

A schematic illustration of the disengagement of hypothetical eluites (migrants), pair A and pair B, as a function of the mean migration distance is shown in Fig. 3.1. The selectivity of the chromatographic system is greater for pair A than for pair B because ΔZ_A increases much faster than ΔZ_B with the average distance migrated. Unit resolution is obtained at a distance where the ΔZ lines and 4σ curves intersect. Due to the higher selectivity of the chromatographic system for pair A than for pair B, a shorter distance suffices for the complete resolution of pair A. Thus, two fundamental factors determine the efficiency of separation by elution chromatography:

(a) The selectivity of the system, represented by the slope of the ΔZ lines and determined by the relative magnitude of the distribution of the eluites between the mobile and stationary phases, should be as high as possible. When it is high, the column and, concomitantly, the analysis time can be short.

(b) The bandspreading per unit column length, as measured by the magnitude of $H = \sigma_L^2/Z$, should be small. Our discussion of the theory of chromatography will therefore be focused on these two phenomena.

3.1.2. Displacement chromatography

Renewed interest in displacement chromatography [9–11] is due to its potential for preparative-scale separations with high-efficiency analytical columns, such as

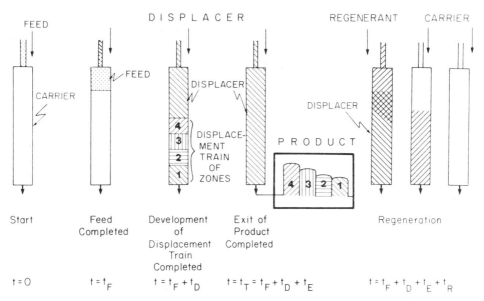

Fig. 3.2. Operational steps in displacement chromatography. The column, equilibrated with the carrier solvent at time 0, is loaded with feed until time t_F. Development with the displacer solution commences immediately and proceeds for the time t_D. Upon completion of development, the displacement train exits the column, a step which takes until time t_E. Finally, the column is stripped of the displacer with a suitable regenerant and re-equilibrated with the carrier, until time t_R. (Reproduced from *J. Chromatogr.*, 218 (1981) 365, with permission [12].)

those employed in HPLC. When the feed mixture is introduced into the column, its components are first sorbed at the top of the column (Fig. 3.2). Then a solution of a displacer, a substance that has stronger affinity for the stationary phase than any of the feed components, is pumped into the column. Provided the column is sufficiently long, the components of the feed will now arrange themselves in a "displacement train" of adjoining square-wave concentration zones of separated components (Figs. 3.2 and 3.3). In the fully developed displacement train all zones move with the velocity of the displacer front, and when the separation is complete, isotachic conditions are reached. The distance/time diagram in Fig. 3.4 shows the trajectories of the concentration steps that occur in the course of separating a feed mixture of three components and the evolution of the zones containing the individual substances. Isotachic conditions are reached when all trajectories become parallel. At that time (t_D), the positions and concentrations of the individual solutes are related to their adsorption isotherms, as shown in Fig. 3.3. The migration velocity of the displacement train, u_D, is given by the velocity of the displacer front.

$$u_D = \frac{u_0}{1 + (\phi C_{S,D}/C_{M,D})} \tag{3.5}$$

where u_0 is the carrier velocity, ϕ is the phase ratio of the column, and $C_{S,D}$ is the

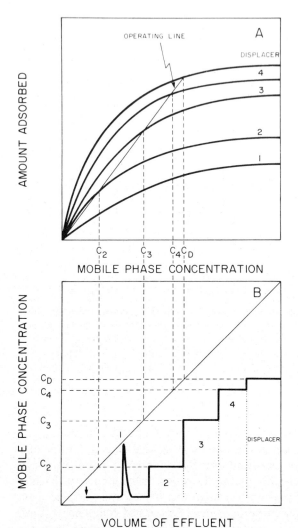

Fig. 3.3. (A) Graph illustrating the adsorption isotherms of individual feed components (1–4) and displacer along with the operating line. (B) Graph illustrating the resulting displacement diagram. The intersections of the operating line with the isotherms determine the concentrations of the feed components in the final product. The isotherm of Component *1* lies wholly beneath the operating line, hence it is eluted ahead of the displacement train. (Reproduced from *J. Chromatogr.*, 218 (1981) 365, with permission [12].)

amount of displacer sorbed per unit volume of stationary phase in equilibrium with a displacer (mobile phase) solution of concentration $C_{M,D}$. The phase ratio is defined as

$$\phi = V_S/V_M \tag{3.6}$$

where V_S and V_M are the volumes of stationary and mobile phases in the column, respectively.

List of symbols on p. A122

As shown in Fig. 3.3A, the chord representing the ratio $C_{S,D}/C_{M,D}$, which is called the operating or speed line, intersects the isotherms of the sample components. Under isotachic conditions, the concentrations of the separated species in the mobile phase will be given by the intersections of their isotherms with the operating line. Thus, the heights of the steps in Fig. 3.3B are determined by the respective isotherms and the displacer concentration. Conservation of mass requires that the widths of the steps for the feed components will be proportional to the amounts present in the feed.

Complete displacement development occurs if the isotherms are convex and the operating line intersects the isotherms of all feed components. If the isotherm of a less retarded component lies below the operating line, that component will be eluted as a peak, illustrated as Component 1 in Fig. 3.3B. Since the occurrence of convex isotherms under conditions commonly employed in HPLC has been verified, the representation in Fig. 3.3A by Langmuir isotherms is probably a true reflection of reality for many displacement chromatographic systems.

At present, elution chromatography is widely practiced and is almost synonymous with chromatography, but displacement development has recently been shown to offer significant advantages in liquid chromatography with high-efficiency columns [12,13]. Displacement development frequently occurs in preparative chromatography when columns are overloaded and it also plays a role in separations by bio-affinity chromatography [14]. Nevertheless, a great deal of experience will be required to exploit the full potential of this kind of chromatography. For this reason and due to the relative simplicity and wide popularity of elution chromatography, further theoretical treatment in this chapter will be focused on the thermodynamic and kinetic phenomena associated with elution development.

3.2. THE CHROMATOGRAM

3.2.1. Evaluation of the chromatogram

A suitable detector, monitoring the column effluent in GC or HPLC, or a photodensitometer scanning a TLC plate produces a signal which is proportional to the concentration of the separated sample components. The time course of this signal produces the chromatogram, i.e. the written record of the experiment. This record may take a variety of forms, including a chart recorder tracing, a spot on a TLC plate, or digitized elements residing in a computer memory. When a sample, containing one component and an inert tracer, is injected into a column, the tracer, which is assumed not to interact with the stationary phase, traverses the column with the mobile-phase velocity and emerges from the column at time t_0 on the chromatogram (cf. Fig. 3.8). The elution time, t_0, is often denoted by t_M in the literature and is called the retention time of an unretained solute or the hold-up time of the mobile phase in the column. The sample component is retarded by the stationary phase and therefore emerges after the inert tracer at a time, t_R, which is called the retention time of that substance. It is the time that elapses between sample

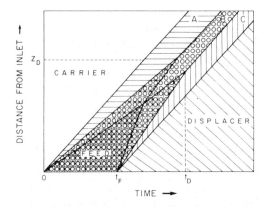

Fig. 3.4. Distance/time diagram, illustrating the separation of a three-component mixture by displacement chromatography. At t_F, the introduction of the feed, containing A, B, and C, is completed and the displacer, D, is introduced. At time t_D, the displacement train is fully developed and requires a column length of Z_D. Some separation occurs by frontal chromatography during the introduction of feed.

introduction and the appearance of the peak center at the end of the column. In the case of Gaussian peaks, the peak maximum (apex) coincides with the center of gravity (first moment) of the concentration distribution and is used for the evaluation of t_R. The retention time is a fundamental parameter of great practical and theoretical significance. It is used to define the adjusted retention time, t'_R

$$t'_R = t_R - t_0 \tag{3.7}$$

$$t_R = t_0 + t'_R \tag{3.8}$$

Eqn. 3.8 shows that the retention time of an eluite is given by the sum of the time spent in the mobile phase, t_0, and the time spent in the stationary phase, t'_R.

In improperly designed instruments, the extracolumn dead volume from the sampling device, connections, and detector is commensurable with the peak volume of the inert tracer and the eluite. Then, the measured t_0 and t_R values will also include the extracolumn hold-up time, t_D. In practice, t_D is usually small with respect to t_0 and may be neglected. Furthermore, in the calculation of the adjusted retention time no correction is necessary, as

$$t'_R = (t_R + t_D) - (t_0 + t_D) \tag{3.9}$$

When the sample size increases above a critical limit, the chromatographic system becomes nonlinear due to the nonlinearity of the sorption isotherm. As a consequence, the peak shape becomes asymmetric and the retention time becomes dependent on the sample size. In such cases, the retention time may have to be evaluated by extrapolation of t_R to zero concentration or by calculation of the first moment of the peak, which is a rigorous measure of the retention and is independent of peak asymmetry.

In GC, t_0 is conveniently evaluated from the position of the "air peak" on the chromatogram. However, some detectors, such as the FID, do not respond to air.

List of symbols on p. A122

When the air peak cannot be measured, some other gas, such as hydrogen, is used as the inert tracer. Alternatively, the gas hold-up time is calculated by extrapolation from the retention time of lower alkanes [15].

There is no universal inert tracer in HPLC and the inertness of a "nonsorbed" component must be established experimentally. To measure the interparticulate space or void volume one needs a tracer that is excluded from the interior of the particles, either by its molecular size or by ionic charge (Donnan exclusion [16]). If the space occupied by solvent within the particles is to be included, one may use an isotopic tracer, such as deuterated water. Whereas in GC the gas hold-up volume in the column can be unambiguously defined at a fixed temperature, in LSC with multicomponent eluents the observed mobile-phase hold-up volume is a function of the eluent composition [17]. In such cases, the actual void volume of the column is obtained by methods other than chromatography [18] or, more appropriately, the thermodynamically rigorous definition of the void volume is used to evaluate the mobile-phase hold-up time from the relationship [19]

$$t_0 = \Sigma t_{R,i}^S \, \phi_i \tag{3.10}$$

where $t_{R,i}^S$ and ϕ_i are the retention time and volume fraction in the eluent of solvent component i. The $t_{R,i}^S$ values are conveniently measured by chromatographing labeled solvents. Sparsely deuterated solvents are eminently suitable for this purpose and can be detected by a differential refractometer. Alternatively, an extrathermodynamic value of t_0 can be obtained from the retention times of homologs governed by linear free-energy relations. A number of methods are described in the literature for evaluating t_0 by using homologous eluite series, but the practical significance of this approach is rather limited by the inherent inaccuracy of the method [20].

Although in analytical work the use of retention times or even retention distances on the chromatogram is quite satisfactory, the retention values that have direct physicochemical significance are the retention volumes. In LC, even at high pressures, the compressibility of the mobile phase may be neglected in the calculation of retention volumes. The retention volume is obtained as the product of the retention time and the volumetric flowrate, F, if the flowrate is maintained constant during elution by a precision pump. Of course, the retention volumes can also be obtained directly by collecting the column effluent during the appropriate time period. The terms mobile-phase hold-up volume and retention volume are used frequently in describing retention volumes. The mobile-phase hold-up volume, V_0 or V_M, is the retention volume of an inert tracer and is given by $V_0 = Ft_0$. The retention volume, V_R, and adjusted retention volume, V_R', are obtained as Ft_R and Ft_R', respectively. In GC, the high compressibility and thermal expansion coefficient of the carrier gas mandate the introduction of the corrected retention volume of the inert gas, V_M, given by $F_c jt_0$, where F_c is the gas flowrate at the column temperature and outlet pressure and j is the gas compressibility factor. The corrected adjusted retention volume, V_N, is called the net retention volume and is evaluated as $F_c jt_R'$. When flow or temperature programing is used, both flowrate and pressure change during the experiment, and retention volumes cannot be calculated in this simple manner.

References on p. A130

3.2.2. Retention factor

A convenient dimensionless measure of retention is given by

$$k = (t_R - t_0)/t_0 = t_R'/t_0 \tag{3.11}$$

where k is the retention factor, also referred to in the literature as the capacity factor. The retention factor is a dimensionless peak locator that measures the position of the eluite peak with respect to the starting point and t_0 on the chromatogram. Accordingly, the retention factor of the nonsorbed inert tracer is zero. The use of k is recommended only when isocratic elution is used, because the physical interpretation of k is more complicated in the case of temperature programing and gradient elution. As the most important quantity that can directly be obtained from the chromatogram, the retention factor has numerous meanings. It is a dimensionless partition or distribution ratio given by

$$k = \frac{\text{amount of an eluite in the stationary phase}}{\text{amount of that eluite in the mobile phase}} \tag{3.12}$$

and therefore is also called the mass-distribution ratio.

The retention volume and the mobile phase volume in the column are related through the retention factor as

$$V_R = V_M(1 + k) \tag{3.13}$$

Eqn. 3.13 is equivalent to the fundamental equation of chromatography, given by

$$V_R = V_M + KV_S \tag{3.14}$$

where K is the thermodynamic equilibrium constant for the distribution of the eluite between the two phases of a given chromatographic system, and V_S is the volume of the stationary phase in the column. The definition of the phase ratio of the column, ϕ, as V_S/V_M and comparison of eqns. 3.13 and 3.14 yields the following relationship between the retention factor and the equilibrium constant:

$$k = \phi K \tag{3.15}$$

The evaluation of ϕ is — at least in principle — straightforward when the stationary phase is a liquid. With solid stationary phases, ϕ and K are subject to different definitions; e.g., surface area and surface concentrations may be used, and the evaluation of column parameters is generally beset with difficulties. Table 3.1 shows typical values of k and ϕ in GC, where packed and open tubular columns may widely differ with respect to these values. Such data are not available for LC, but in HPLC with bonded phases ϕ can be assumed to be on the order of unity.

The probabilities, P_S and P_M, that the eluite during its travel through the column is in the stationary and mobile phases, respectively, are given by

$$P_S = \frac{k}{1 + k} \tag{3.16}$$

and

$$P_M = \frac{1}{1 + k} \tag{3.17}$$

TABLE 3.1

RETENTION FACTORS (k) AND PHASE RATIOS (ϕ) TYPICAL IN GC
K = thermodynamic equilibrium constant.

Column	Support	Particle size, mm	Percent liquid, v/w	ϕ	k at	
					$K = 50$	$K = 1000$
Packed columns						
Standard	Chromosorb	0.15–0.17	16	7	7.1	143
Low-loaded	Chromosorb	0.15–0.17	1	205	0.24	4.9
Low-loaded	Glass beads	0.15–0.17	0.05	417	0.12	2.4

Column		Tube ID, mm	Film thickness, μm	ϕ	k at	
					$K = 50$	$K = 1000$
Open tubular columns						
Standard (liquid-coated)		0.25	0.578	123	0.41	8.1
Standard (liquid-coated)		0.25	0.147	405	0.12	2.4
Porous layer (liquid-impregnated)		0.50	–	35.5	1.4	28

Furthermore P_S and P_M also express the fraction of the eluite in the column present in the stationary and mobile phase, respectively. P_M is equivalent to the retardation factor that is frequently used in the literature and is denoted by R. Accordingly, the physical meaning of R is

$$R = \frac{\text{velocity of eluite zone}}{\text{velocity of mobile phase}} = \frac{\text{amount of an eluite in the mobile phase}}{\text{amount of that eluite in both phases}} \qquad (3.18)$$

For uniform chromatographic systems, the retention factor is related to the retardation factor by

$$k = (1 - R)/R \qquad (3.19)$$

In planar chromatography the positions of spots are measured by the R_F values,

$$R_F = \frac{\text{distance of spot from start}}{\text{distance of eluent front from start}} \qquad (3.20)$$

Whereas R and R_F are formally equivalent, their physicochemical interpretation is likely to be different, because in planar chromatography the properties of both the mobile and stationary phases vary along the path of the migrant, whereas in CC the column is assumed to be axially uniform under isocratic conditions. In practice, the relationship between the two parameters is approximated [21] by $R = R_F/Q$, where Q ranges from 0.8 to 0.9.

The logarithm of the retention factor has particular significance as a measure of the free energy change for retention at a given temperature. The logarithmic

References on p. A130

retention factor, κ or κ_e, is expressed by

$$\kappa = \log_{10} k \tag{3.21}$$

or

$$\kappa_e = \ln k \tag{3.22}$$

In planar chromatography, the corresponding quantity is denoted by R_M and is evaluated from the retardation factor by

$$R_M = \log_{10}\left(\frac{1 - R_F}{R_F}\right) \tag{3.23}$$

The use of κ and R_M is most extensive in linear free energy relationships, as will be seen in Chap. 3.6.

3.2.3. Flow velocity

The linear flow velocity of the mobile phase is a significant operational parameter that affects the time of separation and the magnitude of bandspreading. Various expressions are used in CC for the flow velocity [22]. In forced-flow CC, e.g., GC or HPLC, the flowrate is usually constant during the experiment. On the other hand, in planar chromatography the flow is time-dependent and the situation is more complicated, as discussed in Chap. 3.7.2.

The superficial or empty-tube velocity, u_s, is given by

$$u_s = F/A_t \tag{3.24}$$

where F is the volumetric flowrate — assumed to be constant — and A_t is the cross-sectional area of the empty column.

The interstitial velocity, u_e, is defined by

$$u_e = u_s/\epsilon_e \tag{3.25}$$

where ϵ_e is the interparticulate (interstitial) porosity given by

$$\epsilon_e = V_e/V_t \tag{3.26}$$

where V_e is the interstitial void volume and V_t is the empty-tube volume, respectively. In LC it is possible to use sufficiently large inert tracer molecules that are totally excluded from the intraparticulate space. The retention time of such a tracer is t_e, and the interstitial velocity is evaluated as

$$u_e = L/t_e \tag{3.27}$$

where L is the length of the column. At constant flow, the interstitial volume is given by

$$V_e = Ft_e \tag{3.28}$$

and the interparticulate porosity is obtained as

$$\epsilon_e = u_s/u_e = Ft_e/V_t \tag{3.29}$$

The chromatographic velocity, u, is derived from the hold-up time of the inert

List of symbols on p. A122

tracer than can enter both the interstitial and intraparticulate spaces occupied by the mobile phase. It is given by

$$u = u_s / \epsilon_T \tag{3.30}$$

where ϵ_T is the total porosity of the column, as defined by

$$\epsilon_T = (V_e + V_i)/V_t = \epsilon_e + \epsilon_i (1 - \epsilon_e) \tag{3.31}$$

where V_i and ϵ_i are the intraparticulate pore volume of the column packing and the corresponding intraparticulate porosity, respectively. The chromatographic velocity is readily evaluated from the column length and the retention time of a suitable inert tracer as

$$u = L/t_0 \tag{3.32}$$

This approach is only as accurate as the method by which t_0 is obtained. In LLC an additional error may be introduced if the tracer explores the stationary phase volume as well [23].

In studies of peak spreading, a dimensionless velocity, the so-called reduced velocity, ν, is frequently used. It is defined as

$$\nu = \frac{u_e d_p}{D_M} \tag{3.33}$$

where u_e is the interstitial mobile phase velocity, d_p is the particle diameter in packed columns, i.e. the characteristic dimension of the system, and D_M is the molecular diffusivity of the eluite in the mobile phase. For open tubular columns the inner diameter of the tube, d_t, is used to express the reduced velocity. In the chemical engineering literature ν is known as the Peclet number, Pe, and is considered as the product of the Reynolds number, Re, and the Schmidt number, Sc [24]. In chromatography, u is easier to measure than u_e and is sometimes used in eqn. 3.33 instead of u_e. For most packed columns the two velocities are related as $u \approx 0.6 u_e$.

3.2.4. Properties of Gaussian peaks

In linear elution chromatography, the column can be considered mathematically as a Gaussian operator on the sample input. Thus, the customary pulse input yields a normal distribution of the eluite concentration in the column effluent that is recorded as a Gaussian peak on the chromatogram.

The dependence of the eluite concentration, C, on time for a Gaussian peak is given by the relationship

$$C = \frac{1}{F} \frac{M}{\sigma_t \sqrt{2\pi}} e^{-0.5[(t_R - t)/\sigma_t]^2} \tag{3.34}$$

where F is the flowrate, M is the amount of solute injected into the column, and σ_t is the standard deviation measured in time units. As shown in Fig. 3.5, the peak width at different ordinate positions is proportional to the standard deviation of the distribution.

References on p. A130

In frontal chromatography a concentration step of the solute is introduced. If the chromatographic system is linear, i.e., the solute concentration in the feed, C_0, is sufficiently low, the concentration profile in the effluent is given by

$$C = \frac{C_0}{2} \, \text{erfc}\left(\frac{t_R^* - t}{\sigma_t} \right) \tag{3.35}$$

where erfc is the error-function complement, which is tabulated in numerous reference books, and t_R^* is the breakthrough time of the solute front. The curves represented by eqn. 3.35 are sigmoidal in shape, passing from $C = 0$ at $t = -\infty$ through $C = C_0/2$ at $t = t_R^*$ to $C = C_0$ at $t = +\infty$. It is easy to show that the approximate integration of the Gaussian distribution function as given in eqn. 3.34 yields eqn. 3.35.

The correct parameters for characterization of the concentration/time relationship represented by the chromatographic peak are the statistical moments that are defined as follows

$$\text{zeroth moment (peak area)} = \int_0^\infty C \, dt = A \tag{3.36}$$

$$\text{first moment (retention time)} = \frac{1}{A} \int_0^\infty Ct \, dt = t_R \tag{3.37}$$

$$\text{second central moment (variance)} = \frac{1}{A} \int_0^\infty C(t - t_R)^2 \, dt = \sigma_t^2 \tag{3.38}$$

The zeroth moment is the peak area A, which is readily obtained by integration and is used in quantitative analysis. The first moment equals the retention time, as can be shown by substituting C from eqn. 3.34 into eqn. 3.37 and integrating. The second moment is the variance and expresses the breadth of the peak. As shown in Fig. 3.5, the standard deviation is readily evaluated graphically from the chromatogram so that it can be used conveniently to estimate the variance of Gaussian or nearly Gaussian peaks. The first and second moments of the peak are independent of the amount of eluite as they are normalized to the peak area. For Gaussian distributions, statistical moments higher than the second have value zero.

The maximum concentration, i.e., the height of a Gaussian peak is given by

$$C_{max} = \frac{A}{\sigma_t \sqrt{2\pi}} \tag{3.39}$$

Rearranging eqn. 3.39, we obtain the area of the Gaussian peak as

$$A = C_{max} \sigma_t \sqrt{2\pi} \tag{3.40}$$

On the other hand, the area of the triangle, A_{tr}, shown by the dashed lines in Fig. 3.5, is given by

$$A_{tr} = 4\sigma_t C_{max} / \sqrt{e} \tag{3.41}$$

List of symbols on p. A122

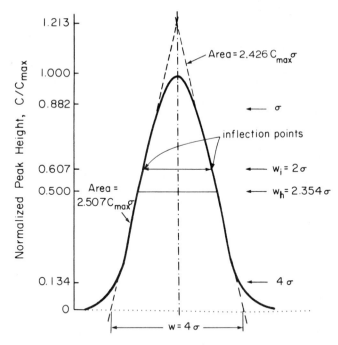

Fig. 3.5. Properties of a Gaussian peak. C_{max}, peak height at maximum; σ, standard deviation, w_i, peak width at inflection points; w_h, peak width at half-height; w, peak width at base (base intercept). The area under the triangle formed by the tangents to the inflection points and the baseline as well as the peak area (zeroth moment) are also shown.

3.2.5. Asymmetrical peaks

True Gaussian curves are rarely seen in real chromatographic peaks. However, the perturbations seen in the quasi-Gaussian peaks that are most commonly obtained in practice may be assumed to be small, and chromatographic parameters may be evaluated as if the peaks were Gaussian in shape. Peak asymmetry, which has an untoward effect on resolution, is nevertheless often recorded as a measure of the inadequacy of a chromatographic system.

The rigorous measure of the deviation from symmetrical peak shape is the skew, S, that is derived from the third central moment of the peak as follows

$$S = \frac{1}{A\sigma_t^3} \int_0^\infty C(t - t_R)^3 \, dt \tag{3.42}$$

A positive value of the skewness indicates tailing of the peak. Another deviation from Gaussian shape, the excess, E, is derived from the fourth statistical moment as

$$E = \frac{1}{A\sigma_t^4} \int_0^\infty C(t - t_R)^4 \, dt - 3 \tag{3.43}$$

If the excess is positive, the peak is more pointed than a corresponding Gaussian

Define Peak Asymmetry as

$$A_s = \frac{b-a}{a} \qquad\qquad A_s' = \frac{b'-a'}{a'}$$

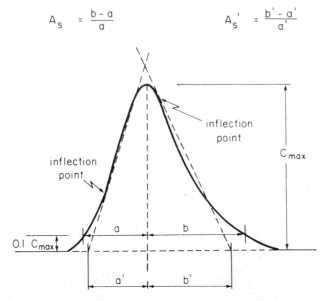

Fig. 3.6. Definition of asymmetry. The asymmetry is defined in terms of the line segments a and b or a' and b', drawn perpendicular to a line which is perpendicular to the baseline and passes through the peak apex. Whereas a and b are measured at an altitude equal to 10% of C_{max} to the leading (a) and trailing (b) edges of the peak, a' and b' measure the baseline from the front (a') to the rear (b') vertex of a triangle constructed of the baseline and lines tangent to the chromatogram at the two points of inflection.

distribution having the same standard deviation. On the other hand, negative excess measures the flattening of the peak.

The skew is preferably evaluated by a computer, although graphical methods are available [25]. Because the measurements are cumbersome and frequently inaccurate in any case, the preferred approach is the use of an asymmetry parameter that can be graphically evaluated from the chromatogram in a simple way. A common method involves the following steps. A line perpendicular to the baseline is dropped from the peak apex and the widths of the two peak halves are evaluated at the altitude of 10% of the peak height. These widths are shown by distances a and b in Fig. 3.6. The asymmetry factor, A_s, is then calculated from the relationship

$$A_s = (b - a)/a \tag{3.44}$$

Alternatively, a triangle can be constructed from the tangents drawn at the two inflection points of the peak and their baseline intercept. The distances a' and b', obtained in a fashion similar to the above procedure as shown in Fig. 3.6, are used to define another asymmetry parameter, A_s', as

$$A_s' = (b' - a')/a' \tag{3.45}$$

In a third method, the peak half-widths, a^* and b^*, at 0.134 C_{max} may be used to

List of symbols on p. A122

define A_s^*, as

$$A_s^* = (b^* - a^*)/a^* \tag{3.46}$$

The usefulness of A_s^* is related to the property of Gaussian peaks that at an altitude of $0.134\ C_{max}$ the peak width is exactly 4σ.

The three asymmetry parameters are closely related, but one may be more useful than another in certain applications. Each asymmetry parameter gives positive and negative values for peaks exhibiting tailing and fronting, respectively, and the asymmetry is zero for symmetrical peaks. It should be kept in mind that the above parameters are purely empirical measures and have no simple relation to the skew, which is the rigorous measure of peak asymmetry. In fact, the magnitude of the three asymmetry parameters depends on both the skew and the excess. This is illustrated in Fig. 3.7, which shows six peaks, having different combinations of S and E, and the pertinent asymmetry factor, A_s, of each. The peaks were generated by using the first three terms of a Gram–Charlier series [25]. Fig. 3.7 shows that, when $S = 0$ there is no asymmetry, and in the case of nonzero skew the value of the asymmetry parameter depends also on the magnitude of E.

The above measures, except skewness, have no theoretical foundations. Peak asymmetry, even if measured as S, is difficult to relate quantitatively to physical events in the chromatographic column. Deviations from Gaussian peak shape due to variations in the thermodynamic equilibrium constant over the concentration range of the eluite in the column are discussed in Chap. 3.5.1.1. Since a chromatographic system sufficiently close to linear can be created by lowering the sample load or by appropriately changing the chemical make-up of the system, the measurement of peak asymmetry from this source has not been very important except in quality control of columns for specific applications. In HPLC with microparticulate packed columns asymmetry is often related to nonuniformity of flow resulting from poor

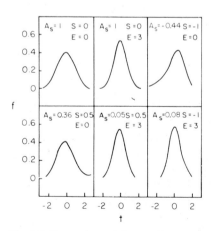

Fig. 3.7. Comparison of the asymmetry parameter, A_s, and skew, S, of peaks having an excess, E, of 0 or 3. The distributions, f, as a function of time were calculated by using the first three terms of the Gram–Charlier series.

References on p. A130

column packing or instrument construction, poor peak shape frequently being due to maldistribution of the sample at the column entrance. The above asymmetry parameters can serve to diagnose and quantify the effect of such phenomena. Because they are empirical measures, it is important that the method chosen to evaluate peak asymmetry be unambiguously defined.

3.3. MEASURES OF COLUMN EFFICIENCY

3.3.1. Plate height and plate number

The magnitude of bandspreading or peak variance measured in column length units, σ_L^2, is proportional to the column length for linear elution in a uniform column. Therefore, the peak variance at the end of the column is given by

$$\sigma_L^2 = HL \tag{3.47}$$

where L is the column length and H is the proportionality constant which depends on the eluite, the operating conditions, and the construction of the column. Rearranging eqn. 3.47, we obtain

$$H = \sigma_L^2/L \tag{3.48}$$

Evidently, the smaller the value of H, the smaller is the magnitude of bandspreading per unit length of the column, i.e., the higher is the efficiency of the column. Indeed, H is a frequently used column efficiency parameter that is called the plate height or height equivalent to a theoretical plate (HETP) following the nomenclature established by the first theory of the chromatographic process [26], the so-called plate theory. The dimension of H is length and its value for efficient columns is commensurate with a characteristic distance in the column, such as the particle diameter in packed columns and tube diameter in capillary columns.

A dimensionless measure of column efficiency, N, is derived by dividing the squared first moment by the second central moment.

$$N = \frac{t_R^2}{\sigma_t^2} = \frac{L^2}{\sigma_L^2} \tag{3.49}$$

N is called the plate number, number of theoretical plates, or simply the plate count of the column. A large plate number signifies that the relative bandspreading is small and that the chromatographic system is highly efficient. For the determination of N, any pair of first and second moments can be used, as long as they are dimensionally consistent. Therefore, N is very easily determined from the retention distance and peak width, measured on the recorder chart paper.

The determination of H does not require the measurement of σ_L^2, as long as N is known, because comparison of eqns. 3.48 and 3.49 yields the simple relation

$$H = L(\sigma_L/L)^2 = L/N \tag{3.50}$$

Thus, plate height can be evaluated conveniently from the column length and data directly obtained from the chromatogram. In Fig. 3.5 the relationship between peak width and standard deviation is illustrated. Accordingly, the width at the inflection points, w_i, the width at half height, w_h, and the baseline intercept, w, are given by by 2σ, 2.354σ, and 4σ, respectively. These values allow us to express the number of theoretical plates in the following ways

$$N = 4\left(\frac{t_R}{w_i}\right)^2 = 5.54\left(\frac{t_R}{w_h}\right)^2 = 16\left(\frac{t_R}{w}\right)^2 \qquad (3.51)$$

3.3.2. Other measures of column efficiency

3.3.2.1. Effective plate height and plate number

Separation in a chromatographic column is associated with the time eluites spend in the stationary phase, i.e. with the adjusted retention time, because the time spent in the mobile phase can be considered idle with regard to the intrinsic separation process. It appears to be reasonable, therefore, to define an effective plate number, N_{eff}, analogous to N, in which t'_R replaces t_R. Thus,

$$N_{eff} = N[k/(1+k)]^2 \qquad (3.52)$$

and the corresponding effective plate height, H_{eff}, is given by

$$H_{eff} = H\left(\frac{1+k}{k}\right)^2 \qquad (3.53)$$

The effective parameters defined above are claimed to be more meaningful than the regular efficiency parameters when one is comparing the column resolving power for eluites having widely different retention factors.

3.3.2.2. Peak capacity

The maximum number of peaks that can be resolved by a chromatographic system under a given set of conditions is called the peak capacity, n. It is a function of the plate number as well as the retention volumes of the first and last peaks, V_α and V_ω, respectively, according to the following relationship

$$n = 1 + \sqrt{N/16} \times \ln(V_\omega/V_\alpha) \qquad (3.54)$$

In interactive chromatography the value of n is determined by operational conditions, such as the allowable separation time or detection sensitivity. In contradistinction, the peak capacity of size exclusion chromatography (SEC) is uniquely defined by the ratio of the total void volume of the column to the interstitial volume, which is usually 2.3 ± 0.3. Therefore, the peak capacity in SEC, n_{SEC}, is severely limited compared to that in interactive chromatography. It can be estimated from

$$n_{SEC} = 1 + 0.2\sqrt{N} \qquad (3.55)$$

The peak capacity of a chromatographic system can be substantially increased when isocratic elution is replaced by temperature programing in GC or gradient

References on p. A130

elution in LC. In fact, the reason for using such anisocratic elution techniques is that the concomitant increase in peak capacity reduces the analysis time and increases the concentration of the late peaks.

3.3.2.3. Axial dispersion coefficient

For the emerging peak of a unit amount of substance chromatographed, eqn. 3.34 can be rewritten as follows:

$$C = \frac{1}{2\sqrt{\pi \mathcal{D} t}} \, e^{-0.5[(L - u_b t^2)/2\mathcal{D} t]} \tag{3.56}$$

where L is the length of the column, u_b is the band velocity, and $\mathcal{D}$ is the so-called axial dispersion coefficient. The latter parameter, which is frequently used in the chemical engineering literature, has the same dimensions as molecular diffusivity and is another measure of bandspreading.

According to the Einstein equation, the variance of the chromatographic peak in column length units, i.e., the axial mean-square displacement, is given by

$$\sigma_L^2 = 2\mathcal{D} t \tag{3.57}$$

Comparison of eqns. 3.47 and 3.57 yields

$$\mathcal{D} = H u_b / 2 \tag{3.58}$$

Thus, the axial dispersion coefficient is proportional to the product of plate height and band velocity. On the other hand, we find that

$$\mathcal{D} = t_R / 2N \tag{3.59}$$

and alternatively

$$2N = L u_b / \mathcal{D} \tag{3.60}$$

Eqn. 3.60 shows that the plate number is equivalent to a dimensionless quantity, which is the product of column length and band velocity divided by the axial dispersion coefficient and is analogous to the Peclet number (cf. eqn. 3.33). Replacing u_b in eqn. 3.60 by the fluid velocity, we obtain a dimensionless number called in the literature the Bodenstein group.

3.4. RELATIVE RETENTION AND RESOLUTION

3.4.1. Relative retention and selectivity

A chromatogram of two eluites is illustrated in Fig. 3.8. The retention of Eluite 2 relative to that of Eluite 1 is denoted as $\alpha_{2,1}$ and can be evaluated from the adjusted retention times or from the corresponding capacity factors as

$$\alpha_{2,1} = t'_{R,2} / t'_{R,1} = k_2 / k_1 \tag{3.61}$$

List of symbols on p. A122

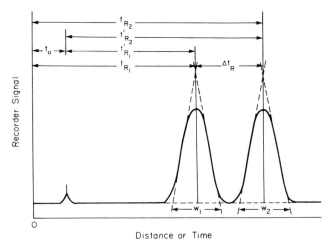

Fig. 3.8. Chromatogram of two eluites, illustrating the evaluation of retention times.

In GC the equivalent relationship

$$\alpha_{2,1} = V_{N,2}/V_{N,1} \tag{3.62}$$

is also frequently used. From eqns. 3.15 and 3.61 it follows that relative retention is the ratio of the thermodynamic equilibrium constants associated with the retention of the two eluites

$$\alpha_{2,1} = K_2/K_1 \tag{3.63}$$

In expressing the relative retention by eqn. 3.61 the faster moving eluite is used as the reference by convention so that the value of $\alpha_{2,1}$ is always > 1. Relative retention values with respect to a given standard are denoted by the symbol r. For instance, $r_{Val/Phe}$ stands for the retention of valine relative to that of phenylalanine. Relative retention values are frequently used to present retention data of an eluite, as the effect of certain errors is reduced when the reference substance and eluite are chromatographed together and thus subjected to the same conditions. However, it should be noted that the relative retention is related to the equilibrium constants (cf. eqn. 3.63) only under isocratic elution conditions. When gradient elution or temperature programing is used, the ratio of retention times may be useful in some correlations, but in such cases the relative retention values are very much dependent on instrumental constants and have much more limited application than the isocratic values.

The relative retention, α, is generally referred to as the selectivity of the chromatographic system toward the two sample components. In GC the term relative volatility is also used for relative retention, although in distillation theory relative volatility denotes the ratio of the vapor pressures of the two components. The two definitions are not the same, since in GC relative retention may be strongly affected by eluite interaction with the stationary phase. If the chromatographic equilibrium constant of one eluite and the relative retention are known, the equilibrium constant of the other eluite can be calculated according to eqn. 3.63.

References on p. A130

3.4.2. Resolution

The extent of separation of the peaks is measured by the resolution, R_s, which is equal to the ratio of the distance between the peak maxima, Δt_R, to the mean band width of the two neighboring peaks, $\bar{w}$,

$$R_s = \frac{\Delta t_R}{\bar{w}} = \frac{2(t_{R,2} - t_{R,1})}{(w_1 + w_2)} = \frac{\Delta t_R}{4\bar{\sigma}_t} \qquad (3.64)$$

where $t_{R,1}$ and $t_{R,2}$ are the retention times, w_1 and w_2 are the peak widths measured by the baseline intercept, as shown in Fig. 3.5, and $\bar{\sigma}_t$ is the mean standard deviation. Peaks are considered to be fully resolved when $R_s = 1.5$, i.e. when their separation is 99.7% complete. In most practical cases, however, $R_s = 1$, corresponding to 98% separation, is usually adequate. According to this definition, $R_s - 1$ peaks would fit between the two peaks in question.

The resolution is a basic measure of the efficacy of the chromatographic system in separating the two components. The speed of separation is conveniently expressed as resolution per unit time, $R_s/t_{R,2}$. For closely spaced peaks the resolution may be expressed as the product of three terms,

$$R_s = \left(\frac{\alpha - 1}{\alpha + 1}\right)\left(\frac{\bar{k}}{1 + \bar{k}}\right)\left(\frac{N}{16}\right)^{1/2} \qquad (3.65)$$

where $\bar{k}$ is the mean retention factor. Eqn. 3.65 can be approximated as

$$R_s = \left(\frac{\alpha - 1}{\alpha}\right) \times \left(\frac{k_2}{1 + k_2}\right) \times \left(\frac{N}{16}\right)^{1/2} \qquad (3.66)$$

$$\text{(Selectivity)} \quad \text{(Retention)} \quad \text{(Efficiency)}$$

Eqns. 3.65 and 3.66 show that the resolution is determined by three factors:

(a) selectivity, which is related to the relative retention values and measures the discriminatory power of the chromatographic system;

(b) retention, which measures the fraction of eluite present in the stationary phase and so expresses the retentive power of the chromatographic system;

(c) efficiency, which measures the relative narrowness of the peaks by the ratio of the retention time to peak width (cf. eqn. 3.51).

Eqns. 3.65 and 3.66 are both valid approximations for column chromatography of two eluites. In planar chromatography eluite spots migrate only a fraction of the total length of the sheet and, if conditions are uniform along the sheet, the resolution is given by

$$R_s = \left(\frac{\alpha - 1}{\alpha}\right)\left(\frac{k_2}{(1 + k_2)^{3/2}}\right)\left(\frac{N}{16}\right)^{1/2} \qquad (3.67)$$

where N is the plate number for the entire length of the sheet.

The above resolution equations shed light on the requirements for chromatographic separations: the two components should have different retention factors, i.e. $\alpha > 1$, and the second component at least must be retained, i.e. $k_2 > 0$. Furthermore,

List of symbols on p. A122

a minimum number of theoretical plates, N_{req}, is needed to carry out the separation. N_{req} can be expressed by setting $R_s = 1$ in eqn. 3.65:

$$N_{req} = 16\left(\frac{\alpha}{\alpha - 1}\right)^2 \left(\frac{k + 1}{k}\right)^2 \tag{3.68}$$

where k is the retention factor of the more retained eluite. The required number of plates can conveniently be used to compare the difficulty of separating particular eluite pairs by various chromatographic systems. Given the plate height, H, the column length required for the separation, L_{req}, can also be calculated from eqn. 3.66 as

$$L_{req} = HN_{req} = 16H\left(\frac{\alpha}{\alpha - 1}\right)^2 \left(\frac{k + 1}{k}\right)^2 \tag{3.69}$$

If resolutions greater than 98% are required, the factor 16 is replaced by 36 in both eqn. 3.68 and eqn. 3.69.

The interplay between α, k, and N in effecting resolution is illustrated in Fig. 3.9. A comparison of A and B shows that the plate number has to be higher for peaks which are eluted close to the mobile-phase hold-up time (A) than for peaks having relatively high retention factors (B) in order to obtain the same resolution. Although the retention factors in A and C are identical, resolution is accomplished with fewer

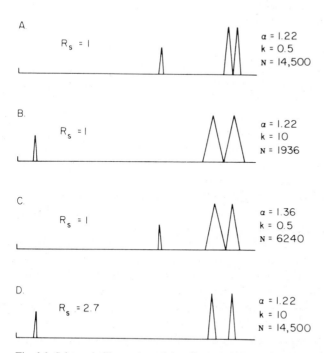

Fig. 3.9. Schematic illustration of the effect of changes in various parameters on the resolution, R_s. α, k, and N are relative retention, retention factor of the second eluite, and plate number, respectively.

References on p. A130

plates in C than in A because the chromatographic selectivity is greater in C. The effect of increasing the plate numbers or the resolution under otherwise identical conditions is illustrated in B and D. Finally, comparison of A to D shows that, at the same selectivity and plate number, an increase in the retention factor may result in improved separation. Chromatograms similar to A and D are encountered mainly in GC with open tubular columns.

3.5. THERMODYNAMICS OF CHROMATOGRAPHIC RETENTION

3.5.1. Fundamental relationships

This section presents a general framework for the thermodynamics of retention in the major forms of chromatography. After an examination of the fundamental relationships between the chemical potential of a solute in the mobile and stationary phases and the equilibrium constant, treatment of the activity coefficient will lead to expressions for the dependence of retention on state variables, such as temperature, pressure, and composition. In addition to the equilibrium distribution of solute between the mobile and stationary phases, which is regarded as the primary equilibrium process, secondary equilibria [27], such as protonation of ionogenic eluites in liquid chromatography will also be considered. The theory presented here will then be applied to specific conditions.

The magnitude of retention is exclusively expressed by the retention (capacity) factor, k, or by the logarithmic retention factor, κ. As shown in eqns. 3.19–3.23 the R_F value used to measure migration in planar chromatography is directly related to k, whereas the R_M values are equivalent to κ values under ideal elution conditions. However, retention data obtained in GC or HPLC are usually easier to interpret in terms of the underlying physicochemical parameters than those obtained in TLC or PC, where nonuniform conditions usually prevail along the migration path.

In the ensuing discussions, eluite retention is assumed to occur by only one mechanism unless otherwise indicated. Frequently, this is an oversimplification of the experimental situation. For example, some of the eluite partitioned into a liquid stationary phase may also be bound at the interface between the stationary phase and the mobile phase. Furthermore, the eluite may also interact with binding sites at the surface of the support for the liquid stationary phase. In such cases a detailed analysis of retention must consider the energetics of each individual process, as exemplified below by the treatment of dual retention mechanisms of interfacial adsorption. In principle, it is possible to isolate the effect of each retention mechanism and to evaluate its contribution to the overall free energy of retention.

In the simplest cases, chromatographic retention is due to the equilibrium distribution of the eluite between the mobile and stationary phases by one of two general mechanisms: partition or adsorption. Partition occurs when eluite molecules are transferred from one bulk phase into another so that in each phase they are completely surrounded by the molecules of that phase. In contrast, when adsorbed at the stationary phase surface, eluite molecules are in an anisotropic environment,

List of symbols on p. A122

composed of both mobile phase molecules and the surface of the bulk stationary phase. Especially in LSC, the composition of the liquid surface layer at the stationary phase surface may be different from that in the bulk mobile phase. As a result, the properties of the surface layer are expected to play an important role in determining the magnitude of the net retention energy.

Historically, the thermodynamics of different chromatographic methods, which evolved separately, have received different formal treatments. However, diversity is also a consequence of differences in volume density of the principal components of each phase. When the mobile phase is a gas, the average interaction energy of the eluite in the gas is much smaller than it would be in a liquid mobile phase because the density in the gas is about three orders of magnitude less than that in the liquid. It follows that retention in GC is largely governed by the energetics of interactions with stationary phase and the free energy of vaporization of the eluite, while the mobile phase apparently serves as an inert medium the main function of which is to sweep the eluites through the column. In contradistinction, molecular interactions in LC are quite strong between eluite and mobile phase components and they contribute significantly to the retention process. Consequently, division of chromatographic methods into two major groups according to the mobile phase, i.e. GC and LC, follows quite naturally from such considerations.

Classification according to the stationary phase, which may be either a liquid or solid, also has thermodynamic justification. Van der Waals forces become negligible beyond a few molecular diameters, and electrostatic forces also decrease rapidly with distance. Thus, in a liquid stationary phase, the eluite, upon transfer (partition) from the mobile phase, is shielded by a "screen" of stationary phase molecules thicker than a few molecular diameters. This is not true when eluite molecules are bound to the stationary phase surface or to covalently attached ligates, because the surface is in intimate contact with the mobile phase. Such cases are somewhat more difficult to analyze, since the physical chemistry at interfaces is incompletely understood. This reasoning can be extended to the thermodynamic treatment of SEC, where retention may be regarded as partitioning of eluite between two "liquids": the interstitial bulk mobile phase and the pore fluid. As the rotational and translational freedom of the eluite is reduced inside the pores of the column material, the pore fluid is believed to be different from the bulk mobile phase. The entropic effect associated with these phenomena is considered to be the major factor governing retention. However, the traditional classification of chromatographic techniques frequently fails, as under practical conditions the boundaries between partition and adsorption may be blurred. As will become clear later, confinement of certain techniques to the procrustean bed of traditional classification schemes cannot be justified.

3.5.1.1. Retention and free energy change

In interactive chromatography, the average interaction with each environment is measured by the Gibbs free energy or chemical potential, which depends on the eluite concentration. Equilibrium obtains when the chemical potentials in every phase are equal. In linear chromatography at sufficiently low eluite concentrations, the equilibrium thermodynamic quantities are considered to be constant and independent of eluite concentration. The ratio of eluite concentrations in the two phases at equilibrium yields the corresponding equilibrium constant, K, which is related to the chemical potentials of eluite in the two phases under standard conditions.

When K is constant, i.e. the sorption isotherm of the eluite is linear, the resulting peak is Gaussian in shape, and the retention factor is independent of the sample size (Fig. 3.10). Nonlinear isotherms, such as the convex and concave isotherms illustrated in Fig. 3.10, result in tailing and fronting of the peak, respectively. Such peak asymmetry is a consequence of the dependence of the migration velocity of the eluite on the slope of the isotherm, which varies with the mobile phase concentration. Retention factors, obtained from retention times measured at the peak apex, show a concomitant dependence on the sample size, as depicted in Fig. 3.10. Although peak asymmetry may arise from other sources, particularly in HPLC with relatively short columns, the peak asymmetry of thermodynamic origin is most important. The phenomenon is prevalent especially in adsorption chromatography, owing to the heterogeneity of binding sites and/or to the overloading in preparative work. However, frequently the relatively slow kinetics of the primary or secondary equilibria involved in the retention process may be responsible for asymmetrical peaks [1,28].

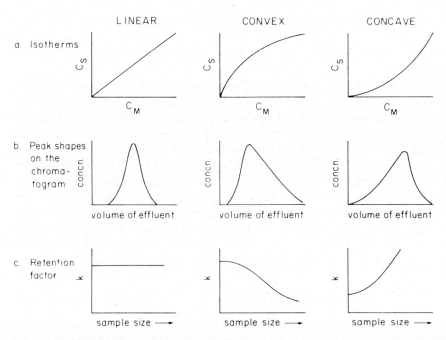

Fig. 3.10. Effect of isotherm shape on certain chromatographic properties. (a) Three different shapes of sorption isotherms encountered in chromatography. (b) Peak shapes resulting from these isotherms. (c) Dependence of the retention factor on the amount of eluite injected.

List of symbols on p. A122

In any case, the magnitude of eluite retention, measured by the first moment of the chromatographic peak, is solely determined by the overall equilibrium distribution of the eluite between the mobile and stationary phases, as shown by eqn. 3.14, where K is often an overall equilibrium constant. At first glance, it may seem peculiar that a thermodynamic property of the system determines the rate of eluite migration through the chromatographic system, but it must be remembered that the equilibrium constant is made up of rate constants according to the principle of microscopic reversibility [29]. In the simplest case, the equilibrium constant is given by the ratio of the rate constants for sorption and desorption

$$K = k_a/k_d \tag{3.70}$$

where k_a and k_d are the rate constants for sorption and desorption, respectively. The expression is more complex when the eluite exists in more than one form [30,31], e.g., as ionogenic species present both as the acid and conjugate base or as rapidly equilibrating isomers.

For an isobaric, isothermal process the equilibrium constant, K, is given as

$$K = \exp(-\Delta G^0/RT) \tag{3.71}$$

where ΔG^0 is the difference in standard Gibbs free energy associated with the transfer of the eluite from the mobile phase to the stationary phase in chromatography. The Gibbs energy for a state is defined as

$$\Delta G^0 = \Delta H^0 - T\Delta S^0 \tag{3.72}$$

where ΔH^0 and ΔS^0 are its enthalpy and entropy, respectively. The dependence of the equilibrium constant on temperature is found by combining eqns. 3.71 and 3.72 to give the Van't Hoff equation:

$$d \ln K/d(1/T) = d(-\Delta G^0/RT)/d(1/T) = -\Delta H^0/R \tag{3.73}$$

where ΔH^0 is the difference in enthalpy associated with the transfer of eluite between the two phases. Under regular conditions the value of ΔH^0 is independent of temperature so that linear Van't Hoff plots of $\ln K$ versus $1/T$ result, but irregular retention behavior is frequently observed in practice and recognized by the dependence of ΔH^0 on the temperature [30].

In general, the differential equation that relates the Gibbs energy of any system to its composition is given as

$$dG = -S \, dT + V \, dP + \Sigma \mu_i \, dn_i \tag{3.74}$$

where V and P are the volume and pressure of the system and μ_i and n_i are the chemical potential and number of moles of component i in the system. The chemical potential μ_i relates the free energy change of the system to a change in the number of moles of i when the temperature, pressure, and the moles of other components, n_j, are held constant, i.e. it is given as

$$\mu_i = (\partial G/\partial n_i)_{T,P,n_j} \tag{3.75}$$

The general requirement for equilibrium is that the Gibbs energy be a minimum, and

References on p. A130

this condition is expressed as

$$\Sigma \mu_i \, dn_i = 0 \tag{3.76}$$

when the pressure and temperature are fixed.

According to eqn. 3.76, chromatographic equilibrium is reached when the chemical potential of the eluite in the mobile and stationary phases are equal. The chemical potential of an eluite will depend on the temperature, pressure, and concentration of all components in the system including the concentration of the eluite itself. For this reason, the chemical potential of the eluite is given by

$$\mu = \mu^0 + RT \ln a \tag{3.77}$$

where μ^0 is the standard chemical potential, i.e. the potential determined under standard conditions, and a is the eluite activity in the phase of interest. The activity of a substance is related to its concentration, C, through the activity coefficient, γ, by the expression

$$a = \gamma C \tag{3.78}$$

Rigorous definitions of activity in liquid and vapor phases are found in Chap. 3.5.1.2.

Also according to eqn. 3.76, at equilibrium the eluite is distributed so that its respective chemical potentials in the stationary and mobile phases, μ_S and μ_M, are equal

$$\mu_S = \mu_M \tag{3.79}$$

so that

$$\mu_S^0 + RT \ln a_S = \mu_M^0 + RT \ln a_M \tag{3.80}$$

The corresponding equilibrium constant (partition coefficient), K, is given by the ratio of the equilibrium concentrations of the eluite in the two phases (cf. eqn. 3.15). In linear elution chromatography K is independent of the eluite concentration.

The logarithm of the equilibrium constant (in concentration units) can be derived from eqns. 3.71, 3.78, and 3.80 as

$$\ln K = (\mu_M^0 - \mu_S^0)/RT + (\ln \gamma_S - \ln \gamma_M) \tag{3.81}$$

Eqn. 3.81 shows that the logarithm of the equilibrium constant pertinent to chromatographic retention is given by the sum of the differences between the standard chemical potentials and the logarithmic activity coefficients. The thermodynamic analysis of retention is equivalent to evaluating the constant K. In light of eqn. 3.81, this requires that the activity coefficients in each phase be known. Various expressions for evaluating the activity coefficients are discussed in Chap. 3.5.1.2.

The retention is expressed in terms of the Henry's law coefficient in GC and in terms of a corresponding equilibrium constant, such as the partition coefficient, in LC. These functions are analogs in eqn. 3.81; in principle, the equilibrium constant is the ratio of the Henry's law coefficients for solution in the mobile and stationary phases.

List of symbols on p. A122

The Henry's law coefficients and equilibrium constants are written as functions of fugacity and activity, respectively. Because the activity is the ratio of the actual fugacity to the fugacity for ideal behavior, the formulations are equivalent, although they differ in the choice of the standard state used. By convention, activity and fugacity are used in the analysis of systems with gaseous and liquid mobile phases, respectively. In the final expressions, only the activity coefficients that are given as the ratio of the activity to the concentration (or pressure) are used.

The dependence of the activity coefficient, γ, on the system variables can be evaluated from the Gibbs–Duhem equation

$$n_1 \, d\mu_1 = -n_2 \, d\mu_2 \tag{3.82}$$

which gives the relationship between the number of moles, n_1 and n_2, of Components 1 and 2 and the corresponding chemical potentials, μ_1 and μ_2, in a single phase.

3.5.1.2. Activity and activity coefficient

3.5.1.2.1. Definitions
The term fugacity refers to the tendency of a substance to escape from the condensed phase to the vapor phase. According to the thermodynamic definition, fugacity can be approximated as the vapor pressure at low pressures. The activity is defined as the ratio of the fugacity of the system to fugacity in a reference state, called the standard state. For gases, the activity is usually defined as the ratio of the actual fugacity of the system to the ideal fugacity expected if the gas were a perfect gas.

The standard state is chosen according to one of two conventions that regard the component either as a solvent or a solute. The first convention assumes that ideal behavior is represented by Raoult's law and, therefore, the activity of a compound is given as the ratio of its fugacity in the vapor phase to its fugacity in a gas composed of it alone. In ideal solutions, the activity is equal to the mole fraction of the solute. Therefore, by this convention, the activity coefficient is defined as the ratio of activity to mole fraction in solution.

The second convention, which is used for solutes, recognizes that Raoult's law usually is not obeyed by solutes at low concentrations. Therefore, a solution is considered ideal at infinite dilution, and the standard state is defined from Henry's law (cf. eqn. 3.84). The activity of an eluite is the ratio of its fugacity to its Henry's law coefficient. The activity coefficient is the ratio of its activity to its mole fraction in solution. This convention is commonly used for the work definition of activity and activity coefficients of eluites in chromatography.

3.5.1.2.2. Fugacity and gas phase activity coefficient
Because in analytical GC the partial pressure of the eluite in the carrier gas is usually very low, the magnitude of retention is determined by the Henry's law coefficient of the eluite for the particular chromatographic system. Therefore, it may be of interest to review the pertinent fundamentals of the physical chemistry of gases.

References on p. A130

According to Raoult's law, the fugacity, f, of a gas above an ideal solution is given by the mole fraction of the solute in the solution, x_1, and the total pressure of the gas, P^0, as

$$f = P^0 x_1 \qquad (3.83)$$

However, eqn. 3.83 is rarely applicable in practice. A more useful expression is given by Henry's law

$$f = K_H x_1 \qquad (3.84)$$

where K_H is the Henry's law coefficient. The difference between these two laws is schematically illustrated in Fig. 3.11.

The effect of temperature on the equilibrium constant is evaluated by the Clapeyron equation, which relates the volume change to the enthalpy change in a phase transition:

$$(V_1 - V_v)\, dP/dT = -\Delta H_v^0/T \qquad (3.85)$$

where V_1, V_v and ΔH_v^0 are the molar volumes of the eluite in the liquid and vapor phases and the enthalpy of vaporization, respectively. The temperature dependence of the vapor pressure is evaluated by integration of eqn. 3.85. If we assume that the molar volume of the vapor obeys the ideal gas law, that the enthalpy change is independent of temperature (i.e. the heat capacity of the eluite is constant in each phase), and that the liquid molar volume is negligible compared to that of the vapor, the form of the integrated Clausius–Clapeyron equation is

$$\ln P^0 = -H_v^0/RT + \text{constants} \qquad (3.86)$$

Vapor pressure data are available from various sources for a wide variety of

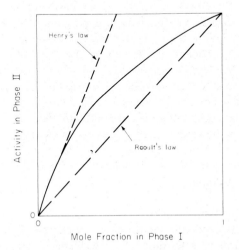

Fig. 3.11. Comparison of the dependence of the activity of a solute in one phase on its composition in the other phase (solid line) according to Henry's and Raoult's laws (broken lines).

List of symbols on p. A122

compounds; eqn. 3.86 yields a satisfactory estimate of vapor pressure in many cases
[8].

In practice, however, heat capacity changes are usually not negligible, so that the
enthalpy of vaporization depends of the temperature. Therefore, integration of the
Clapeyron equation leads to an expression of the form

$$\log P^0 = C' - A'/T + B' \log T \tag{3.87}$$

where A', B', and C' are constants. As this expression is difficult to use because the
coefficients are not readily available, the simpler Antoine equation is more popular
for vapor pressure estimation. It is given by

$$\log P^0 = C - A/(B + T) \tag{3.88}$$

where A, B, and C are experimentally measured coefficients. The Antoine equation
formally resembles eqn. 3.87 but differs from it in that the zero on the temperature
scale is not $0°K$ but $-B°K$. This change in temperature scale greatly simplifies the
analysis of vapor pressure data. The Antoine equation should be used only within
the temperature range over which the coefficients are determined. Extensive collec-
tions of Antoine coefficients are found in the chemical engineering literature [32,33].

In the preceding analysis we have neglected nonideality of the carrier gas or eluite
vapor and interactions between eluite and the carrier gas mixture as well as those
between the carrier gas and the stationary phase. Apparently, the error introduced
by disregarding eluite interactions with the carrier gas is usually small [34,35]. The
simplest correction for nonideality uses only the solute vapor pressure fugacity and
yields satisfactory results in many applications. In fact, it has been found that
activity coefficients obtained with the fugacity correction alone agreed with those
obtained by static measurements or calculated from more detailed expressions [36].
Detailed treatment of corrections can be found in monographs [7].

3.5.1.2.3. Evaluation of electrolyte activity

The definition of electrolyte activity coefficients is based on the Henry's law
convention. Molality replaces mole fraction as the concentration scale. At high
dilution, the fugacity of an electrolyte that yields v ions on dissociation is

$$f = mK_H \tag{3.89}$$

where K_H is the Henry law coefficient. The activity, activity coefficient $\gamma_\pm$, and
molality of a salt that yields v^+ cations and v^- anions upon dissociation are related
as

$$\gamma_\pm = a_\pm / (m_+^{v+} m_-^{v-})^{1/v} \tag{3.90}$$

where $a_\pm$, v^+, v^-, and v are the activity of the salt and number of cations, anions,
and total ions, respectively.

The now classical treatment of activity coefficients of simple ions and salts is
given by the Debye–Hückel equation, which relates the logarithm of activity

coefficients to the ionic strength as

$$\ln \gamma_{\pm} = -1.825 \times 10^6 |Z_+ Z_-| \left| \frac{I\rho_0}{\epsilon^3 T^3} \right|^{1/2} \tag{3.91}$$

In eqn. 3.91, cgs units are used and ρ_0, ϵ, Z_+ and Z_- are the solvent density, dielectric constant, and the charge on the cation and anion, respectively. The ionic strength, I, is defined as

$$I = \frac{1}{2} \sum_i m_i Z_i^2 \tag{3.92}$$

where summation is made over all ionic species. Extension of eqn. 3.91 to more concentrated systems is represented by the Davies equation [37], which takes the form

$$\ln \gamma_{\pm} = -A|Z_+ Z_-| I^{1/2} + BI \tag{3.93}$$

More complex and exact solutions that can be used at high electrolyte concentrations have also been developed [38,39].

3.5.1.2.4. Activity coefficients in nonionic solutions

Regular solution theory [40,41] has frequently been used for the estimation of activity and the interpretation of experimental results in chromatography. This approach is applicable when the molecules are similar in size. When the molar volumes of the stationary phase constituents and the eluite are markedly different, large errors occur in the predicted mixing entropy because of the divergence of the volume fraction scale (which is the proper basis of entropy calculation) from the mole fraction scale. Corrections for the mixing entropy are available as functions of the ratio of the sizes of eluite and stationary phase components [8], obtained from statistical mechanical analyses of polymer solutions [40,42,43].

One defect of regular solution theory is that it cannot be reliably used to analyze behavior in polar solvents, especially water, or in mixtures that contain polar components. However, no widely accepted method for treating such systems exists, because the thermodynamic theory of such solutions is incomplete. A simple approach to the prediction and/or interpretation of equilibrium constants of the Henry's law type is the solvophobic theory, which is applicable not only to aqueous systems [44–46] but also to hydro-organic media [47,48]. In the latter cases, the theory is still somewhat primitive and, due to the complexity of the system, it entails some assumptions that may be considered oversimplifications. The theory is outlined in the analysis of reversed-phase chromatography (Chap. 3.5.5).

3.5.1.2.5. Activity coefficients in multicomponent nonionic solutions

The theory of solutions is not sufficiently advanced to describe the variation of activity coefficient with composition in mixed solvents in a rigorous fashion. Nevertheless, simple formulations describing the change in activity coefficient with composition do exist. The simplest approach regards the mixed solvent as the "sum"

List of symbols on p. A122

of two solvents, each of which has a certain activity coefficient and may be nonideal. However, the two solvent components are assumed not to interact with each other. This is the basis of the "diachoric" equation [49], which relates partition into a mixed liquid stationary phase in GC to the corresponding partition coefficients in the neat liquid phases

$$K_{AB} = \phi_A K_A + \phi_B K_B \tag{3.94}$$

where K_{AB}, K_A and K_B are the partition coefficients for the mixed solvent and for neat solvents A and B, respectively. The volume fractions of A and B are given by ϕ_A and ϕ_B, respectively. The behavior predicted by eqn. 3.94 is shown in Fig. 3.12a for the case in which the GLC retention factor is a linear function of the liquid stationary phase composition. Eqn. 3.94 has been the starting point for treatments of retention in adsorption and reversed-phase partition chromatography [50].

An alternative approach takes into account interactions between solvent components. In this case, the activity coefficient of the solute in a binary mixture is expressed by

$$\ln \gamma_{AB} = \phi_A \ln \gamma_A + \phi_B \ln \gamma_B - \bar{v}_{AB} \beta \phi_A \phi_B \tag{3.95}$$

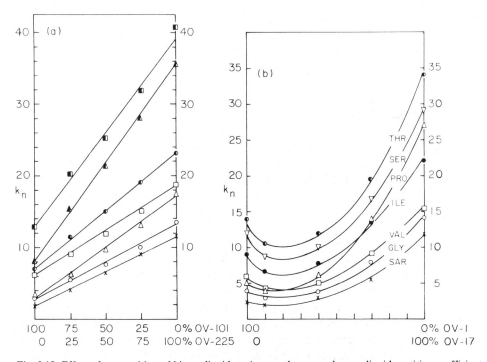

Fig. 3.12. Effect of composition of binary liquid stationary phases on the gas–liquid partition coefficient. In the simplest case, K_H is a linear function of the stationary phase composition according to eqn. 3.94, as shown in (a). Alternatively, the function is more complex, as given in eqn. 3.95 and shown in (b). (Reproduced from *J. Chromatogr.*, 167 (1978) 291, with permission [51].)

References on p. A130

where γ_{AB}, γ_A, and γ_B are the activity coefficients of the solute in the binary mixture and in the neat solvents A and B, respectively. The composition of the mixture is given by the volume fractions of A and B, ϕ_A and ϕ_B, whereas $\bar{v}_{AB}$ and β are the (fictitious) molar volume of pure liquid solute and an interaction coefficient for A and B, which can be evaluated from regular solution theory [51]. Eqn. 3.95 has been shown to describe the dependence of solute retention on stationary phase composition in GLC. An example is seen in Fig. 3.12b, where the retention factor in GLC of derivatized amino acids is a quadratic function of the stationary phase composition. The definition of the activity coefficients used in the treatment of retention with polar and nonpolar stationary phases is similar to, but not identical with, the definition given in eqn. 3.95.

3.5.1.3. Adsorption

Adsorption on a surface is complicated by the fact that the surface is covered by adsorbed mobile phase molecules which must be displaced by the eluite before binding occurs. The displacement step can be represented by the reaction scheme:

$$A_M + B_S \rightleftharpoons A_S + \nu B_M \tag{3.96}$$

where ν molecules of B present at the stationary phase surface are displaced by one molecule of A from the mobile phase and the subscripts S and M indicate stationary and mobile phase concentrations, respectively. If the mobile phase is a gas, the relationship between surface coverage and mobile phase concentration is given by a Langmuir-type isotherm as

$$y_{A,S} = \frac{y_{max} K_A [A]}{1 + K_B [B]^\nu + K_A [A]} \tag{3.97}$$

where $y_{A,S}$ and y_{max} are fractional and maximum surface coverage, respectively, by Substance A. Parameters K_A and K_B are constants for binding A and B to the stationary phase, whereas [A] and [B] are concentrations in the mobile phase [7,52]. The retention factor, k, is obtained from eqns. 3.12 and 3.97 as

$$k = \phi y_{AS} / [A] = \phi y_{max} K / \left(1 + K_B [B]^\nu + K_A [A]\right) \tag{3.98}$$

where ϕ is the phase ratio.

Whereas the concentration of A will usually be vanishingly small under elution conditions, eqn. 3.98 shows that the magnitude of retention depends on the extent to which the surface is covered by the eluite and the more strongly adsorbed mobile phase component, which depends on the concentration of each mobile phase component. Eqn. 3.98 predicts that in linear adsorption chromatography the reciprocal of the retention factor is a linear function of the concentration of the more strongly adsorbed mobile phase component, raised to the νth power (i.e. Solvent A in eqn. 3.98). In practice, usually $\nu = 1$. This qualitative conclusion seems to hold true for adsorption from liquid mixtures. However, adsorption from solution may be complicated by solvation of the surface [53]. Furthermore, recent analysis suggests that retention is governed by the surface excess concentration, which is defined as the difference between the surface concentration and the bulk-phase concentration in consistent units [19].

The limits of this analysis, as well as the problem of adsorption, can be illustrated by three examples:

(a) An eluite may bind much more weakly than the eluent to the stationary phase proper, so that it is either excluded or it partitions into the layer of strongly bound solvent at the surface. Under certain circumstances, this might be viewed as a special case of LLC.

(b) The eluite may bind much more strongly than the solvent, in which case the role of solvent displacement in retention is negligible, so that K_B in eqns. 3.97 and 3.98 approaches 0.

(c) The binding strength of solvent and eluite are comparable, i.e. K_A and K_B are of the same order of magnitude. This case may be important in the analysis of retention in reversed-phase chromatography with ternary mobile phases. However, this model has not been treated in detail, except for adsorption chromatography when interactions between the mobile phase and eluite are negligible [4,54].

The diversity in behavior discussed above is responsible for present ambiguities in demarcating adsorption and partition chromatography, particularly when multicomponent eluents are used. Advances in HPLC are expected to provide a clearer theoretical framework and an adequate experimental data base for the treatment of adsorption from liquid mixtures.

3.5.1.4. Complex formation

The eluite may form a complex with components of the mobile phase. The simplest general reaction takes the form

$$\nu_A A + \nu_B B \rightleftharpoons \nu_C C \tag{3.99}$$

where A, B, and C are, respectively, the uncomplexed sample component, the complexing agent, and the eluite complex, and ν_A, ν_B and ν_C are their respective stoichiometric coefficients. The conditions for equilibrium in each phase are obtained from eqn. 3.74 as

$$\Sigma \nu_i \mu_{i,S} = 0 \tag{3.100}$$

and

$$\Sigma \nu_i \mu_{i,M} = 0 \tag{3.101}$$

where ν_i values corresponding to ν_A and ν_B in eqn. 3.99 are negative.

The retention factor is related to the total amount of eluite, which is the sum of the free and complexed forms in each phase. Therefore, the observed retention factor is expressed as

$$k = \frac{m_{A,S} + m_{C,S}}{m_{A,M} + m_{C,M}} \tag{3.102}$$

where $m_{i,j}$ is the mass of species i in phase j, with A and C representing the free and complexed eluite species, respectively.

The condition for chromatographic equilibrium when the chemical potential for transfer between the two phases is zero, the relationship between retention factor and the free energies of transfer and reaction is found by combination of eqns. 3.100 and 3.102 to obtain

$$k = \frac{k_A + k_C K_f [A]^{r_A - 1} [B]^{r_B}}{1 + K_f [A]^{r_A - 1} [B]^{r_B}} \tag{3.103}$$

where

$$k_i = \phi_{\exp}[(\mu_{iM} - \mu_{iS})/RT] \tag{3.104}$$

$$K_f = [C]/[A]^{r_A}[B]^{r_B} \tag{3.105}$$

$$K_f = \exp[(r_A \mu_{A_EM} + r_B \mu_{BM} - \mu_{CM})/RT] \tag{3.106}$$

$$r_i = \nu_i/\nu_C \tag{3.107}$$

Therefore, the observed retention factor is given by the retention factors of the free (A) and complexed (C) eluite, weighted by the extent of complex formation in the mobile phase.

Eqn. 3.103 is the basis for estimation of stability constants and for evaluation of the magnitude of interactions with stationary phase components. The reader is directed to a review of the chromatographic determination of physicochemical quantities [36]. Expressions similar to eqn. 3.103 have been used for the determination of complex formation constants by GLC [55] and also in LLC [36] and reversed-phase chromatography for the evaluation of mobile phase complex formation constants, including acid dissociation constants [56].

According to eqn. 3.103, complex formation does not cause departures from linearity in elution chromatography when the A:C stoichiometry is 1:1 and the concentration of the complexing agent, B, is sufficiently high, i.e. much greater than any local concentration of the free eluite (A) or the complex (C) in the column. With 1:1 stoichiometry, the term $[A]^{r-1}$ in eqn. 3.103 is unity at all concentrations, so that the retention factor is independent of the concentration of A. However, if the ratio r_A is different from 1, the retention factor will depend on the concentration of A in the peak. As a consequence, the elution volume will depend on the mass of injected sample and the peak shape may not be Gaussian [1,31]. Such results have been observed in the gel chromatography of dissociating protein systems [57,58]. It also follows that if the local concentration of B is not constant at all points in the chromatograph, retention must be predicted by using eqn. 3.103.

Complex formation is used in many ways to enhance selectivity in chromatography. For instance, stationary phases in GC can be impregnated with Ag^+ in order to enhance specifically the retention of alkenes. In reversed-phase chromatography the mobile phase frequently contains a complexing agent, which has been called hetaeron (from the Greek word for companion). In ion-pair chromatography [59], a hydrophobic ion is added to the eluent in order to enhance specifically the retention of oppositely charged sample components [27,48,60]. In some cases, components of the buffer used to maintain the pH of the eluent constant may also form complexes with certain eluites [61].

The effect of complexation on retention is conveniently measured by the retention modulus, η, which is given by

$$\eta = k/k_0 \tag{3.108}$$

where k is the retention factor of the eluite in question with the complexing agent (hetaeron) present in the eluent, and k_0 is the retention factor obtained without the hetaeron but under otherwise identical conditions as far as the column, the temperature, and other operating conditions are concerned. The value of the modulus is greater than unity when complex formation enhances retention and smaller than unity when the complex is eluted faster than the free eluite [56]. In the following analyses of the thermodynamic basis of retention, retention is assumed to be unaffected by complexation. The expressions given can then be modified in light of eqn. 3.103 to correct for this effect when it is present.

3.5.1.5. Secondary adsorption effects

With liquid stationary phases, interfacial adsorption may also contribute to retention. In GLC the net retention volume per gram of packing, V_g, may also depend on the surface area of the stationary phase [62]:

$$V_g = KV_S + K_a A_S \tag{3.109}$$

where K, V_S, K_a and A_S are the gas/liquid partition coefficient, the volume of liquid stationary phase, the interfacial adsorption coefficient, and the surface area of the stationary phase, respectively. Plots of V_g/A_S versus V_S/A_S, using data obtained on different columns, yield K as the slope and K_a as the intercept, so that by using eqn. 3.109 both equilibrium constants can be evaluated. The situation is further complicated by possible adsorption of eluite at the support surface, which can be especially significant with polar supports, such as silica or alumina. The phenomenon has been extensively treated in the literature [36,63,64]. The contribution of adsorption to retention can be analyzed by appropriate plots of retention data, obtained on columns which vary in stationary phase load.

3.5.2. Gas–liquid chromatography

3.5.2.1. Role of carrier gas

The mobile phase in GLC is most frequently a chemically inert gas, such as nitrogen or helium, which does not interact with the sample components. Although these gases dissolve in the stationary phase, their role is passive insofar as they provide an inert medium in which eluite molecules not dissolved in the stationary phase are swept through the column.

References on p. A130

The partition coefficient between two phases is given as the ratio of the activity in the stationary phase and the fugacity in the vapor phase so that the net retention volume, V_N, is given as

$$V_N = \phi x_1 / P^0 \tag{3.110}$$

where x_1 is the mole fraction of 1 in the liquid phase and P^0 is the standard pressure. The retention is related to the heats of vaporization, ΔH_v^0, and heat of mixing, ΔH_m^0, in the stationary phase at a given temperature by

$$\log V_N = (\Delta H_v^0 - \Delta H_m^0)/RT - (\Delta S_v^0 - \Delta S_m^0)/R + \Phi \tag{3.111}$$

where Φ is the logarithm of the phase ratio, ϕ.

Eqn. 3.111 is frequently expressed in terms of the differential heat of vaporization from solution at infinite dilution, ΔH_e^0, which is given by

$$\Delta H_e^0 = \Delta H_v^0 - \Delta H_m^0 \tag{3.112}$$

3.5.2.2. Determination of retention volume

The retention volume is usually determined indirectly from the retention time and flow velocity of the carrier gas, corrected for the pressure drop across the column. The retention volume of an unretained component, usually air, methane, or hydrogen [65], is used in the calculation of the retention factor.

An alternative method for void volume determination capitalizes on the observation that plots of the logarithmic net retention volume of n-alkanes versus the number of carbons in the alkane are usually straight lines, as illustrated in Fig. 3.13. This relationship can be exploited in order to evaluate V_m by the use of the retention volumes of three or more homologs [15,20].

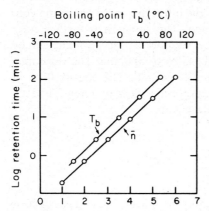

Fig. 3.13. Dependence of the logarithm of the retention time, obtained in GSC at 60°C, on the number of carbons in the n-paraffin eluite and on the boiling point of the paraffin. (Reproduced from *Anal. Chem.*, 27 (1955) 170, with permission [66].)

List of symbols on p. A122

3.5.2.3. Determination of thermochemical quantities

Thermochemical data, such as the latent heat of vaporization of an eluite, can be obtained by using eqn. 3.111 and Van't Hoff plots from retention measurements on stationary phases with which it forms ideal or athermal solutions [67,68].

Boiling points can be estimated from the heat of vaporization by use of Trouton's rule, although better results are obtained by combination of eqn. 3.111 and the general form of eqn. 3.86 to obtain

$$\ln V_N = A T_b + B \tag{3.113}$$

at a fixed temperature. The boiling point, T_b, can be estimated from the corrected retention volume of a solute by interpolation of plots of $\ln V_N$ versus known T_b.

Solute vapor pressure is determined by

$$\ln V_N = -B \ln P^0 + C \tag{3.114}$$

were B and C are constants and the system is isothermal and nearly ideal. Unknown vapor pressures may be determined by interpolation in plots of $\ln V_N$ versus $\ln P^0$ for eluites of known vapor pressure [36]. This method has been used to estimate vapor pressures of fatty acids, fatty acid esters, hydrocarbons, alcohols, and chloroalkanes [69]. An alternative method uses the specific retention volumes at the temperature of interest and the known boiling temperature [7].

The molecular weight of stationary phase constituents can be determined from retention on a chemically similar phase having a known molecular weight [7]. It is possible to extract both the activity coefficient and the second virial coefficient, B_{12}, which accounts for carrier gas/solute interactions [36,70]. Activity coefficients of hydrocarbons and chloroalkanes in squalene and dinonylphthalate are in good agreement with statically measured values [34,71,72]. B_{12} has been determined for the interactions of hydrocarbons, aromatics, and other organics with H_2, N_2, Ar, O_2, CO_2, He, or CH_4 in the carrier gas. A critical review found that chromatographically determined values of B_{12} agree well with those determined by other methods [36]. The determination of activity coefficients by GC has been the subject of a recent review [73] and more extensive monographs [7,52].

3.5.3. Gas–solid adsorption chromatography

In GSC, the eluite is retained by adsorption at the stationary phase surface. Retention can be formally visualized as the result of the combined effects of condensation from the vapor phase and weak binding interactions with the surface. Generally, the number of binding sites is finite and the sites are often not energetically uniform. As a result, the degree of saturation of the surface affects the Gibbs free energy of retention, except at very low surface coverage, where linear conditions prevail.

The retention volume, V_N, is related to the activity of the eluite in the mobile and stationary phases according to eqn. 3.77 and, by combination of eqns. 3.77 and 3.81, it is found to be

$$\ln V_N = -\Delta H_a^0 / RT + \Delta S_a^0 / R + \Phi \tag{3.115}$$

References on p. A130

where ΔH_a^0 and ΔS_a^0 are enthalpy and entropy of adsorption, respectively. The retention volume depends upon energetic factors that include the energy of adsorption and the activity coefficients in both the gas and surface phases. Whereas in GLC the energies of vaporization and mixing comprise the retention energy, in GSC it is composed of the energies of vaporization and adsorption. Consequently, the retention energy of an eluite would not be expected to be the same in the two methods, although they might be identical coincidentally. As a consequence, efforts to extract physicochemical quantities, other than the enthalpy and entropy, associated with the overall adsorption process generally fail. However, correlations between the retention volume or enthalpy and properties of the pure solute can be obtained if the effects of adsorption are properly accounted for. This is discussed more fully in Chap. 3.6.

GSC is not extensively used in analytical work, because the bandspreading and peak asymmetry are greater than in GLC, owing to the surface heterogeneity of the solid stationary phases. On the other hand, chromatography may be used for the characterization of the adsorbent. The adsorption isotherm, $f(P)$, can be obtained as an implicit function of gas pressure, P,

$$f(P) = \theta/(1-\theta) \tag{3.116}$$

where θ is the fractional coverage of the surface.

The full characterization of the binding properties of a surface requires knowledge of the surface area and the enthalpy of binding. Problems associated with the measurement of the surface area are fully treated in specialized monographs [7]. The heat of adsorption can also be evaluated by using eqns. 3.115 and 3.116. Plots of the degree of saturation (or surface coverage) versus partial pressure of the eluite are prepared from retention volumes, determined at various operating pressures and at several different temperatures. Van't Hoff plots of the logarithm of adjusted retention volume, evaluated at constant surface coverage, versus reciprocal temperature yield the "isosteric" enthalpy of adsorption. Determinations of the stability constant, specific surface area, and isosteric adsorption energy are used for the GSC characterization of catalysts [74].

3.5.4. Liquid–liquid chromatography

LLC employs liquid mobile and stationary phases. The phases must be mutually immiscible, or very nearly so, in order to minimize loss of the stationary phase from the column, and thus obtain a stable chromatographic system. "Bleeding" can be minimized by temperature control and by presaturating the mobile phase with the liquid stationary phase. Adsorption at the interface and the column surface also must be minimized. In spite of the need for these precautions, LLC is a potential tool for the determination of physicochemical properties of sample components. Retention is determined by the partition coefficient between the two phases. The activity coefficient in one phase can be determined from the retention factor when the activity in the other phase is known.

In order to analyze the thermodynamics of retention in LLC [75], each phase is regarded as a two-component solution in equilibrium at column pressure $\bar{P}$ and temperature T. The chemical potential of the solute in each phase is given by eqn. 3.77. The column pressure is taken as the mean of the column inlet and outlet pressures. The specific retention volume is given as the adjusted retention volume per gram of support, V_g.

$$\ln V_g = \left(\frac{\ln \gamma_M M_M}{\ln \gamma_S M_S \rho_M} \right) + \left(\frac{\bar{P} - 1}{RT} \right) (\bar{v}_M - \bar{v}_S) \qquad (3.117)$$

where γ is the activity coefficient and $\bar{v}$ is the partial molar volume of the eluite in the mobile or stationary phase having molecular weight M. The mobile phase density is ρ_M, and the reference pressure is usually taken to be 1 atm. If the difference in partial molar volume of eluite between the two phases is small, the second term on the right-hand side of eqn. 3.117 is negligible and the specific retention is given by

$$V_g = \gamma_M M_M / \gamma_S M_S \rho_M \qquad (3.118)$$

The prediction of eqn. 3.118 that retention volume is determined by the ratio of activity coefficients in the mobile and stationary phases has ample experimental support. For instance, the retention behavior of hydrocarbons with diethylene glycol and triethylene glycol as the stationary phase and heptane as the mobile phase conforms to that predicted by eqn. 3.118 with activity coefficients from extra-chromatographic sources [75]. Retention volumes extrapolated to 60°C from data obtained over the range 25–45°C agreed well with those predicted at that temperature by use of eqn. 3.118 and independently determined activity coefficients [76].

Chromatographic selectivity can also be predicted by using eqn. 3.118. The selectivity between two sample species, 1 and 2, is obtained from eqns. 3.62 and 3.118 as

$$\alpha_{2,1} = \gamma_{1,S} \gamma_{2,M} / \gamma_{2,S} \gamma_{1,M} \qquad (3.119)$$

Two methods for modulating chromatographic selectivity are implied by the above relationship:

(a) One of the phases may be replaced in order to obtain more favorable activity coefficient ratio. For example, the selectivity between 2,3-butanedione and dimethyl-carbonate can be increased from 1.07 to 1.33 by changing the mobile phase from methylcyclohexane to toluene [75].

(b) Differences in the temperature dependence of the coefficients may be exploited to manipulate selectivity. While the retention enthalpy in LLC is on the order of 5 kcal/mol [77], differences in enthalpies are likely to be small. However, in light of the Van't Hoff equation (eqn. 3.73), even differences as small as 2 kcal/mol will cause the selectivity to increase by a factor of 1.23 when the temperature increases from 25°C to 45°C, provided the more strongly retained component has greater enthalpy.

Eqns. 3.118 or 3.117 can be used to determine the ratio of activity coefficients in the two phases for the eluite as well as the partial molar excess free energy, enthalpy, and entropy associated with the chromatographic retention process. Although little progress has been made in the area of the determination of thermochemical data by LLC, the activities of alcohols in glycerol have been determined [77] and the activity coefficients of hydrocarbons in aniline and/or acetonitrile at 25°C were predicted successfully on the basis of eqn. 3.118.

Discrepancies found between chromatographically and statically determined values have been ascribed to adsorption at the interface [75] or to the slight solubility of one phase in the other. When corrections are made to account for the presence of the minor components in each phase, the experimental and predicted activity coefficients agree to within ±1%. In addition to the general treatment followed here [75], statistical mechanical analysis has also been used to develop the theory of partition chromatography [78].

3.5.5. Reversed-phase chromatography

3.5.5.1. The stationary phase

LC carried out with a nonpolar stationary phase and polar mobile phase is generally known as reversed-phase chromatography. The bonded stationary phase usually consists of hydrocarbonaceous ligates, covalently attached to the surface of a siliceous support via siloxane bonds. In fact, this type of chromatography is the most prominent representative of "bonded-phase" chromatography in which a solid stationary phase with covalently bound organic functions is employed [79].

According to various models of the thermodynamics of retention in reversed-phase chromatography [48,80], the logarithmic retention factor is proportional to the change in surface area upon binding of the eluite to the stationary phase. That change is proportional to the surface area of either the eluite or the binding site, whichever is smaller. Generally, retention increases with the surface coverage by organic functions. However, with an incompletely modified surface the mechanism of retention may be different. At low coverage the ligates may be scattered on the surface so that only a few or no binding sites of optimal size would be formed [81]. With increased coverage, more such sites are generated, and the retention increases exponentially or linearly with surface coverage, depending on whether the sites are too small or too few at low coverage. The data regarding these effects are not yet clear, and plots of retention versus coverage yield either linear or logarithmic relationships [48]. Above a critical carbon load, the value of which depends on the surface area and geometry of the particle, no increase in retention is observed.

Some data suggest that retention is dependent on the chain length of the stationary phase ligates [80], at least with incompletely covered phases. However, an analysis of retention data obtained on fully loaded and capped phases indicates that the free energies of retention on octyl- and octadecylsilica phases are indistinguishable. Furthermore, the retention free energy is independent of the provenance of the silica support [82]. However, bonded stationary phases having sterically highly constrained ligates, such as an adamantyl group, or short-chain ligates, such as ethyl, are energetically distinct from the commonly used octyl- and octadecylsilicas. In view of these results, a thermodynamic analysis of reversed-phase chromatography retention that neglects peculiarities of the support seems justified only as long as water-rich eluents are used and specific interactions of eluites with residual silanol groups at the surface are negligible.

List of symbols on p. A122

TABLE 3.2

PROPERTIES OF SOLVENTS WITH POTENTIAL USE IN REVERSED-PHASE CHROMATOGRAPHY [48]

	MW	BP (°C)	n^a	UV^b (nm)	ρ^c (g·cm^{-3})	η^d (cP)	ϵ^e	μ^f (Debye)	γ^g (dyn·cm^{-1})	E^h
Acetone[i]	58.1	56	1.357	330	0.791	0.322	20.7	2.72	23	0.56
Acetonitrile	41.0	82	1.342	190	0.787	0.358	38.8	3.37	29	0.65
Dioxane	88.1	101	1.420	215	1.034	1.26	2.21	0.45	33	0.56
Ethanol	46.1	78	1.359	205	0.789	1.19	24.5	1.68	22	0.88
Methanol	32.0	65	1.326	205	0.792	0.584	32.7	1.66	22	0.95
2-Propanol	60.1	82	1.375	205	0.785	2.39	19.9	1.68	21	0.82
1-Propanol	60.1	97	1.383	205	0.804	2.20	20.3	1.65	23	0.82
Tetrahydrofuran	72.1	66	1.404	210	0.889	0.51	7.58	1.70	27.6	0.45
Water	18.0	100	1.333	170	0.998	1.00	78.5	1.84	73	

[a] Refractive index at 25°C.
[b] UV cut-off; the wavelength at which the optical density of a 1-cm thick neat sample is unity as measured against air.
[c] Density at 20°C.
[d] Viscosity at 20°C.
[e] Dielectric constant.
[f] Dipole moment.
[g] Surface tension.
[h] Eluotropic value of alumina according to Snyder [84].
[i] Not suitable for use with UV detector.

3.5.5.2. Mobile-phase effects

The mobile phase in reversed-phase chromatography is more polar than the stationary phase. It is most frequently a mixture of water, or an aqueous buffered solution, and a suitable miscible organic solvent, such as methanol, acetonitrile, or tetrahydrofuran. The properties of several solvents for use in reversed-phase chromatography are given in Table 3.2. Of these properties, the dielectric constant and the surface tension of .he mobile phase have been found to be important in determining retention, as predicted by the "solvophobic" theory [85] (vide infra), which predicts that retention increases with a decrease in dielectric constant or an increase in surface tension. The eluite diffusivity depends on the mobile phase viscosity, which thus has an effect on the column efficiency. Among the solvents listed in Table 3.2, water has the greatest polarity and surface tension. Therefore, water is the weakest eluent used, and in most applications pure methanol or acetonitrile is the stronger eluent in reversed-phase chromatography.

Eluents of intermediate strength are usually obtained by mixing one of these solvents with water or an aqueous buffer. Figs. 3.14 and 3.15 show the viscosity, surface tension, and dielectric constants of such mixtures as a function of composition. In each case, the surface tension and the dielectric constant decrease monotonically with increasing organic solvent content. On the other hand, the viscosity first increases with the organic solvent content and, after reaching a maximum, decreases.

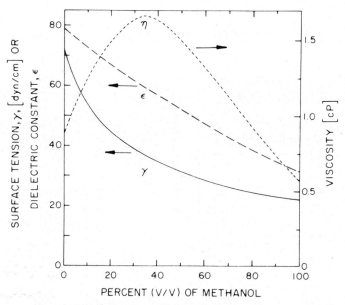

Fig. 3.14. Dependence of solvent properties of interest in reversed-phase chromatography on the composition of water–methanol mixtures at 25°C. γ = Surface tension, η = viscosity, ϵ = dielectric constant. Data were taken from refs. 86, 87, and 88, respectively. (Reproduced from *J. Chromatogr. Sci.*, 15 (1977) 393, with permission [83].)

List of symbols on p. A122

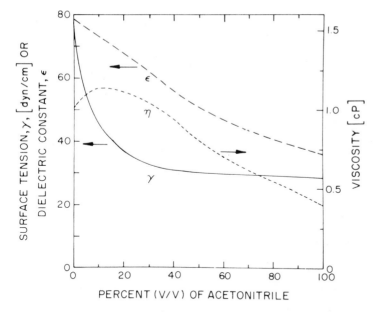

Fig. 3.15. Dependence of solvent properties of interest in reversed-phase chromatography on the composition of water–acetonitrile mixtures at 25°C. γ = Surface tension, η = viscosity, ϵ = dielectric constant. Data were taken from refs. 86, 86, and 89, respectively. (Reproduced from *J. Chromatogr. Sci.*, 15 (1977) 393, with permission [83].)

This effect is particularly pronounced in the case of methanol–water mixtures. Most work has been done with binary mobile phases containing water and acetonitrile or methanol, but there is a growing interest in the use of ternary systems. Although exceptions have been noted [90], for binary eluents the logarithmic retention factor, κ, has been observed to be a linear function of the volume fraction of organic cosolvent, φ, given by

$$\kappa = \kappa_0 + \beta\varphi \tag{3.120}$$

where κ_0 is the logarithmic retention factor obtained with plain water or aqueous buffer [48,91]. The effects of acetonitrile concentration and eluite size are shown in Fig. 3.16. The slopes of κ versus φ plots are expected to be proportional to the molecular surface area of the eluite, according to the solvophobic theory [48].

With ternary solvent systems the linearity between κ and φ is no longer strictly observed. On the other hand, the addition of a third solvent component to the mobile phase often confers novel selectivity on the chromatographic system. The third solvent component may form complexes with certain eluites in the mobile phase and thereby modify retention and selectivity. For example, different selectivities toward various functional groups are obtained with water–methanol, acetonitrile–water, and tetrahydrofuran–water mixtures, even at compositions which give the same retention factor for benzene [93]. The retention of phenols, nitrobenzene, and nitrobenzaldehydes are enhanced, and retention of alkylbenzoates are

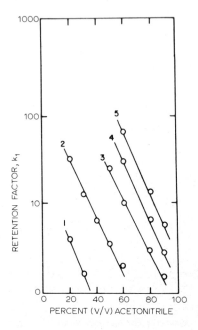

Fig. 3.16. Plots of the logarithmic retention factors of polyaromatic hydrocarbons against the composition of acetonitrile–water mixtures in reversed-phase chromatography. The data were obtained with (1) phenol, (2) benzene, (3) anthracene, (4) benz[a]anthracene, and (5) benzo[a]pyrene as eluites. (Reproduced from *J. Chromatogr.*, 126 (1976) 421, with permission [92].)

reduced in tetrahydrofuran–water (1:3) compared to that expected on the basis of the retention in methanol–water (1:1) and on the assumption that eqn. 3.120 holds [94]. Furthermore, small volume fractions of hexafluoroisopropanol, trifluoroethanol, trichlorotrifluoroethane, or chloroform in the eluent have produced significant changes in selectivity [95]. The effects of such complex formation [48] need to be considered in a complete thermodynamic analysis of retention.

Ion-pair chromatography represents an especially timely example of the use of a ternary system for modulation of retention. In these systems, a hydrophobic ion (hetaeron) is included in the mobile phase. Although the process has been extensively studied, its mechanism remains an open question. An increase in retention can occur if the hetaeron binds to the stationary phase to form a dynamically coated ion-exchange surface at which the eluite is retained, or if the hetaeron–eluite complexes formed in the mobile phase are less polar and larger than the eluite molecule and therefore more strongly retained than the latter. An analysis of the available data suggests that while neither mechanism operates under all conditions, each of them, as well as other mechanisms, may operate under particular conditions [96]. Recent reviews describe the method [60,97] and include a thermodynamic analysis [96].

List of symbols on p. A122

3.5.5.3. Solvophobic theory

In reversed-phase chromatography — in contrast to other chromatographic systems — polar eluites are eluted before nonpolar eluites. Theoretical treatment of the process may be attempted in three different ways:

(a) The first employs regular solution theory [98,99], which models interactions in nonpolar solvents and has been extended to polar solvents [100]. The predictions from this theory are not always satisfactory, as the use of several adjustable parameters is required [101].

(b) The second approach involves theories dealing with the hydrophobic effect in neat aqueous media, but these theories cannot be readily extended to treat interactions in hydro-organic solvents, such as those used in reversed-phase chromatography.

(c) The third approach is based on the "solvophobic" theory [44,47], which holds a promise of a unified treatment of solute behavior in neat aqueous, neat organic, and mixed hydro-organic solvents. The theory was originally developed as a generalized treatment of the "hydrophobic effect" for any solvent and was applied to the kinetics or equilibria of a few processes [46]. It has since been used to model the aqueous solubilities of alkanes [102], adsorption onto charcoal [102], and protein solubilities [103]. It has the virtue that the parameters required can be found in standard handbooks and in the literature or they can be adequately estimated. The solvophobic theory has been successfully adapted to analyze the thermodynamics of retention in reversed-phase chromatography [85], and a detailed description of this approach is available [48].

3.5.5.3.1. The original model

The original model used in the solvophobic theory was developed for the Henry's law coefficient of a solute in a solvent [45]. For that purpose, the solution process is divided into two steps, as illustrated in Fig. 3.17. In the first step, a cavity in the solvent is created of the same shape and size as the incoming solute. The free energy change, ΔG_c, required for this is the product of the surface area of the cavity and the solvent surface tension, γ, which has to be corrected to microscopic dimensions by a factor $\kappa^e(r)$. In the second step, the molecule is placed in the cavity and the resulting interaction energy is calculated. This energy is comprised of a Van der Waals and an electrostatic component. A final term accounts for the difference in free volume between the condensed and gas phases [48].

The Van der Waals term is calculated from a Kihara potential, corrected for the reduction in the intermolecular potential by intervening molecules in the condensed state. It was developed on the basis of a statistical mechanical treatment of a dense system of spherical particles [44]. The electrostatic term includes all contributions that are polar in nature, such as dipole–dipole interactions and ionic effects. The appropriate quantitative expressions are available [48]. If required, the energies of hydrogen bond or charge transfer complex formation can be included in this term.

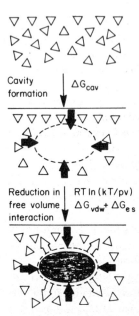

Fig. 3.17. Schematic illustration of the processes that determine solubility according to the solvophobic theory. First, a cavity is formed in the solvent to accept the solute. Thereafter, the solute interacts with the solvent molecules surrounding the cavity. Reproduced from *Activated Carbon Adsorption from the Aqueous Phase*, Ann Arbor Sci. Publ., 1980, p. 65, with permission [102].)

3.5.5.3.2. Free energy change in retention

The original model adapted for chromatography assumed the retention process to consist of complex formation between the eluite and the ligate at the stationary phase surface. The free energy for the Henry coefficient is equivalent to the chemical potential of each species at infinite dilution, and the retention factor can be found by a term-by-term evaluation of the Henry coefficients for each species.

The clearest implication of the solvophobic theory in the interpretation of chromatographic data [48,104] is that the retention is proportional to the surface area change on binding of the eluite to the surface, which is itself proportional to the appropriate molecular surface area. The Van der Waals term is also proportional to the surface area, but this contribution is opposite in sign to the cavity term. The two terms together account for the linear relationship between κ and the carbon number of the eluite [48]. The solvophobic theory has also been used to account for the effect of structure on retention parameters in ion-pair chromatography [104] and the dependence of retention on ionic strength [59]. The relationship also implies that retention is proportional to the surface tension of the mobile phase, although the relationship is complicated by the observed [85,104] composition dependence of $\kappa^e(r)$ that has not yet been expressed as a solvent property.

A more detailed analysis of thermodynamic approaches to retention in reversed-phase chromatography is included in a recent review [48]. An alternative analysis [50] views retention as due only to competitive binding between eluite and eluent, or it utilizes the diachoric equation (eqn. 3.94). Still another model holds that retention and selectivity are inversely proportional to the solubility of the solute in the eluent. The resulting relationship has been used to calculate solubilities of aromatic hydrocarbons [105] with the assumption that stationary phase interactions are independent of eluent composition.

3.5.6. Adsorption chromatography

The stationary phase used in adsorption chromatography is a polar adsorbent such as silica or alumina or a bonded phase with polar ligates. Linear adsorption chromatography is treated in a monograph [4], and a compilation of various bonded stationary phases used in HPLC may be found in recent reviews [106,107].

The mobile phase is usually a nonpolar solvent, e.g., hexane or cyclohexane, and contains a polar "modulator", such as an alcohol or chloroform. Properties of commonly used solvents are listed in Table 3.3. Experience shows that more polar solvents are stronger eluents. However, this property of the eluent cannot be quantified by the dielectric constant and/or the refractive index, because these are indicators of eluent strength only in the sense that the molecular polarizability is related to the dielectric constant and the refractive index.

In order to express the experimentally relevant eluotropic properties of the

TABLE 3.3

ELUOTROPIC STRENGTH, ϵ^0, AND SOLUBILITY PARAMETER, δ, FOR SOLVENTS USED IN CHROMATOGRAPHY

	ϵ^0	δ		ϵ^0	δ
Fluoroalkanes	− 0.25		Dichloromethane	0.42	4.1
n-Pentane	0.00	5.9	1,2-Dichloroethane	0.44	4.8
Isooctane	0.01	7.6	Methyl ethyl ketone	0.51	4.6
Petroleum ether	0.01	6.7	1-Nitropropane	0.53	4.5
n-Decane	0.04	10.3	Triethylamine	0.54	7.5
Cyclohexane	0.04	6.0	Acetone	0.56	4.2
Cyclopentane	0.05	5.2	Dioxane	0.56	6.0
1-Pentene	0.08	5.8	Tetrahydrofuran	0.57	5.0
Carbon disulfide	0.15	3.7	Ethyl acetate	0.58	5.7
Carbon tetrachloride	0.18	5.0	Methyl acetate	0.60	4.8
Xylene	0.26	7.6	Diethylamine	0.63	7.5
Diisopropyl ether	0.28	5.1	Nitromethane	0.64	3.8
Isopropyl chloride	0.29	3.5	Acetonitrile	0.65	10.0
Toluene	0.29	6.8	Pyridine	0.71	5.8
1-Propyl chloride	0.30	3.5	Dimethylsulfoxide	0.75	4.3
Benzene	0.32	6.0	1- or 2-propanol	0.82	8.0
Ethyl bromide	0.35	3.4	Ethanol	0.88	8.0
Ethyl sulfide	0.38	5.0	Methanol	0.95	8.0
Chloroform	0.40	5.0	Ethylene glycol	1.1	8.0

References on p. A130

eluents [4] quantitatively, the eluotropic strength, ϵ^0, is determined for a given eluent from the retention volume of standard eluites in the eluent. The logarithmic retention factor is given by

$$\kappa = \log V_S + \alpha\left(S^0 - A_E \epsilon^0\right) \tag{3.121}$$

where V_S is the volume of adsorbent in the column, α is a parameter proportional to the average surface energy of the adsorbent, which can be interpreted as the degree of surface activation, S^0 is the (dimensionless) adsorption energy for a standard solvent on fully activated adsorbent, and A_E is the dimensionless molecular area of the eluite. Methods for calculation of A_E, which is usually written A_S in the literature, are available [4]. The eluent strength, ϵ^0, is determined from the ratio of the κ values for a sample component, obtained in two solvents as

$$\kappa = \kappa_r + \epsilon^0 A_E \tag{3.122}$$

where κ_r is the logarithmic retention factor with pentane as solvent, for which ϵ^0 equals zero by definition.

The theory of linear adsorption chromatography is well established [54]. According to the "displacement" [4] model, the retention process entails the displacement of solvent molecules from the stationary phase surface by the eluite. As a result, the interactions between eluite and stationary phase govern the energetics of retention. On the other hand, the "diachoric" [50,108] model assumes that retention is governed by mobile phase interactions. Both models predict a decrease in retention as the concentration of the more polar component of a binary mobile phase increases. The relationships between retention and mobile phase composition are qualitatively similar, but not identical, except in one special case [50]. The "diachoric" model apparently does describe the effect of eluent composition on retention, but it suffers from a number of thermodynamic and internal inconsistencies [54]. The displacement model is simple and understandable in light of the previous thermodynamic analysis of adsorption. Adequately accurate predictions for the retention of a given eluite in one mobile phase can be made if its retention in another is known. Furthermore, the retention factor of an eluite of known chemical structure that has not been chromatographed previously can be estimated if the retention factor of another eluite with similar size and structure is known.

The displacement model invokes a competition between the eluite and the solvent molecules for the adsorbent surface. The adsorption of an eluite, E, is assumed to occur according to the equilibrium

$$E_M + n\, S_S \rightleftharpoons E_S + n\, S_M \tag{3.123}$$

where one eluite displaces n adsorbed solvent molecules. Because the surface is completely covered by an adsorbed monolayer, the area occupied by an adsorbed eluite is just equal to that required by n solvent molecules. The net energy of adsorption, ΔG, for to the above binding equilibrium can be expressed as

$$\Delta G = \Delta G_{E,S} + n\,\Delta G_{S,M} - \Delta G_{E,M} - n\,\Delta G_{S,S} \tag{3.124a}$$

where $\Delta G_{E,S}$, $\Delta G_{E,M}$, $\Delta G_{S,S}$, and $\Delta G_{S,M}$ are the partial molal free energies of the eluite

List of symbols on p. A122

and solvent in the stationary or mobile phases, respectively, made dimensionless by division by RT.

In most adsorption systems of interest, the energy terms associated with the mobile phase, $\Delta G_{S,M}$ and $\Delta G_{E,M}$, are much less significant than the corresponding stationary phase terms, $\Delta G_{S,S}$ and $\Delta G_{E,S}$, and therefore

$$\Delta G = \Delta G_{E,S} - n \, \Delta G_{S,S} \tag{3.124b}$$

An alternative argument leading to this result is that the magnitudes of the interactions with the mobile phase are nearly equal and, therefore, the difference is approximately zero.

The free energies of solute binding, $\Delta G_{E,S}$, and solvent binding, $\Delta G_{S,S}$, per unit area are given the symbols S^0 and ϵ^0, respectively. The stoichiometry, n, is given as the ratio of solute to solvent area. Combination of these definitions with eqn. 3.124 yields

$$\Delta G = S^0 - A_E \epsilon^0 \tag{3.125}$$

where A_E is the surface area of the eluite molecule. Combination of eqns. 3.15, 3.71, and 3.125 yields eqn. 3.121. A correction, Δ, for interactions between eluite and solvent can be included to obtain

$$\ln k = \ln V_S + S^0 - \epsilon^0 A_E + \Delta \tag{3.126}$$

A somewhat more complex analysis is required for binary (or ternary) mobile phases. The form of eqn. 3.121 is unchanged but, ϵ^0 has to be redefined for a binary mixture of A and B as

$$\epsilon_{AB}^0 = \epsilon_A + \frac{\log\left(x_B 10^{\alpha n_B(\epsilon_B - \epsilon_A)} + 1 - x_B\right)}{\alpha n_B} \tag{3.127}$$

where x_b and n_b are the mole fractions and molecular area of the stronger solvent component. A generalized approximation to ϵ^0 for multicomponent eluents is given by

$$\epsilon^0 = \epsilon_g + \frac{\log\left(x_h 10^{\alpha n_h(\epsilon_h - \epsilon_g)} + x_g\right)}{\alpha n_h} \tag{3.128}$$

where h is the more strongly adsorbed of the two most strongly adsorbed components, g and h.

The molecular areas of eluites, A_E, can be calculated from the additivity relationship

$$A_E = \Sigma n_i a_i \tag{3.129}$$

where a_i is the area for group i. The assumption that the binding energies of molecular constituents are linearly additive is borne out experimentally. The values of a_i that have been calculated from strictly geometric considerations compare quite well with the corresponding experimentally determined values on silica, alumina, and other adsorbents [4] — with some exceptions, which have been ascribed to

References on p. A130

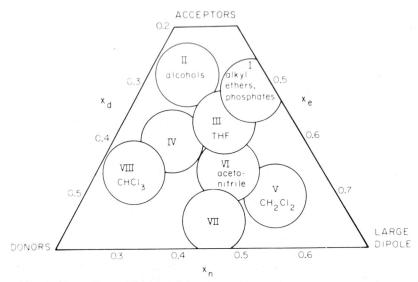

Fig. 3.18. Classification of liquids used as stationary phases in GC and as mobile phases in adsorption chromatography. The solvents cluster into eight classes as hydrogen bond acceptors or hydrogen bond donors, according to the normalized selectivities toward ethanol, x_e, dioxane, x_d, and nitromethane, x_n, as measured on the scales at the sides of the "solvent" triangle. (Reproduced from *High Performance Liquid Chromatography. Advances and Perspectives,* Vol. 1, Academic Press, New York, 1980, p. 208, with permission [109].)

"localization". This term refers to preferential and strong adsorption of certain groups, such as the specific interaction between amino groups in the eluite and silanol group on the silica surface. Localization can be related to the sample group binding free energy and is treated along with special solvent effects, such as hydrogen bonding and charge transfer interactions between solute and solvent [4].

Retention data for 82 solvents have been evaluated in order to determine their polarity, which is related to the adjusted logarithmic retention factors of ethanol, dioxane, and nitromethane in GC with the 82 solvents as the stationary phase. Selectivity parameters, defined as the contribution to polarity due to interactions associated with those test compounds, were also calculated. A triangular plot of solvent selectivity, reproduced in Fig. 3.18, shows that the phases fall into eight classes with respect to hydrogen bond donor and acceptor activity or strong interactions, as measured by selectivity toward ethanol, dioxane, and nitromethane. The groups at the vertices show the greatest differences in selectivity. These results should facilitate rational choice of phases on the basis of desired selectivity and polarity [4,110]. The effect of solvent selectivity with nonhydrogen bonding donor solvents and solutes on alumina has been analyzed [84].

3.5.7. Ion-exchange chromatography

In principle, the thermodynamics of ion exchange can be derived from eqns. 3.73, 3.77 and 3.78 with appropriate chemical potentials, obtained from the activity coefficients of ions, which can be evaluated by using eqns. 3.91–3.96. A relatively simple example is ion exchange with a cation exchanger

$$b[A_M] + a[B_S] \rightleftharpoons b[A_S] + a[B_M]$$ (3.130)

where A and B are co-ions in the mobile phase and stationary phase as indicated by the subscript M and S, respectively, and a and b are the appropriate stoichiometric coefficients.

The corresponding equilibrium constant can be expressed as

$$K = \frac{[A_S]^{|b|}[B_M]^{|a|}}{[A_M]^{|b|}[B_S]^{|a|}}$$ (3.131)

$$= K_d \frac{\gamma_{AS}^{|b|}\gamma_{BM}^{|a|}}{\gamma_{BS}^{|a|}\gamma_{AM}^{|b|}}$$ (3.132)

where K_d is the thermodynamic selectivity (exchange) coefficient and $\gamma_{A,M}$, γ_{BM}, γ_{AS}, and γ_{BS} are the activity coefficients of ions A and B in the mobile and stationary phases, respectively. The retention factor for A is defined as

$$k = \phi[A_S]/[A]$$ (3.133)

and combination of eqns. 3.131–3.133 yields

$$k = \phi \frac{[B_S]^{|a/b|}}{[B_M]^{|a/b|}} = K_d^{\frac{1}{|b|}} \frac{\gamma_{AS}}{\gamma_{AM}} \left(\frac{\gamma_{BM}}{\gamma_{BS}}\right)^{|a/b|}$$ (3.134)

In the analysis of such phenomena it is frequently assumed that the ion exchanger acts simply as a concentrated polyelectrolyte solution. A more complete analysis of the ion-exchange equilibria begins at eqn. 3.74 and takes into account the chemical potential for exchange as well as the work required to expand the exchanger resin due to change in osmotic pressure of the resin, π. The resulting expression for the retention factor is

$$\ln k = \Phi + \ln \frac{\gamma_A^{|b|}}{\gamma_B^{|a|}} + \ln \frac{\gamma_{BS}^{|a|}}{\gamma_{AS}^{|b|}} + \frac{\pi}{RT}(|a|\bar{V}_B - |b|\bar{V}_A)$$ (3.135)

where v_A and v_B are partial molar volumes of A and B.

Eqn. 3.135 has been tested and was found to describe the behavior of ion exchangers and to be useful in predicting retention [111]. The activities of ions in resins can be derived [112] from that of water by using the Gibbs–Duhem equation (cf. eqn. 3.82). The exchange is determined by the activity coefficient ratios, inasmuch as the magnitude of the last term of eqn. 3.135, which expresses the effect of swelling on retention, is small, even in highly crosslinked resins [111–113].

Donnan exclusion, in which ions of the same charge as the resin are excluded from the resin and thereby create concentration differences, occurs in ion-exchange resins. If the salt $A_x X_a$ is distributed between the mobile and stationary phases as

$$A_x X_a \rightleftharpoons (A_x X_a)_S$$ (3.136)

where A and X are the coion and counterion respectively, the equilibrium condition is related to the concentrations in the two phases as

$$[A_M]^{|x|}[X_M]^{|a|}\gamma_{\pm M}^{|a|+|x|} = [A_S]^{|x|}[X_S]^{|a|}\gamma_{\pm S}^{|a|+|x|} \tag{3.137}$$

where $\gamma_{\pm M}$ and $\gamma_{\pm S}$ are mean ionic activity coefficients in the mobile and stationary phases, respectively. In this expression, the effects of osmotic pressure are neglected.

According to the principle of electroneutrality

$$[A_M] = |x/a|[X_M] \tag{3.138}$$

and

$$[A_S] = |r/a|[R] + |x/a|[X_S] \tag{3.139}$$

where $[R]$ and r are the concentration of the ion exchanger site and the charge at the site. Combination of eqns. 3.137–3.139 yields

$$[X_M]^{|x|+|a|} = \{|r/X_M|[R_S] + [X_S]\}^{|x|}[X_S]^{|a|}(\gamma_{\pm S}/\gamma_{\pm M})^{|x|+|a|} \tag{3.140}$$

This expression shows that the uptake of counterion by the exchanging ion is enhanced at high external concentrations and is reduced at high concentrations of exchange sites, such as are found in highly crosslinked resin. Furthermore, its exclusion will be greater if the absolute value of the charge on the counterion is greater than the charge on the central ion [114]. Although these effects have been observed in the practice of ion exchange, the theoretical predictions are not always reliable, especially when the resin and the distribution of exchange are heterogeneous [115]. As a nonstoichiometric model, the Stern–Chapman–Gouy theory has also been used to treat electrolyte uptake [116].

Various effects, such as solvation and swelling of the resin, play significant roles in ion exchange. In hydro-organic solvents, the swelling of strong anion and cation exchangers increases with solvent polarity. Ion-exchange selectivity in hydro-organic media arises from the competition of ions for the medium that provides the best solvation. The mobile phase being usually more polar, the smaller ion of the exchanging pair goes into that phase. However, the opposite order is found when dioxane–water mixtures are used as mobile phase, because water is preferentially adsorbed by the resin [117]. Similarly, inversions in the retention order are found in cation exchangers when water–rich water–2-propanol is used as the mobile phase.

Analysis of retention on ion exchangers is further complicated if hydrophobic interactions between the eluite and the resin matrix [118] also have to be taken into account. In fact, ion-exchange chromatography of biological substances involves a number of phenomena, among others, partition between the eluent and the pore fluid of the ion-exchange resin [119]. A satisfactory thermodynamic treatment of ion-exchange chromatography of complex molecules is yet to be found. This branch of chromatography is perhaps the most difficult to analyze in rigorous physico-chemical terms and the maxim still holds that "ion-exchange chromatography is as far from exchange of ions as chromatography is from color writing" [120].

List of symbols on p. A122

3.5.8. Exclusion chromatography

In exclusion chromatography the column material consists of rigid porous particles or a gel, the interparticulate volume of which is occupied by the stagnant mobile phase. Retention occurs when the eluite diffuses from the moving interstitial liquid into a stagnant pore fluid so that its migration in the axial direction is arrested until it returns to the interstitial fluid. Theories of retention in SEC have asserted either that retention is determined by hydrodynamic (i.e. kinetic) properties of the mobile phase and eluite or by equilibrium partitioning of eluite between the interstitial and pore fluids. The latter approach seems best to describe the retention behavior and will be discussed below. Reviews have critically examined the evidence in support of the hydrodynamic and thermodynamic theories of retention [121,122].

The thermodynamics of SEC can be developed in a fashion analogous to the treatment of interactive chromatography. In the latter case, eluite concentrations at equilibrium are different in the two phases as a consequence of differences in the pertinent eluite interactions in those phases. However, in SEC the equilibrium concentrations of the eluite in the accessible stationary phase space and in the interstitial mobile phase are the same, because the fluid has the same properties in both places. The mass of eluite in the stationary phase pores is equal to the product of the concentration and the available pore volume, V_A, and the mass in the mobile phase is given as the product of the concentration and interstitial volume, V_e. The retention factor is obtained by combining these relationships with eqn. 3.77 to obtain

$$k = V_A/V_e \tag{3.141}$$

The available pore volume is less than or equal to the total intraparticulate pore volume, V_i, and is related to it through

$$V_A = KV_i \tag{3.142}$$

Combination of eqns. 3.141 and 3.142 yields

$$k = KV_i/V_e \tag{3.143}$$

By using the definition of retention factor in eqn. 3.11, the retention volume, V_R, is found to be

$$V_R = V_e + KV_i \tag{3.144}$$

so that

$$K = (V_R - V_e)/V_i \tag{3.145}$$

Because the pore volume of the support is not always known, an alternative definition of K has been developed [120] for the analysis of experimental data, as follows

$$K_{av} = (V_R - V_e)/(V_t - V_e) \tag{3.146}$$

where V_t is the total volume of the column, i.e. the mobile phase plus packing.

References on p. A130

Rigid-rod Molecules   Spherical Molecules   Flexible Chains

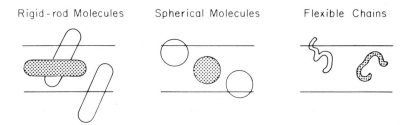

Fig. 3.19. Schematic illustration of the shape and size of eluite molecules, limiting the volume of pores in which the molecular center of mass can be located. The open figures represent configurations that are physically impossible, because the eluite occupies space which is also occupied by pore walls. (Reproduced from *J. Phys. Chem.*, 72 (1968) 4397, with permission [123].)

The thermodynamic problem rests with the evaluation of K. Exclusion is a function of both support and eluite properties. Fig. 3.19 shows that molecules cannot invade the entire pore volume of a uniform pore support, because occupancy of some spaces implies that a portion of the molecule would also occupy space already occupied by the support. Therefore, exclusion depends on the molecular dimensions of sample components in a system of uniform pores. On the other hand, the magnitude of the exclusion also depends on the geometry of the eluite molecules, as shown in Fig. 3.20. Very compact molecules can invade areas from which less compact molecules or molecules with high aspect ratios are excluded. In addition, the particular distribution of the pore diameter and pore volume of the column material need to be included in an analysis of K.

The theory of the relationship between the size and shape of eluites and their retention was first developed from statistical mechanical analyses [123] of the exclusion of rigid molecules in which the mean external length, $\overline{L}$, was used to

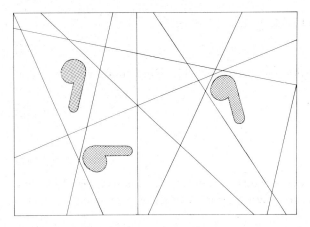

Fig. 3.20. Schematic illustration of the effect of nonuniform pore structure in SEC. The smallness of some of the enclosed spaces precludes occupation by the eluite. (Reproduced from *J. Phys. Chem.*, 72 (1968) 4397, with permission [123].)

List of symbols on p. A122

characterize a molecule. $\bar{L}$ is a function of the aspect ratio, M

$$M = L_0/L_1 \tag{3.147}$$

where L_0 and L_1 are the diameters and lengths of an ellipsoid of revolution. The parameter s measures the ratio of gel surface area to free volume. The product $s\bar{L}$ is used to examine the effects of pore structure and eluite size on retention. Some relationships between $s\bar{L}$ and retention factors are presented in Figs. 3.21 and 3.22. Fig. 3.21 shows that the partition coefficient depends significantly on the pore type, but that the values of K converge, as the dimensionless parameter sL_0 approaches 1, i.e. as the ratio of pore width to molecular diameter increases. Therefore, size exclusion is highly sensitive to eluite geometry at small pore diameters. On the other hand, the general convergence of the curves in the region commonly explored, $0.2 < K < 1$, implies that the parameter s may be well suited to characterizing a gel. Fig. 3.22 shows the dependence of K on the overall length of molecules, $\bar{L}$, of various aspect ratios. Because the curves very nearly coincide and are, therefore, nearly independent of shape, $\bar{L}$ was suggested to be the parameter of choice in the characterization of a polymer [123].

Of the experimentally accessible parameters, the radius of gyration best mimics $\bar{L}$ and, therefore, it is the most fundamentally interesting parameter in the determination of retention. This provides the basis of the so-called universal calibration plots. Similar studies have related the partition coefficients of random-coil polymers and rigid polymers to their molecular diameters and to the number and length of freely jointed chains in them [124]. The dependence of K on the square root of the ratio of molecular size to pore equivalent radius is illustrated in Fig. 3.23.

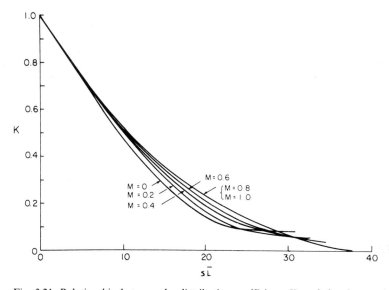

Fig. 3.21. Relationship between the distribution coefficient, K, and the characteristic length, $s\bar{L}$ of the eluite in a cylindrical pore for different aspect ratios, M, of the eluite. (Reproduced from *J. Phys. Chem.*, 72 (1968) 4397, with permission [123].)

References on p. A130

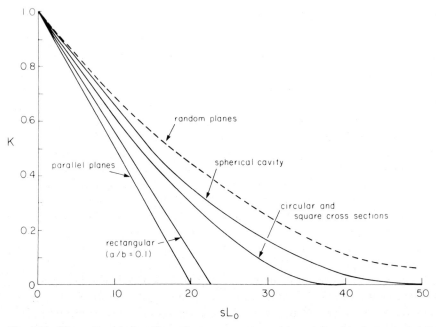

Fig. 3.22. Illustration of the effect of pore geometry on the relationship between the distribution coefficient and characteristic length of the eluite. (Reproduced from *J. Phys. Chem.*, 72 (1968) 4397, with permission [123].)

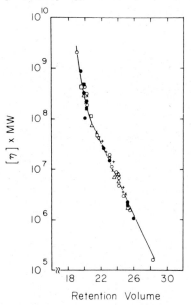

Fig. 3.23. Universal calibration plot in size exclusion chromatography. The hydrodynamic volume parameter, $[\eta]MW$, is plotted against the retention volume with tetrahydrofuran as the eluent and polystyrenes, poly(methacrylate), poly(vinyl chloride), poly(phenyl siloxane), and polybutadienes as eluites. (Reproduced from *J. Polym. Sci., Part B*, 6 (1968) 803, with permission [125].)

List of symbols on p. A122

The preceding treatments assume that partitioning is governed by thermodynamic properties rather than by hydrodynamic properties. This assumption has ample support in a variety of systems [122,126]. For example, retention has been found to be independent of flowrate [127]. Ab initio calculations of K agreed well with values of K for polystyrene samples on porous-glass columns [127]. The relationship between $\log K$ and molecular weight of glucose oligomers is linear, as expected for rigid rods [128]. However, deviations from the thermodynamic model can be observed in swelling gels [124,125,129]. For example, the partition coefficients for proteins, determined statically and chromatographically on Sephadex columns, agreed well except when the gels were highly swollen [57,130]. These results suggest that nonequilibrium effects can be important in highly swollen gels. In addition, adsorption on the gel matrix can make a significant contribution to retention [129,131].

The models presented here imply that the chromatographic process is entropically driven and, therefore, retention should be temperature-independent. Indeed, invariance of retention with temperature has been generally observed in practice. However, adsorption on the support may give rise to temperature effects, because adsorption is governed by the enthalpy of solute transfer to the surface [132]. Molecular weight determination of proteins by means of chromatography on controlled-pore glass suffers from this difficulty. However, adsorption is obviated if amino acid buffers [133], urea, or sodium dodecyl sulfate (SDS) are added to the mobile phase [134]. Temperature-induced changes in gel morphology may also generate a temperature dependence of retention in the gel chromatography of proteins [121].

SEC is frequently used to estimate the molecular weight or some associated measure of molecular dimensions. The above considerations provide the rationale for the so-called "universal calibration plot", which is based on the fact that K is determined by the molecular radius of gyration [123,129,131]. For flexible polymers the relationship between radius of gyration, R_G, and molecular weight is given by

$$[\eta]M = 10\pi N\xi^3 R_G^3/3 \qquad (3.148)$$

where N is Avogadro's number, $[\eta]$ is the intrinsic viscosity and ξ relates R_G to the radius of an equivalent sphere, R_e, as

$$R_e = \xi R_G \qquad (3.149)$$

and takes the value 0.835 in ideal solvents [135]. A similar relationship approximates the case for rigid macromolecules. Plots of retention volume versus $[\xi M]^{1/3}$ would nearly duplicate those of K versus $\bar{L}$ in Figs. 3.21 and 3.22. This allows estimation of the molecular weight according to a plot that is quite insensitive to molecular shape and may therefore be properly regarded as being appropriate for all molecules.

In the universal calibration plots, $\log[\eta]M$ is plotted versus retention volume. The universal calibration technique has been validated by several investigators [136–139]. Eqn. 3.148 provides the rationale for the use of SDS solutions in the determination of the molecular weight of proteins, because in these solutions proteins are usually present as random coils [140]. Fig. 3.23 is an example of such a plot, including data from several different polymers. Deviations from eqn. 3.148 may occur due to gel/solute interactions [141], which can be modulated by change of solvent composition [138] or by adding SDS to the eluent.

The properties of size-exclusion supports and the techniques used are discussed in several monographs [121,122,142,143]. Bandspreading has been the subject of recent reviews [126,144].

3.6. LINEAR FREE ENERGY RELATIONSHIPS

3.6.1. Substituent effects

The term linear free energy relationships (LFER) stems from the observation that the free energy change involved in one process, e.g., chromatographic retention, is frequently a linear function of that involved in another process, e.g., vaporization. It is natural to assume that such processes, which are subject to LFER, have certain common features and that they can be related to the structure of the molecules involved. They have been known and used in chromatography since Martin [145] analyzed the effect of molecular structure of the eluite on its retention.

The usual assumption in the use of LFER in chromatography is that the chemical potential for the retention of a compound is a linear function of potentials that can be assigned to its molecular fragments as

$$\Delta\mu^0 = \Sigma n_i \Delta\mu_i^0 \tag{3.150}$$

where n_i and $\Delta\mu_i^0$ are the number of fragments and the corresponding chemical potentials, respectively. For instance, the chemical potential for acetone may be expressed as

$$\mu_{CH_3COCH_3}^0 = 2\mu_{CH_3}^0 + \mu_{CO}^0 \tag{3.151}$$

Several alternative formulations are also possible, e.g., potentials could be assigned to the different atoms, and positional or geometric effects could be included explicitly [146]. However, the use of atomic group potentials is usually avoided, because it offers few advantages over the use of molecular fragment potentials.

If two compounds, 1 and 2, are similar except that 2 contains the additional molecular fragment X, eqn. 3.150 may be used to relate the chemical potential of 2 to that of 1 as

$$\Delta\mu_2^0 = \Delta\mu_1^0 + \Delta\mu_X^0 \tag{3.152}$$

The corresponding logarithmic retention factors are given by eqns. 3.153 and 3.154

$$\kappa_1 = \Delta\mu_1^0/2.3RT + \Phi \tag{3.153}$$

$$\kappa_2 = \Delta\mu_2^0/2.3RT + \Phi \tag{3.154}$$

and the logarithmic relative retention is given by

$$\log\alpha_{1,2} = \Delta\mu_X^0/2.3RT \tag{3.155}$$

List of symbols on p. A122

An implication of eqn. 3.155 is that the retention of 2 relative to that of 1, i.e. the selectivity of the chromatographic system toward the two eluites, is independent of the properties of 1 under fixed chromatographic conditions and depends only on the structural difference. Therefore, the relative retention between eluites that contain the group X and otherwise identical eluites that lack X is a constant value. Of course, it is necessary that the X group is indeed the same among the eluites in order for eqn. 3.155 and the above statement to be valid. For instance, if group X is ionizable, it must be ionized to the same extent in all eluites under comparison. This requirement can be satisfied by adjustment of the mobile phase pH to a value well removed from the pK_a values of the eluites so that ionization is either complete or completely suppressed. For similar reasons, the use of mobile phase components that interact strongly with the group in question should be avoided if one wishes LFER to hold.

The validity of eqn. 3.155 has been verified in all areas of chromatography. It is most frequently manifested in linear plots of the logarithmic retention factor versus the number of carbon atoms of n-alkanes or their derivatives. It has been observed in GC [147], adsorption [4], partition [148], and reversed-phase chromatography [148,149]. Results obtained in GC are illustrated in Fig. 3.24, where for each family of eluites the logarithmic retention factor increases by a constant value with the addition of each methylene group in the homologous series. The results in Fig. 3.25 demonstrate that this behavior is not restricted to methylene groups, because the logarithmic retention factor increases linearly also with the number of alanyl residues in oligoalanines [150]. The logarithmic retention factor has been found to be proportional to the number of amino acid residues in oligopeptides [151] and to the number of oxyethylene groups in oligoethyleneglycols [30].

Under certain circumstances LFER do not hold. Linear dependence of the

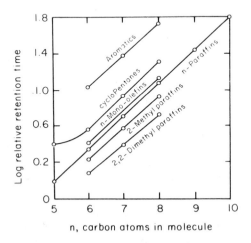

Fig. 3.24. Relationship between the number of carbon atoms of members of various homologous series and the logarithm of the retention time in GC with a benzyl diphenyl phase at 78.5°C. (Reproduced from *Anal. Chem.*, 29 (1957) 320, with permission [147].)

References on p. A130

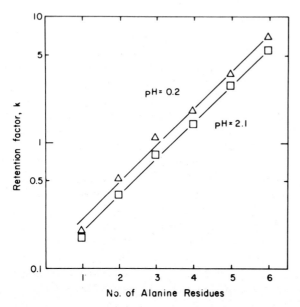

Fig. 3.25. Plots of the logarithmic retention factors, log k, against the number of alinine residues in oligoalanines. (Reproduced from *J. Chromatogr.*, 142 (1977) 623, with permission [150].)

logarithmic retention factor on the number of oxyethylenes in oligoethyleneglycols was not observed at certain temperatures and with certain mobile phase compositions due to conformational changes in the eluites [30]. Stereochemical effects can also cause a significant departure from linear relationships. For instance, the retention factors of corresponding D–D and L–L dipeptides are identical, but they are different from those for the corresponding D–L and L–D dipeptides [152]. Exceptions to the simple formulations of LFER notwithstanding, the concept of additivity of group energies seems to be broadly valid in chromatography and can be used to develop quantitative structure/retention relationships [153].

A more general formulation of LFER leads to relationships between the retention factor of an eluite and its equilibrium constant in another process, K, as

$$\ln k = a_1 - a_2 \ln K \tag{3.156}$$

where a_1 and a_2 are empirical constants that can be evaluated from the behavior of many eluites in the two systems under examination. Thus, plots of the logarithmic retention factor against the logarithmic equilibrium constant in a second process for several eluites will be linear. Of course, the second process may be retention under different chromatographic conditions, so that another set of retention factors can be used to express K in eqn. 3.156. The relationship between octanol/water partition coefficients and retention factors in reversed-phase chromatograpy, depicted in Fig. 3.26, is a manifestation of eqn. 3.156, which has been found to hold broadly in chromatography. R_F values of peptides, calculated by this approach, agreed well with those experimentally determined [154]. The differential heat of vaporization in

List of symbols on p. A122

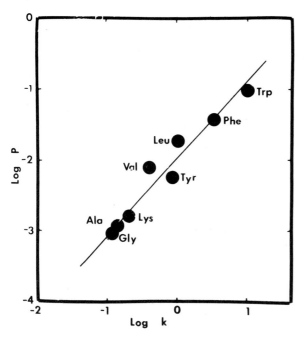

Fig. 3.26. Correlation between the logarithmic retention factor, log k, and the water/octanol partition coefficient, log P, for eight amino acids. The data were obtained in reversed-phase chromatography on an octadecyl-silica column with 0.1 M phosphate buffer, pH 6.7, as eluent. (Reproduced from *J. Chromatogr.*, 142 (1977) 623, with permission [150].)

GC is related to the heat of vaporization of neat solute [155].

Retention indices of phenols on polar stationary phase were found to correlate with the Kováts' index (Chap. 3.6.3) on nonpolar stationary phase plus the refractivity of the whole phenol molecule [156]. Group constants have been obtained for substances in GC and adsorption LC [4,157]. The latter measurements provide the basis of solvent strength calculations. Linear relationships between the logarithm of the water/octanol partition coefficient, log P, and the number of structural elements for a substance provide the basis of the π index of hydrophobicity [158]. There is ample evidence that log P values correlate with the logarithmic retention factor in reversed-phase chromatography [150]. Thus, the logarithm of the retention factor of phenols could be expressed as a linear function of the π parameter [159]. The π-index system has been modified to account for folding or other conformational changes [160], and the effect of such phenomena on chromatographic retention is under investigation. Quantitative structure/retention relationships have been discussed more fully than is possible here in a review that focuses on the relationships between R_F values and octanol/water partition coefficients [161]. There is also a review that deals exclusively with quantitative structure/retention relationships [162].

References on p. A130

3.6.2. Enthalpy–entropy compensation

The enthalpy and entropy changes associated with a process vary among members of a homologous series involved in that process in such a way that the observed free energy changes between members of the series are less than those expected on the basis of the change in enthalpy alone. In this sense, the increment in entropy with change in structure "compensates" for the increment in enthalpy to reduce its effect on the overall free energy. This phenomenon, called "enthalpy–entropy compensation" can also be observed when data taken under different experimental conditions, e.g., with mobile phases having different composition, are compared. Enthalpy–entropy compensation has been observed in a wide variety of chemical reactions [155,163]. It is manifested in, and diagnosed by the use of linear plots of enthalpy change versus entropy change. The slope has the dimension of temperature, and it is called the compensation temperature. Thus, the retention enthalpy for eluites 1 and 2 is related to the retention entropy as

$$\Delta H_1^0 - \Delta H_2^0 = T_c\left(\Delta S_1^0 - \Delta S_2^0\right) \tag{3.157}$$

where the value of the compensation temperature, T_c, is constant for several eluite pairs.

So-called statistical compensation may occur as a consequence of errors in the evaluation of enthalpy that are reproduced in the entropy, if the entropy is determined in the usual way from the equilibrium constant and the enthalpy. In order to minimize this effect in chromatography, the use of plots of κ versus ΔH^0 is preferred [164,165] in the determination of compensation behavior. Appropriate plots of the retention data for a variety of eluites reveal compensation at fixed solvent composition. Compensation behavior is also observed in reversed-phase chromatography when the composition of the mobile phase is changed. The value of T_c has been found to be approximately 625°K over a wide range of conditions [165]. Compensation behavior has been observed on bonded reversed phases [104,149] for a variety of mobile phases and solutes [149,166,167] as well as on pyrocarbon [168].

Enthalpy–entropy compensation is an extrathermodynamic phenomenon the mechanism of which is not understood. It is believed to arise from a single process that governs the overall equilibria in the systems under consideration and may be related to changes in solvation that occur in the course of the process [163]. In view of this, compensation in reversed-phase chromatography may be due to variation in the solvation of the eluite and ligate upon complex formation. In this case, the magnitude of the corresponding ΔH^0 and ΔS^0 changes is expected to be proportional to the contact area, which is usually proportional to the surface area of the eluite [48]. The special significance of enthalpy–entropy compensation in reversed-phase chromatography is that it may allow the effects of composition and temperature on retention to be analyzed explicitly, as long as regular retention behavior prevails. As the effect of sample structure is implicit in such an analysis, it may allow the extraction of structure-related retention parameters from chromatographic data [169] and offers the basis for a powerful retention index system in reversed-phase chromatography.

List of symbols on p. A122

3.6.3. Retention index systems

Indexing systems in chromatography are designed to provide a framework in which retention parameters can be related to the chemical structure of eluites. Perhaps the best known is the Kováts index system [170], which is used in GC. The index, I, for a given eluite is calculated as

$$I_i = 100 \frac{\ln(V_i/V_N)}{\ln(V_{N+1}/V_N)} + 100 n_C \tag{3.158}$$

where V_i, V_N, and V_{N+1} are the net retention volumes of the eluite, n-paraffin having n_C carbons and n-paraffin with $n_C + 1$ carbon atoms, respectively. The C_N and C_{N+1} reference paraffins are chosen such that they are eluted before and after the eluite, respectively, and their retention values are as close as possible to the eluite under consideration. The index can be interpreted as 100 times the carbon number of a hypothetical paraffin having the same retention as the eluite. The use of 100 as the multiplier results in retention indices with values conveniently larger than unity. The index of an eluite is composed of contributions from the structural elements of the eluite molecule [170,171] and, therefore, it may contain structural information.

The use of such retention indices is further expanded by the term ΔI, which is the difference between the I values of a substance obtained on two different stationary phases, chosen so that one of the reference phases is polar and the other is apolar. Retention indices depend on the number and kind of functional groups in the eluite molecule, shielding of functional groups in the molecule, and the geometry and bond moments of polarizability of the stationary phase. The retention index on an apolar stationary phase is determined by the number and spatial arrangement of the carbon atom skeleton of the eluite, the number, type, and arrangement of heteroatoms in the molecule, and geometric effects peculiar to the liquid stationary phase. As a consequence, the ΔI values contain structural information and may be of value for the tentative identification of the sample components [170,172].

The effects of geometry and substitution in the sample molecule on the ΔI value have been extensively reviewed [172]. Other, more special retention indices, based on other reference compounds have also been proposed [173,174], as well as systems based on data from temperature-programed GC [175,176]. The temperature coefficient of the index, dI/dT, has been used as a further aid in the characterization of sample components [177]. Methods for the prediction of Kováts indices on columns containing mixed liquid stationary phases have also been proposed [178].

The effects of stationary phase and sample polarity on retention in GC have been examined with respect to the retention indices [179,180] and the effect of polar interactions on the retention index is represented by products of "polarities", attributed to the eluite and the stationary phase. In the final form, the effect of sample orientation, charge transfer donor or acceptor strength, and hydrogen bonding donor or acceptor strength on ΔI is expressed as

$$\Delta I = ax + by + cz + du + es \tag{3.159}$$

where the parameters a, b, c, d, and e characterize the eluite, and the corresponding terms for the stationary phase are x, y, z, u, and s. The values for various stationary phases are found in the literature [179,180] and are summarized in review articles [62,180,181]. Alternative methods for the characterization of liquid stationary phases have also been reviewed recently [182].

An attempt has been made to establish a retention index system, analogous to the Kováts system, for reversed-phase chromatography by using 2-alkylketones as the standards [183]. The chief defect of this approach is that the retention index of polar eluites changes markedly with changes in mobile phase composition. In reversed-phase chromatography, interactions with the eluent are significant, and the composition of the eluent may vary within a broad range. In contradistinction, the carrier gas in GC is inert, and its composition is invariant. This problem may be circumvented by use of a formal scheme that takes into account the dependence of retention on mobile phase composition and temperature [149]. In this approach, κ, the logarithm of the retention factor, is related to the volume percent of organic cosolvent in a hydro-organic mobile phase, φ, and to the temperature, T, as

$$\kappa = A_1\varphi(1 - T_c/T) + A_2/T + A_3 \tag{3.160}$$

where the A terms are parameters peculiar to the eluite (although A_3 also includes the phase ratio) and T_c is the compensation temperature. Eqn. 3.160 has been found to given an adequate description of the magnitude of retention in reversed-phase chromatography with hydro-organic eluents containing methanol, acetonitrile, dioxane, or tetrahydrofuran [149,166]. Eqn. 3.160 is also applicable to polar eluites, but to treat ionic species it must be modified [169]. The parameters of eqn. 3.160 can be related to the molecular structure of the eluite. They are composed of substituent contributions as

$$A_i = \Sigma n_j \alpha_{i,j} \tag{3.161}$$

where $\alpha_{i,j}$ is the contribution of substituent j to A_i, an n_j is the number of substituents j in the eluite molecule. Eqns. 3.160 and 3.161 embody a generalization of the Martin equation (eqn. 3.150), as they also explicitly account for the dependence of retention on eluent composition and temperature — at least under conditions encountered in reversed-phase chromatography. It is expected that eqn. 3.160 will be used in conjunction with a series of reference eluites, such as 2-ketones, to account for changes in mobile phase composition and temperature. This will allow an orthogonal retention index system to be established for characterizing hydrophobic properties of eluites, for measuring the strength of various eluents, and to facilitate identification of unknown sample components.

3.7. FLOW THROUGH POROUS MEDIA

3.7.1. Flow of the mobile phase

Flow of the mobile phase (carrier gas, eluent, or developing solvent) is an essential part of all chromatographic techniques. While sweeping the sample compo-

List of symbols on p. A122

nents through the column by the mobile phase is responsible for the separation, the continuous flow and finite rate of mass transfer preclude eluite equilibration between the two phases and result in band broadening. Additional bandspreading arises from nonuniformities in the flow profile, i.e., in the spatial distribution of flow velocities throughout the column. Thus, flow phenomena greatly influence the efficiency of separation. Moreover, the flow resistance of the column and the flowrate of the mobile phase determine the pressure drop, and important operating parameter in forced-flow chromatography. On the other hand, differences in flowrates of the developing solvents are responsible for the greatly different separation times in PC and TLC. In this section, some of the elementary concepts related to flow in chromatographic systems are outlined.

Laminar flow through circular open ducts, such as capillary columns, is amenable to simple mathematical treatment. The flow profile, i.e. the flow velocity, v, as a function of radial position, r, is given by

$$v = v_{max}\left[1 - \left(\frac{r}{R}\right)^2\right] \tag{3.162}$$

where R is the tube radius and v_{max} is the maximum velocity at the tube center. Eqn. 3.162 represents a parabolic flow profile. The volumetric flowrate, F, is given by

$$F = \frac{(P_i - P_0)R^4\pi}{8\eta L} \tag{3.163}$$

where L is the tube length, η is the fluid viscosity, and P_i and P_0 are the inlet and outlet pressures, respectively. Eqn. 3.163 describes the flow in the laminar region where the value of the dimensionless Reynolds number, Re, is smaller than 2100. The Reynolds number is defined as

$$\text{Re} = \frac{ud\rho}{\eta} \tag{3.164}$$

where u is the mean linear flow velocity in the conduit, having a characteristic distance (diameter) d, and ρ is the density of the fluid.

The flow pattern in packed columns is rather complicated, as suggested by Fig. 3.27. Although several models for the flow have been developed, no simple mathematical treatment is available to calculate the flow profile. The interstitial space in the packed columns where fluid motion occurs is often considered as a bundle of channels, having a certain shape and diameter. It has been recognized the nonuniformity of channel dimensions and holes in the packing result in maldistribution (channeling) of flow. Since the resulting nonuniform flow profile adversely affects chromatographic results, it is necessary that the packing structure in columns be very uniform.

The linear phenomenological law that governs fluid flow through porous media is Darcy's law, which states that the superficial flow velocity is proportional to the pressure gradient

$$u_s = \frac{B^0}{\eta}\frac{P_i - P_0}{L} \tag{3.165}$$

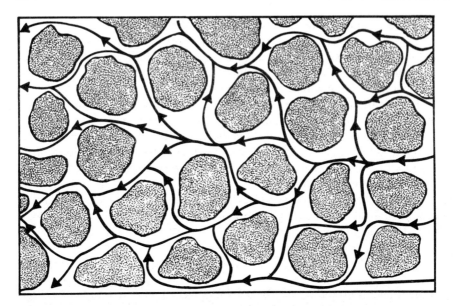

Fig. 3.27. Schematic illustration of the anfractuous path of mobile phase flow in packed columns.

where B^0 is the specific permeability coefficient and is measured in darcies (1 darcy $= 10^{-8}$ cm^2).

The interstitial velocity, u_e (cf. eqn. 3.25), is given by

$$u_e = \frac{B^0}{\epsilon_e \eta} \tag{3.166}$$

where ϵ_e is the porosity of the medium and has a value of 0.4 ± 0.03 for uniform, randomly packed columns.

Numerous expressions have been derived to relate the specific permeability to the particle diameter and porosity of the medium. The Kozeny–Carman equation is the most popular:

$$B^0 = \frac{d_p^2 \epsilon_e^3}{180(1 - \epsilon_e)^2} \tag{3.167}$$

Substitution of B^0 from eqn. 3.165 into eqn. 3.167 yields an expression appropriate for the superficial velocity in laminar flow through packed columns having $\epsilon_e < 0.5$.

In packed columns, stream splitting (cf. Fig. 3.27) is assumed to occur over a distance of one particle diameter so that an eddy diffusion coefficient, E, is expressed as $E = \lambda d_p u_e$, where λ is a measure of the flow inequality in the column. As shown in Chap. 3.8.3.2 (cf. eqn. 3.181), eddy diffusion is assumed to contribute independently to bandspreading.

3.7.2. Flow in planar chromatography

Flow and migration processes occurring in planar chromatography, such as TLC, are markedly different from those in CC. In planar chromatography, the sample is applied to the dry sheet and then an appropriate solvent is applied to a portion of the sorbent that does not contain the sample. The eluent moves along the sorbent by capillary flow, eventually passing the sample spot, and thus elution begins. Due to the very nature of the flow process that causes the advance of the solvent front, the linear velocity is not uniform across the cross-section of the sheet. Rather, the solvent advances most rapidly along the narrower channels and, as a result, the density profile of the mobile phase in the direction of flow is nonuniform. The driving force for the flow in planar chromatography is the capillary pressure difference on either side of the solvent front, as the chromatogram is developed. This capillary pressure drop is proportional to the surface tension of the solvent, and inversely proportional to the size of the particles in the porous migration medium [184]. A simple model [21] of interconnected capillaries gives the velocity of the solvent front, u_f, as

$$u_f = \frac{dZ_f}{dt} = \frac{\phi \gamma d_p}{\eta Z_f} = \frac{\kappa_0 d_p}{2Z_f} \tag{3.168}$$

where Z_f is the distance traversed by the front, t is time, ϕ a constant, γ and η are the surface tension and viscosity of the solvent, κ_0 is a constant, and d_p is the average particle size. Thus, the front travels slower in a layer of smaller particles and slows down as it moves along the sorbent. Furthermore, solvents with low surface tension or high viscosity exhibit a slower movement of the front. The relationship given by eqn. 3.168 is in agreement with the frequently cited empirical relationship for Z_f as a function of time [21]

$$Z_f^2 = \kappa t = \kappa_0 d_p t \tag{3.169}$$

where κ and κ_0 are constants for a given system. Eqns. 3.168 and 3.169 are important because in planar chromatography the flow velocity can be controlled only indirectly and, thus, it is not an operating parameter as in CC. Fig. 3.28 shows a diagram of the height of the solvent front as a function of time for thin layers made from particles of different sizes. The front advances much more slowly in layers with small particles than in layers with larger particles. The curves in Fig. 3.28 were calculated from eqn. 3.169 by using a correlation [184] for κ_0.

The movement of the mobile phase in planar chromatography is a very complex process involving mass transfer to and from the vapor phase surrounding the sorbent as well as mass transfer along the sorbent. The mobile phase evaporates during the run, since the vapor is never truly saturated with the solvent, and at the same time the vapor components are adsorbed on the dry sorbent ahead of the solvent front. Moreover, if a mixed eluent is used, the components of the eluent advance at different rates, giving rise to a degree of frontal chromatography. Due to these complications, no rigorous treatment of the subject is available.

References on p. A130

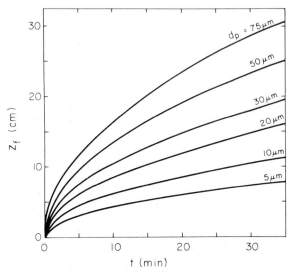

Fig. 3.28. Distance/time diagram for the migration of the eluent front in TLC. The height, Z_f, of the front above the solvent level is plotted against time for layers made from particles of different size. Chromatographic conditions in ref. 184. Data plotted according to eqn. 3.169 with $\kappa_0 = 60.86\ d_p$, corresponding approximately to chloroform as the eluent and a sorbent layer with a specific permeability of 0.008.

3.7.3. Performance index and separation impedance

It is well established that in packed columns interstitial mass transfer is accompanied by a higher energy dissipation than the radial mass transfer in open tubes [185]. The introduction of capillary columns in GC [186] has exploited this result and proved that the same number of theoretical plates can be obtained with a lower pressure drop when an open tubular column is used rather than a packed column. Alternatively, at a given column inlet pressure a higher number of plates is attained with open tubular columns. A quantitative measure of this is the "performance index" [186] that expresses the relationship between the column efficiency and the pressure drop across it.

For HPLC, a very similar but much simpler measure, the separation impedance, E, has been defined [187] as

$$E = \left(\frac{t_0}{N}\right)\left(\frac{\Delta P}{N}\right)\left(\frac{1}{\eta}\right) = \frac{H^2}{B^0} \tag{3.170}$$

Columns exhibiting $E \leqslant 1000$ are considered to be excellent, whereas poor columns have a large separation impedance ($E > 10,000$). In evaluating the pressure drop across the column, it is essential to ascertain that no pressure drop occurs outside the column packing proper, e.g. in the fritted end plates or connecting tubes of the HPLC columns.

List of symbols on p. A122

3.8. BANDSPREADING

3.8.1. Additivity relationships

The fundamental measure of bandspreading is the second central moment of the concentration distribution or, for Gaussian peaks, the variance. According to statistical theory, the variance of a complex random process equals the sum of the variances generated by the individual processes, as long as they are independent, i.e. the processes are not coupled. For a chromatographic peak, therefore, the observed variance, σ^2, may be expressed as

$$\sigma^2 = \sigma_{inj}^2 + \sigma_{col}^2 + \sigma_{conn}^2 + \sigma_{det}^2 \tag{3.171}$$

where σ_{inj}^2, σ_{conn}^2, and σ_{det}^2 are the variances associated with the extracolumn band-spreading due to the injector, connections, and detectors, respectively, and σ_{col}^2 is the variance contributed by the chromatographic process in the column. Extracolumn bandspreading has received detailed treatment in the literature [188,189].

The resolution of a pair of peaks, as given by eqn. 3.64, depends on the standard deviation, i.e. the square root of the variance. It follows that σ is dominated by the main contributor to bandspreading and is only slightly affected by the other processes. As an example, let us assume that $\sigma_{col} = 10$ sec, $\sigma_{inj} = \sigma_{conn} = 2$ sec, and $\sigma_{det} = 1$ sec. Then the standard deviation of the resulting peak is $\sigma = \sqrt{109} = 10.44$. The upshot is that extracolumn effects contribute only 4.4% of the total standard deviation, even though the sum of the standard deviations due to these effects is 50% of that generated by axial dispersion in the column proper.

The plate height, H, is proportional to the peak variance according to eqn. 3.48, and so it is expected to obey the same additivity rule as the variance. Therefore, the plate height of a chromatographic column can be expressed as the sum of increments arising from the processes that contribute independently to bandspreading. The most important plate height increment are associated with the following phenomena: longitudinal diffusion, $H_{l.d.}$; maldistribution of flow, H_f; mass transfer resistances, $H_{m.t.r.}$; and kinetic resistances, H_{kin}. Thus, the plate height can be expressed as

$$H = H_{l.d.} + H_f + H_{m.tr.} + H_{kin} \tag{3.172}$$

In the following sections, the terms of eqn. 3.172 will be evaluated individually and, thereafter, the resulting plate height equations for GC and LC will be examined.

3.8.2. Longitudinal molecular diffusion

Eluite molecules undergo random molecular diffusion during their journey through the column. The variance, or mean square displacement, that arises from this process, $\sigma_{l.d.}^2$ is readily evaluated from the Einstein equation as

$$\sigma_{l.d.}^2 = 2Dt \tag{3.173}$$

where D is the appropriate diffusion coefficient and t is time. The longitudinal diffusion in the mobile phase goes on for a time given by $t = L/u$ so that the resulting variance $\sigma^2_{M,l.d.}$, is given by

$$\sigma^2_{M,l.d.} = \frac{2D_{M,eff}L}{u} \tag{3.174}$$

where $D_{M,eff}$ is the effective diffusion coefficient in the mobile phase. The corresponding plate height contribution, $H_{M,l.d.}$, is given by

$$H_{M,l.d.} = \frac{\sigma^2_L}{L} = \frac{2D_{M,eff}}{u} \tag{3.175}$$

The effective diffusion coefficient is obtained as

$$D_{M,eff} = \gamma D_M \tag{3.176}$$

where γ is the obstruction factor that corrects the diffusivity in packed beds for the hindering effect of the packing structure and has a value of about 0.6. In open tubular columns γ is unity.

There are numerous methods for the estimation of molecular diffusivities. In liquids the diffusion coefficient of nondissociating small and medium-sized molecules is usually calculated from the Wilke–Chang equation

$$D = 7.4 \times 10^{-8} \frac{(\psi_B M_B)^{1/2} T}{\eta \bar{V}_A^{0.6}} \tag{3.177}$$

where $\bar{V}_A$ is the molar volume of solute in cc/gmole (as a liquid at its normal boiling point), M_B is the molecular weight of solvent B, T is the absolute temperature, η is the viscosity of the solution in centipoise, and ψ_B is an "association factor" for the solvent. The latter is 1.0 for nonpolar solvents, such as benzene, aliphatic hydrocarbons, and ether, 1.5 for ethanol, 1.9 for methanol, and 2.6 for water.

Binary diffusion coefficients in the gas phase can be estimated by the relationship [190]:

$$D = \frac{10^{-3}T^{1.75}}{P\left[(\Sigma v_i)_A^{1/3} + (\Sigma v_i)_B^{1/3}\right]} \left(\frac{1}{M_A} + \frac{1}{M_B}\right)^{1/2} \tag{3.178}$$

where T is the absolute temperature, P is the pressure in atmospheres, and M_A and M_B are molecular weights. The v_i values are empirical atomic diffusion volumes (Table 3.4), which are summed for the molecules of the solute and mobile phase to give the appropriate molecular volumes.

In LC the plate height contribution of longitudinal diffusion in the stationary phase, $H_{S,l.d.}$, also must be considered. It is usually of the same order of magnitude as the term for diffusion in the mobile phase and is given by

$$H_{S,l.d.} = \frac{2kD_{S,eff}}{u_e} \tag{3.179}$$

The above expression for $H_{S,l.d.}$ is obtained in a way similar to that for $H_{M,l.d.}$, but the time spent in the stationary phase, i.e. the time of diffusion, is taken as as Lk/u.

List of symbols on p. A122

TABLE 3.4

SPECIAL ATOMIC DIFFUSION VOLUMES [190]
Atomic and structural diffusion volume increments

C	16.5	(Cl)	19.5
H	1.98	(S)	17.0
O	5.48	Aromatic or hetero-	
(N)	5.69	cyclic rings	− 20.2

Diffusion volumes of simple molecules

H_2	7.07	CO_2	26.9
D_2	6.70	N_2O	35.9
He	2.88	NH_3	14.9
N_2	17.9	H_2O	12.7
O_2	16.6	(CCl_2F_2)	114.8
Air	20.1	(SF_6)	69.7
Ne	5.59		
Ar	16.1	(Cl_2)	37.7
Kr	22.8	(Br_2)	67.2
(Xe)	37.9	(SO_2)	41.1
CO	18.9		

In adsorption chromatography the surface diffusivity, $D_{S,eff}$, is believed to be of about the same order of magnitude as the bulk liquid diffusivity.

3.8.3. Flow profile effects and diffusion in the mobile phase

3.8.3.1. Open tubular columns

In capillary columns the flow is usually laminar, having a parabolic flow profile. In such cases, the combined effect of radially nonuniform flow and eluite diffusion in the mobile phase produce a plate height contribution, H_f, that can be rigorously evaluated [186] to yield

$$H_f = \frac{(1 + 6k + 11k^2)d_t^2 u_e}{96(1 + k)^2 D_M} \qquad (3.180)$$

where d_t is the inner diameter of the tube. Eqn. 3.180 shows that the magnitude of axial dispersion increases with the tube diameter and mobile phase velocity, since the effect of flow nonuniformity is amplified. On the other hand, bandspreading decreases with increasing diffusivity of the eluite, because rapid diffusion relaxes the effect of radial nonuniformity of flow.

According to eqn. 3.180, the plate height contribution due to nonuniform flow increases with the retention factor in the range of $0 < k < 10$ and levels off thereafter. Eqn. 3.180 also shows that an unretained tracer ($k = 0$) is also subject to bandspreading.

In coiled tubes, a secondary flow pattern [191] is superimposed on the parabolic flow profile, and convective radial mixing results. This is tantamount to an apparent increase in D_M as far as eqn. 3.180 is concerned and, therefore, bandspreading is reduced by secondary flow. Nonetheless, the enhancement of radial mass transfer by secondary flow does not appear to be large enough to affect the efficiency of capillary LC with tubes having relatively large ($d_t > 0.2$ mm) inner diameter [192].

3.8.3.2. Packed columns

The anfractuous flow path in packed columns (cf. Fig. 3.27) gives rise to a rather complex flow profile that is greatly dependent on the packing structure and defies rigorous analytical treatment. Consequently, the plate height contribution arising from radial flow nonuniformities can only be estimated. The classical theory of eddy diffusion [193] arrives at a velocity-independent plate height increment, $H_{f,e.d.}$, given by

$$H_{f,e.d.} = 2\lambda d_p \tag{3.181}$$

where d_p is the particle diameter and λ is a measure of flow inequality in the packed column.

On the other hand, diffusional resistances in the mobile phase stream are believed to give rise to another plate height increment, $H_{f,diff}$, expressed by

$$H_{f,diff} = \frac{\omega d_p^2 u_e}{D_{M,eff}} \tag{3.182}$$

where ω is a column packing parameter.

Plots of H versus u of data obtained over a relatively narrow velocity range frequently support the reality of a velocity-independent plate height increment, such as that given in eqn. 3.181. However, it is reasonable to believe that over a sufficiently wide range of conditions lateral diffusion counteracts the effect of flow maldistribution and that the two phenomena are coupled [194]. Then the appropriate plate height increment, H_f, is expressed as

$$H_f = \frac{1}{H_{f,e.d.}} + \frac{i}{H_{f,diff}} \tag{3.183}$$

The most recently developed expression [22] for H_f is given as

$$H_f = \frac{2\lambda d_p}{1 + \dfrac{\omega D_M^{1/3}}{d_p^{1/3} u^{1/3}}} \tag{3.184}$$

Other H_f terms of this type differ from eqn. 3.184 in that the exponent is not $1/3$ but 1 [194] or $1/2$ [195].

List of symbols on p. A122

3.8.4. Mass transfer resistances

A major source of bandspreading in the chromatographic column is the resistance to mass transfer, involved in the equilibrium distribution of the eluite between the mobile and stationary phases. In fact, the concentration pulse of the eluite is not in equilibrium between the phases except at its center, due to restraints imposed by the continuous flow. As Fig. 3.29 shows, the eluite concentration at a point in the column just ahead of the center of the zone is always somewhat higher in the stationary phase and lower in the mobile phase than the equilibrium value. The situation is reversed after the zone center has passed through that point in the column. Thus, the zone center moves with a velocity corresponding to thermodynamic equilibrium, whereas bandspreading arising from mass transfer and kinetic resistances in the system measures the magnitude of the departure from equilibrium, that is, the extent of nonequilibrium.

3.8.4.1. Open tubular columns

The stationary phase in most capillary columns is a liquid film which coats the inner wall of the tube. The effect of mass transfer resistances in the mobile phase on the plate height is expressed by the H_f value in eqn. 3.180. The analogous plate height increment arising from resistance to mass transfer in the stationary phase

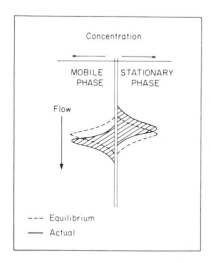

Fig. 3.29. Illustration of the eluite concentration profile in both the mobile and stationary phases within the column. The shaded areas represent the actual positions of the eluite zones, whereas the dashed profiles would be obtained if instantaneous equilibration took place in the column. However, the actual profile in the mobile phase moves faster and in the stationary phase slower than the corresponding profiles at equilibrium.

References on p. A130

[186] is given by

$$H_{\text{S,m.tr.}} = \frac{k^3}{24(1+k)^2} \frac{d_f^2 u_e}{K^2 D_S} = \frac{2k}{3(1+k)^2} \frac{d_f^2 u_e}{D_S} \qquad (3.185)$$

where K is the partition coefficient, d_f the thickness of the liquid film, and D_S the diffusivity of the eluite in the stationary phase.

In order to increase the sample capacity and retention, the liquid stationary phase is sometimes applied as a thin layer to a porous solid support on the inner wall of the tube. This method increases the amount of stationary phase over that in ordinary capillary tubes, but the liquid film is still relatively thin. For such support-coated open tubular (SCOT) columns [196] the $H_{\text{S,m.tr.}}$ term is, of course, more complicated than that for wall-coated open tubes (WCOT) in eqn. 3.185.

3.8.4.2. Packed columns

3.8.4.2.1. Film resistance

As Fig. 3.30 shows, eluite molecules diffusing into a particle from the moving bulk fluid first encounter a diffusional boundary layer before penetrating the interior of the porous stationary phase. The contribution to plate height arising from the film resistance at the particle boundary $H_{\text{m.tr.e.}}$, has been evaluated [197] for spherical particles as

$$H_{\text{m.tr.e.}} = \frac{1}{15} \frac{(k_0 + k + k_0 k)^2 d_p^{5/3} u_e^{2/3}}{(1+k_0)^2 (1+k)^2 D_M} \qquad (3.186)$$

where k_0 is the ratio of the intraparticulate void volume to the interstitial void space

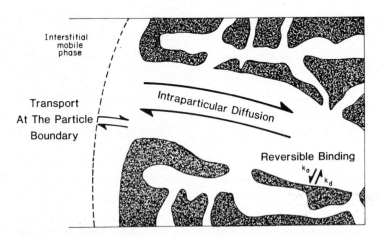

Fig. 3.30. Schematic illustration of the diffusion resistances at the boundary and interior of stationary phase particles as well as the kinetic resistances associated with reversible binding. (Reproduced from *J. Chromatogr.*, 149 (1978) 43, with permission [197].)

List of symbols on p. A122

in the column. $H_{\text{m.tr.e.}}$ is usually small compared to other plate height increments, and can therefore be neglected.

3.8.4.2.2. Intraparticular diffusion resistance

Resistance to diffusion inside the porous spherical adsorbent particles (Fig. 3.30) leads to the plate height contribution, $H_{\text{m.tr.i.}}$

$$H_{\text{m.tr.i.}} = \frac{\theta(k_0 + k + k_0 k)^2 d_p^2 u_e}{30 D_M k_0 (1 + k_0)^2 (1 + k)^2} \qquad (3.187)$$

where θ is the tortuosity factor for the pore structure of the particles. Under practical conditions, where major kinetic resistances are not important, this type of mass transfer resistance is the most important contributor to bandspreading. Corresponding terms for various configurations of the stationary phase can be found in the literature [1]. The simplest expression for $H_{\text{m.tr.i.}}$, used in GC is

$$H_{\text{m.tr.i.}} = \frac{2k}{3(1 + k)^2} \frac{d_f^2 u_e}{D_S} \qquad (3.188)$$

where d_f is the average film thickness for the liquid stationary phase, dispersed on the surface of the porous support, and D_S is the eluite diffusivity in the stationary phase. The diffusion resistance in the stagnant gaseous mobile phase inside the particle is neglected in eqn. 3.188, because it is small compared to that in the liquid stationary phase. On the other hand, the term given in eqn. 3.187 expresses the plate height contribution arising from diffusion resistances in the stagnant mobile phase in the intraparticulate space. Therefore, eqn. 3.187 is applicable to LC, where diffusion in the stagnant mobile phase within the intraparticulate space is relatively slow and its effect on bandspreading is expected to be significant. In LC with multicomponent eluents the value of k_0 is a function of the eluent composition, since the intraparticulate space occupied by the stagnant mobile phase may change due to solvation of the stationary phase surface [17,19]. When a liquid stationary phase is used, the interfacial mass transfer resistance may also be significant and will contribute an additional plate height increment for which numerous expressions can be found in the literature.

In order to reduce the path length for intraparticulate diffusion, pellicular [198] stationary phases were used in HPLC at first. The configuration of this type of column material is a spherical shell supported by a fluid-impervious core [199]. Ion-exchange resins prepared in this form were particularly useful in rapid separations of biological substances [200]. Pellicular stationary phases served as the basis for the development of HPLC instrumentation and significantly improved chromatographic performance before technology for the preparation of uniform microparticulate silica was available and before the full potential of reversed-phase chromatography was recognized.

References on p. A130

3.8.5. Kinetic resistances

In chromatography with solid stationary phases the relative slowness of the actual sorption kinetics may also contribute to bandspreading. The rate of eluite binding to the surface and that of desorption (Fig. 3.31) are characterized by the rate constants k_a and k_d, respectively. Thus, the retention factor, k, the thermodynamic equilibrium constant, K, and the rate constants are related by

$$k = \phi K = \phi \frac{k_a}{k_d} \tag{3.189}$$

In the case of the simplest binding kinetics [197], the appropriate plate height increment, H_{kin}, is given by

$$H_{kin} = \frac{2ku_e}{(1+k_0)(1+k)^2 k_d} = \frac{2k^2 u_e}{(1+k_0)(1+k)^2 \phi k_a} \tag{3.190}$$

H_{kin} is independent of the characteristic length (diffusion path) in the chromatographic system and, therefore, its magnitude cannot be reduced by decreasing the particle diameter. In contradistinction, all other plate height increments with the exception of those that arise from longitudinal diffusion are proportional to some power of the particle diameter.

In HPLC columns packed with very small particles the chromatography of complex macromolecules may involve various binding groups. In such cases, kinetic resistances may be significant in determining the magnitude of axial dispersion. The relative importance of the effect is conveniently estimated from the ratio $H_{kin}/H_{m.tr.}$.

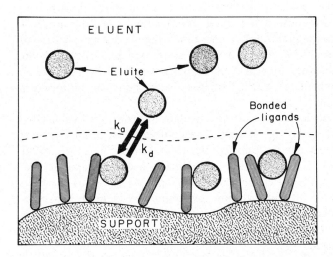

Fig. 3.31. Schematic illustration of the reversible binding of the eluite to the covalently attached ligates at the stationary phase surface. The rate constants for sorption and desorption are k_a and k_d, respectively. (Reproduced from *J. Chromatogr.*, 149 (1978) 43, with permission [197].)

List of symbols on p. A122

For conditions believed to be typical in the chromatography of small polar molecules that ratio is plotted against particle diameter in Fig. 3.32. It shows that with
relatively large particles ($d_p > 15$ μm) the ratio is much smaller than unity and the
effect of kinetic resistances can be neglected. This may be the reason why this effect
was ignored in studies of classical sorption kinetics, where measurements were made
on relatively large particles. For particles between 5 and 10 μm in diameter, H_{kin}
becomes larger than $H_{m.tr.}$. On this basis, bandspreading may be expected to be
governed by kinetic resistances in uniform columns, packed with very small particles
and operated at relatively high flowrates, because under such conditions the value of
the other plate height increments may be smaller that H_{kin}.

With complex molecules, particularly those of biological origin, the effect of
relatively slow binding kinetics on column efficiency is expected to be significant in
the usual practice of HPLC. Furthermore, the slow kinetics associated with secondary equilibria of the eluite in the mobile phase [31,200] may have a major effect
on bandspreading and may in fact, control column efficiency in HPLC. Improvement in both cases may be effected by changing the chemical composition of the
eluent, by increasing the temperature, or by decreasing the flowrate, rather than by
replacing the column.

Slow desorption rates in GSC with an adsorbent having an energetically nonuniform surface are known to engender excessive bandspreading. This effect, which has
been investigated in detail [1,28], is one of the reasons why conventional GSC is less
efficient than GLC. Bonded stationary phases having relatively uniform surfaces
usually exhibit favorable kinetic properties in both GC and LC. The use of
microparticulate columns in HPLC for the separation of complex substances has
been facilitated by the introduction of novel sorbents, such as bonded phases. A
highly important feature of these materials is that they exhibit kinetic resistances

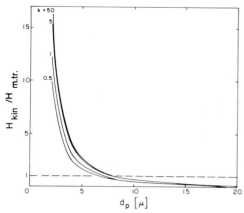

Fig. 3.32. Graph illustrating the dependence of the ratio $H_{kin}/H_{m.tr.}$ on the particle diameter, d_p, with the
retention factor, k, as the parameter. Conditions employed are assumed to be typical in reversed-phase
chromatography of small molecules. (Reproduced from *J. Chromatogr.*, 149 (1978) 43, with permission
[197].)

References on p. A130

that are significantly lower than those encountered with many classical stationary phases.

3.8.6. Plate height equations

Studies on the dependence of the plate height on flow velocity have greatly benefited the accurate interpretation of chromatographic results, facilitated diagnosis of chromatographic columns, and led to significant improvements of separation efficiency. The relationship between H and u is expressed by various "plate height equations", the first of which was the so-called Van Deemter equation [201], written in simplified form as

$$H = A + \frac{B}{u} + Cu \qquad (3.191)$$

where the terms A, B/u and Cu are the plate height increments given in eqns. 3.175, 3.181, and 3.188, respectively. Thus, A expresses the contribution of eddy diffusion, B/u that of longitudinal diffusion, and C that of mass transfer resistances.

A plot of eqn. 3.191 yields a hyperbola, as illustrated in Fig. 3.33. At low flow velocities the magnitude of bandspreading is determined by longitudinal diffusion, whereas at high flow velocities the mass transfer resistances control column efficiency. In between there is an optimum velocity, u_{opt}, at which the plot has a minimum plate height, H_{min}. The values of u_{opt} and H_{min} are readily evaluated by differentiating eqn. 3.191 and setting the result equal to zero as

$$u_{opt} = \sqrt{B/C} \qquad (3.192)$$

and substituting u_{opt} into eqn. 3.191 to obtain

$$H_{min} = A + 2\sqrt{BC} \qquad (3.193)$$

In chromatographic practice there is some flexibility in choosing the flow veloc-

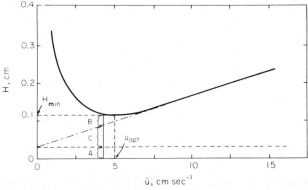

Fig. 3.33. Graph illustrating the plot of plate height against carrier gas velocity in GC with packed columns. The points of minimum plate height, H_{min}, and optimum velocity, u_{opt}, are shown, together with the contributions of the three terms of eqn. 3.191.

List of symbols on p. A122

ity; in fact, it is usually of advantage to operate the column at mobile phase velocities higher than u_{opt} so that the time of analysis can be reduced. Fig. 3.34 illustrates that the loss in resolution is less than 20% of its maximum value obtained at u_{opt}, even if the flow velocity is almost three times higher than the optimum.

The various plate height contributions discussed previously can be summed up to obtain a general plate height equation that correctly expresses H over a wide velocity range. In such cases, it is convenient to plot the reduced plate height, h, against the reduced velocity, ν, as shown in Fig. 3.35. The right-hand side of the plate height equation used in the calculation is the sum of the plate height contributions — in reduced form — given in eqns. 3.175, 3.184, and 3.187. As long as the chromatographic systems are dynamically similar, i.e. provided the kinetic resistances are negligible and the retention factors are identical, all data will fall on a simple curve on such reduced plots. As Fig. 3.35 shows, the practical span of reduced velocity is rather small compared to the range covered by the plate height equation.

Separation of small molecules by both GC and LC usually takes place in the reduced velocity range of 1 to 10. When the separation of macromolecules is attempted under the operating conditions employed in HPLC of small molecules, the reduced plate height is increased, because the reduced velocity which is inversely proportional to the diffusivity increases with the molecular weight. In order to carry out macromolecular separations in the optimal range of reduced velocity with a column efficiency comparable to that obtained with small molecules either the

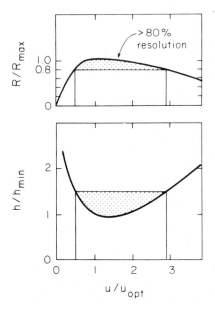

Fig. 3.34. Resolution relative to its maximum value and plate height relative to its minimum value as functions of the ratio of gas velocity to the optimum gas velocity. (Reproduced from *Dynamics of Chromatography, Part I, Principles and Theory*, Dekker, New York, 1965, with permission [1].)

References on p. A130

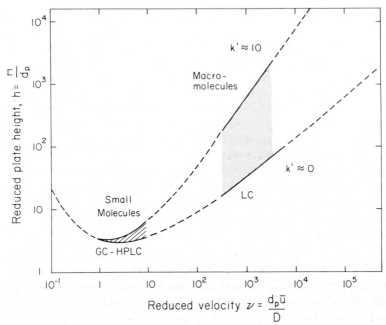

Fig. 3.35. Plot of reduced plate height versus reduced velocity and illustration of the domains of GC and HPLC for the separation of small molecules. The domain of macromolecular chromatography under similar operating conditions is also illustrated. In order to obtain comparable column efficiencies with both classes of substances, the reduced velocity range should be the same. In order to accomplish this, macromolecular chromatography requires lower flow velocity and/or a column containing smaller particles.

particle diameter or the flow velocity must be reduced. At present, lowering the flow velocity appears to be the more practical approach, even if an increase in separation time ensues. Moreover, the effect of kinetic resistances is also relaxed as flow velocity is decreased.

Although the use of plate height versus velocity plots, also called HETP curves, has greatly contributed to the development of chromatography, accurate evaluation of physico-chemical parameters from experiments is difficult if not impossible in many practical cases. Furthermore, effects not treated above may also contribute to the observed bandspreading. In LC, e.g., at high flowrates and high column inlet pressures a nonuniform radial temperature profile may result from viscous dissipation [202].

Within a relatively narrow range of practical conditions the velocity dependence of the plate height can be expressed by simple relationships. However, the parameters of such simplified plate equations are not expected to be amenable to to rigorous interpretation as meaningful physico-chemical quantities. The general plate height equation, for instance, reduces at sufficiently low reduced velocities to the form [197]

$$h \approx \frac{\mathcal{A}}{\nu} + \mathcal{B}\nu^{1/3} + \mathcal{C}\nu \tag{3.194}$$

List of symbols on p. A122

where

$$\mathcal{Q} = 2\gamma \tag{3.195}$$

$$\mathcal{B} = \frac{2\lambda}{\omega} \tag{3.196}$$

and

$$\mathcal{C} = \frac{\theta(k_0 + k + k_0 k)^2}{30 k_0 (1 + k_0)^2 (1 + k)^2} + \frac{2k D_M}{(1 + k_0)(1 + k)^2 d_p^2 k_d} \tag{3.197}$$

according to eqns. 3.175, 3.184, 3.187, and 3.190, respectively. The second term in eqn. 3.194 accounts for effects of slow binding kinetics on bandspreading.

Eqn. 3.194 is illustrated in Fig. 3.36, and plots of the individual terms as functions of flow velocity are also depicted by using numerical coefficients encountered in practice. The first and last terms of eqn. 3.194 are due to longitudinal diffusion and slow equilibration rate, respectively, and have sufficient theoretical foundation, as discussed earlier. The second term corresponds to H_f/d_p; its dependence on the $1/3$ power of velocity has been found from experiments in reduced velocity ranges of practical interest [203].

At relatively high reduced velocities a further simplification of the general plate

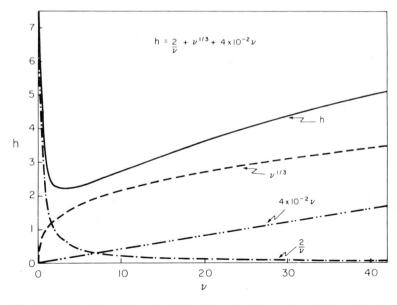

Fig. 3.36. Plots of the reduced plate height and various reduced plate-height increments against the reduced velocity, according to eqn. 3.194 with the parameter values $\mathcal{Q} = 2$, $\mathcal{B} = 1$, and $\mathcal{C} = 0.04$. The plot shows that in the practical flow velocity range bandspreading arises mainly from the term $\mathcal{B}^{1/3}$, where $\mathcal{B}$ is determined by the uniformity of the packing structure.

References on p. A130

height eqn. 3.194 yields the relationship

$$h \approx 2\lambda + Cv \tag{3.198}$$

which predicts a linear dependence of the plate height on the velocity. Such behavior has indeed been observed, and an equation of the form of eqn. 3.198 has been used to analyze experimental data [204]. Reduced parameters facilitate comparison of dynamic behavior in GC and LC. In the absence of kinetic resistances, h versus v plots obtained with eluites having the same retention factors should be identical for different chromatographic systems. As Fig. 3.35 shows, the separation of small molecules by HPLC is carried out in the reduced velocity range of 1 to 10. When the same column and flowrate are used to attempt a separation of macromolecules with molecular diffusivities two orders of magnitude lower than those of small molecules, the reduced velocities will be higher by two orders of magnitude and, as a result, the plate height will be substantially greater. The low column efficiency thus obtained may not suffice for adequate resolution of the components. In order to reduce plate height, the particle diameter and/or the flow velocity have to be decreased. Since kinetic resistances may be significant with macromolecules, the separation should be performed at flow velocities significantly lower than those employed in HPLC of small molecules. Gradient elution can be a particularly useful adjunct in the separation of macromolecular mixtures by interactive chromatography, because the plate height contribution due to slow equilibration decreases with the retention factor.

3.8.7. Planar chromatography

For many of the reasons discussed in Chap. 3.7.2 for flow processes, bandspreading is a more complicated process in planar chromatography than in CC. In particular, mobile phase velocity and density change axially and with the time. As a result, the phase ratio, retention factor, and plate height also vary. Quantitative analysis of these parameters is therefore less straightforward than in CC. The width, w, of the eluite spot due to simple diffusion is given by

$$w^2 = 16\sigma^2 = 32\gamma D_M t + w_{in}^2 \tag{3.199}$$

where σ is the standard deviation, γ is the obstruction factor for the sorbent, D_M is the diffusivity of the eluite in the mobile phase, t is the time, and w_{in} is the width of the spot initially applied to the sorbent. Assuming that the solute density in the spot is represented by a Gaussian distribution, the usual definitions of plate number and height give

$$N = \frac{16R_F^2 Z_f^2}{w^2} \tag{3.200}$$

and

$$H = \frac{R_F Z_f}{N} \tag{3.201}$$

Combination of eqns. 3.198, 3.199, and 3.201, as well as the the empirical equation
for the distance moved by the solvent front, eqn. 3.169, gives the plate height as

$$H = \frac{2\theta D_{\mathrm{M}} Z_{\mathrm{f}}}{R_F \kappa} + \frac{w_{\mathrm{in}}^2}{16 R_F Z_{\mathrm{f}}} \tag{3.202}$$

Eqn. 3.202 shows that the size of the initial spot can contribute significantly to the
final spot diameter. The importance of minimizing the initial spot within the
constraints of detectability is evident from the second-power dependence of H on
w_{in}. Because both R_F and Z_{f} change during chromatographic development, it is
evident that the plate height given by eqn. 3.202 is not a characteristic of the system
but changes in the course of an experiment.

The plate height expression given by eqn. 3.202 assumes that the broadening of
the spot occurs by diffusion of the sample. This assumption is valid for the low
mobile phase velocities encountered in sorbents of very small particle size, such as in
the so-called high-performance thin-layer chromatography (HPTLC). In order to
describe the dynamics in planar chromatography, comprehensive studies [184,205–
208] have made use of the plate height equation (cf. eqn. 3.194) and resulted in an
expression for the local plate height, H_{loc}, when the initial spot width is negligible

$$H_{\mathrm{loc}} = \frac{2\gamma D_{\mathrm{M}}}{u} + \frac{A d_{\mathrm{p}}^{4/3}}{D_{\mathrm{M}}^{1/3}} u^{1/3} + \frac{C d_{\mathrm{p}}^2 u}{D_{\mathrm{M}}} \tag{3.203}$$

where γ is the obstruction factor, and A and C are constants for a given system. Eqn.
3.203 is analogous to the plate height expression used in CC in that the first term is
associated with longitudinal diffusion, the second with mass transfer resistances in
the mobile phase, and the third with slow equilibration rates. The measurable
quantity, though, is not H_{loc} but, rather, the average plate height, $\overline{H}$, at the end of
the chromatographic development, obtained by integrating H_{loc} over the distance
traversed by the sample

$$\overline{H} = b(Z_{\mathrm{f}} + Z_0) + \frac{a}{Z_{\mathrm{f}} - Z_0}\left(Z_{\mathrm{f}}^{2/3} - Z_0^{2/3}\right) + \frac{c}{Z_{\mathrm{f}} - Z_0} \ln \frac{Z_{\mathrm{f}}}{Z_0} \tag{3.204}$$

where

$$a = A\frac{3}{2}\left(\frac{d_{\mathrm{p}}^5 \kappa_0}{2 D_{\mathrm{M}}}\right)^{1/3} \tag{3.205}$$

$$b = \frac{Z\theta D_{\mathrm{M}}}{\kappa_0 d_{\mathrm{p}}} \tag{3.206}$$

$$c = C\frac{\kappa_0 d_{\mathrm{p}}^3}{2 D_{\mathrm{M}}} \tag{3.207}$$

In eqn. 3.204, w_{in} is assumed to be negligible and u is eliminated from eqn. 3.203 by
using eqn. 3.169. The first term in eqn. 3.204 corresponds to the first term in eqn.
3.202, except that in the former diffusion is assumed to take place in both phases.

References on p. A130

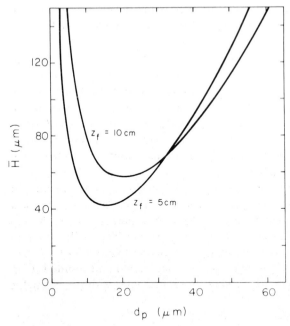

Fig. 3.37. Plots of the dependence of the average plate height, $\bar{H}$, on particle diameter, d_p, in TLC. Calculations were based on eqn. 3.204 for experiments in which the solvent front advanced 5 cm and 10 cm past the origin. Other parameters: $\kappa_0 = 60.86$ (cf. Fig. 3.28), $\theta = 0.7$, $D_M = 3 \times 10^{-5}$ cm^2/sec, $\mathcal{Q} = 1$, $\mathcal{C} = 0.01$, $Z_0 = 0.5$ cm. All parameters except κ_0 were taken from ref. 206.

The plot of $\bar{H}$ versus d_p in Fig. 3.37 was drawn by using typical parameter values given in the literature [206]. Apparently, in planar chromatography there is an optimum particle size at which the plate height is a minimum. Below this particle size, the mobile phase velocity is so low (cf. eqn. 3.168) that longitudinal diffusion tends to broaden the spot, while above it other mechanisms dominate the band-broadening. The curves in Fig. 3.37 are drawn for two values of the development distance, Z_f, i.e. the distance the solvent front has advanced past the origin. Thus, with the shorter development distance, the minimum in the plate height curve occurs at a smaller particle size, but a further decrease in the particle size greatly impairs the sorbent efficiency.

3.9. PROCEDURES IN MULTICOMPONENT ELUTION CHROMATOGRAPHY

3.9.1. Problems in isocratic separation of multicomponent mixtures

Chromatography is a multicomponent separation technique par excellence. Although most of the preceding treatment has dealt with the behavior of single eluites and the separation of eluite pairs, most practical applications aim at the resolution of more than two substances. The expression of resolution in eqn. 3.65 suggests that the separation of two neighboring peaks can be improved by increasing the selectivity of the system and/or by increasing the retention factor until the term $\bar{k}/(1+\bar{k})$ reaches a plateau. However, the peaks of multicomponent samples have a wide range of retention factors and relative retentions under isocratic conditions. Experience teaches that changes in the chromatographic system rarely result in an overall improvement in resolution without undue increases in separation time or other untoward consequences. Therefore, in order to bring about the separation by isocratic elution in a single column, the plate count must be increased. This is often not practical, because it may involve an unacceptable increase in separation time or column inlet pressure. Moreover, as eqn. 3.65 shows, the resolution is not proportional to N but increases with the square root of plate number. Fortunately, a number of procedures are at our disposal to circumvent a shortage of theoretical plates in the separation of multicomponent mixtures. These may be of practical interest whenever more than two components have to be separated. Of course, the separation of two peaks can always be carried out isocratically with a limited number of plates by devising a chromatographic system of sufficient selectivity.

Before discussing such procedures, it is appropriate to divide the problem associated with isocratic separation of multicomponent mixtures into two categories. When complex samples containing many components having a wide range of retention factors are separated, the selectivity may be too high and the separation time too long. Furthermore, late peaks may become excessively broad and undetectable with the available detectors. Fig. 3.38 illustrates such a situation, which has been referred to as the "general elution problem" [209]. The composition of the mixture is such that there is a constant difference between the free energies associated with the retention of neighboring components. This retention behavior, which manifests itself in a logarithmic progression of the peaks, occurs with most homologous series and may also be expected with samples that contain randomly selected components. In Fig. 3.38A the median peak is eluted with a retention factor of about 3, which is considered to be optimum. However, under such conditions, early peaks are crowded and poorly resolved, whereas late peaks are strongly retained so that the separation time is long and their concentration is low. The resolution of early peak may be improved by using a weaker eluent (Fig. 3.38B), but the retention times of late peaks will become impractically long and the peaks will be so broad that detection may be difficult. In contrast, by selecting a stronger eluent, the retention time and width of the late peaks will become acceptable (Fig. 3.38C), but the early peaks will not be resolved because they are eluted close to the inert tracer. The three chromatograms obtained by isocratic elution illustrate the general elution problem, i.e. no equiresolutive retention behavior can be obtained by isocratic elution.

Of course, one way to obtain satisfactory results would be to increase the column efficiency enough to allow the resolution of the early peaks in Fig. 3.38C. But there is another way to accomplish a complete separation: a gradual decrease in the retentive power of the chromatographic system in the course of the chromatographic

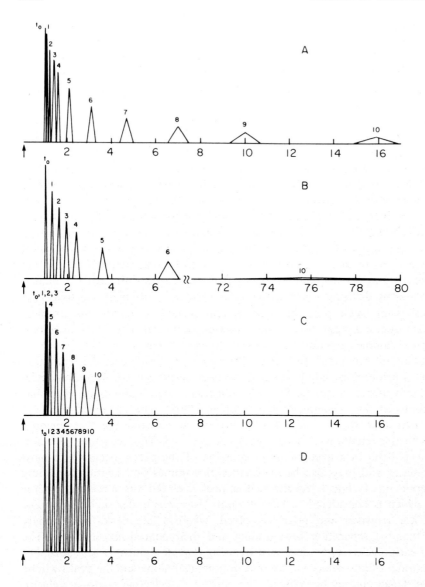

Fig. 3.38. Separation of the members of a homologous series in reversed-phase chromatography by isocratic elution with three eluents of different strengths and by gradient elution. (A) Isocratic elution at intermediate eluent strength: early peaks are not resolved, late peaks are very strongly retained, intermediate peaks are eluted optimally. (B) Isocratic elution with weak eluent: early peaks well resolved, intermediate and late peaks are eluted much too slowly. (C) Isocratic elution with strong eluent: early and intermediate peaks are unresolved, late peaks are eluted fast and are well separated. (D). Gradient elution with eucratic gradient. Schemes A–C illustrate the "general elution problem" [209], as the retention energies for the sample components change by about equal amounts and the sample may be regarded as randomly selected. This picture also applies to GC when eluent strength and gradient elution are replaced by temperature and temperature programing, respectively.

List of symbols on p. A122

development. This is accomplished by temperature programing and gradient elution in GC and LC, respectively. In the application of these anisocratic elution techniques the excessive intrinsic selectivity of the systems under isocratic conditions is "traded" for improved separation. In actuality, the peak capacity is enhanced by gradient elution or temperature programing without changing the intrinsic efficiency of the column, as illustrated in Fig. 3.38 [210]. The enhanced peak capacity makes the employment of these techniques in trace analysis particularly attractive.

The essential feature of anisocratic elution is illustrated by a distance/time diagram for gradient elution. Fig. 3.39 shows the movement of the peaks through the column when the eluent strength is gradually increased with time. The peaks do not move with constant speed but their velocity increases exponentially in the column. A peak emerges from the column when its trajectory reaches the end of the column at $Z/L = 1$. Similar distance/time diagrams apply to temperature-programed chromatography. The two anisocratic elution methods yield analogous results in the case of the most commonly used linear eluent gradient or temperature program.

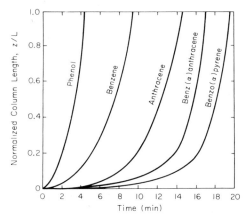

Fig. 3.39. Distance/time diagram for gradient elution in reversed-phase chromatography with a system where the logarithmic retention factor is a linear function of the volume fraction of the organic solvent component in an aqueous eluent. The ordinate is the reduced distance in the column, which is unity at the column outlet where the peaks egress. The curves show the axial positions of the peak centers within the column. (Reproduced from *J. Chromatogr.*, 126 (1976) 421, with permission [92].)

Another problem of multicomponent elution arises when the retention factors of the components span a narrow range and the components of the sample cannot be separated isocratically, with the exception of a few eluite pairs. Employment of another eluent usually is not a practical solution, even if the previously unresolved eluites are separated because the resolution of other solute pairs deteriorates, as shown in Fig. 3.40. Anisocratic elution is not the solution to this problem, which stems from inadequate selectivity of the chromatographic system. Only an increase in column efficiency could generate narrower peaks with a concomitant increase in peak capacity so that all components of the mixture would be resolved within a practical retention factor range [211]. If it is not practicable to increase the efficiency

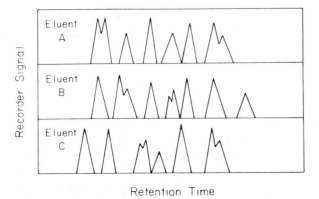

Fig. 3.40. Schematic illustration of isocratic separation of a multicomponent mixture in approximately the same retention factor range with three different eluents. Due to inadequate column efficiency, complete separation is not obtained. Changing the eluent only varies the positions of the unresolved peaks. (Reproduced from *An Introduction to Separation Science*, Wiley-Interscience, New York, 1973, with permission [211].)

of the column, the use of multiple column chromatography offers a solution, particularly in the case of iterant separations.

3.9.2. Anisocratic elution techniques

3.9.2.1. Temperature programing

Temperature programing, used almost exclusively in GC, involves raising the temperature of the column at a predetermined rate (0.5–50°C/min) during chromatography [212]. Since the viscosity of the carrier gas increases with temperature, the flowrate rather than the column inlet pressure is regulated. Temperature-programed operation at constant flowrate is called isorheic operation. Since direct control of flowrate is difficult with capillary columns, isobaric (constant inlet pressure) conditions are maintained. Small-diameter columns are generally used in order to reduce bandspreading due to nonuniform radial temperature profile.

At the low starting temperature of the program, the sample components are very strongly retained at the column inlet. With increasing temperature they begin to move so that their velocity doubles with an increase of approximately 30°C. Under optimal programing conditions [213] each peak reaches the middle of the column when the temperature is about 30°C below its retention (elution) temperature, i.e. the column temperature at which the center of the peak leaves the column. The retention temperature is a fundamental parameter in temperature-programed operation. It is characteristic for the chromatographic system and increases with the logarithmic heating rate, but it is rather unaffected by small changes in the carrier gas flowrate, column length, and starting temperature. In the case of a linear temperature program, the retention temperature is proportional to the logarithmic

List of symbols on p. A122

retention time. Thus, plots of the retention temperature against the number of recurring molecular increments in a homologous series are linear, provided the starting temperature is sufficiently low. Therefore, the Kováts retention index can be extended to data obtained by temperature programing simply by using retention temperatures or times instead of the logarithm of these quantities [214]. The retention temperature is always higher than the so-called "significant temperature" at which an isothermal (isocratic) experiment would yield the same performance. It has been shown [213] that the significant temperature is about 45°C lower than the retention temperature.

The starting temperature is properly selected when the peaks of members of a homologous series (e.g., n-alkanes) are equidistant on the chromatogram, and its value depends on the boiling point of the most volatile component. The terminal temperature is determined by the retention temperature of the least volatile sample component or the maximum allowable temperature of the stationary phase, whichever is lower. The heating rate and the flowrate of the mobile phase are coupled in determining the retention temperature. The effect of heating rate is comparable to that of temperature in the case of isothermal elution, i.e. the resolution decreases with increasing heating rates.

Another elution method that employs changing column temperature, called "chromatothermography", has been introduced in GC. Unlike temperature programing, in which the temperature of the whole column varies uniformly, in this technique a coaxial heater is used to establish a temperature gradient [215] and it is moved from the inlet to the outlet of the column. The bands of eluites occupy different positions in the column and move in the zone of their characteristic temperature with the velocity of the moving furnace. This technique offers certain advantages in trace analysis.

3.9.2.2. Gradient elution

An increase in eluent strength during the chromatographic development is accomplished by gradient elution [109]. The name of this technique originates from its characteristic feature: the eluent strength is changed gradually so that a solvent composition gradient is generated in the column. This continuous change in solvent composition has been found superior in general applications to stepwise elution, i.e. discontinuous changes in the composition of the eluent. Nevertheless, stepwise elution is widely used in certain specific applications.

The shape of the gradient, i.e. the gradient profile or particular dependence of the eluent composition on time, has a significant effect on the resolution of a complex mixture (Fig. 3.41). The most commonly used gradients are linear, i.e. the starting eluent, A, is mixed with the gradient-forming solvent, B, so that the volume fraction of B increases linearly with time. Particularly useful are linear solvent strength gradients, which result in the following dependence of the logarithmic retention factor, κ, on elution time, t:

$$\kappa = \kappa_0 - bt/t_0 \tag{3.208}$$

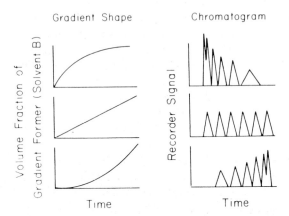

Fig. 3.41. Effect of gradient shape on the separation of a multicomponent mixture. Top: convex gradient; middle: linear gradient; bottom: concave gradient. (Reproduced from *Introduction to Modern Liquid Chromatography*, 2nd Edn., Wiley-Interscience, New York, 1979, with permission [216].)

where κ_0 is the logarithmic retention factor of the eluite obtained by isocratic elution with neat solvent A, the starting eluent, and b is the gradient steepness parameter, which has the same value for all components eluted by a given linear solvent strength gradient. It is given by

$$b = \left(V_M/Ft_g \right) \log(k_A/k_B) \qquad\qquad (3.209)$$

where t_g is the time of the gradient development, and k_A and k_B are the isocratic retention factors of a given eluite in neat A and neat B, respectively. Eqn. 3.209 shows that, at fixed gradient time, b decreases with increasing flowrate and/or decreasing column length.

A particular type of linear gradient, yielding a linear dependence of the retention time (or volume) on the number of recurring molecular units for members of a given homologous series may be of importance. Such a gradient is conveniently termed eucratic. Just as temperature-programed and isothermal elution have analogous features in GC, the correspondence of key chromatographic parameters in gradient and isocratic elution are shown in Table 3.5. Gradient elution is widely used in HPLC under precisely controlled conditions.

3.9.3. Multiple chromatography

3.9.3.1. Recycling and unidimensional multiple chromatography

In preparative chromatography, recycling of the column effluent through the column augments the efficiency of separation [217,218]. The procedure effects an increase in the number of plates and has been used mainly in SEC, where peak capacity is severely constrained. In such systems, the column effluent is monitored

List of symbols on p. A122

TABLE 3.5

COMPARISON OF THE EXPRESSIONS FOR KEY CHROMATOGRAPHIC PARAMETERS IN ISOCRATIC AND LINEAR SOLVENT STRENGTH GRADIENT ELUTION [109]

t_g = retention time in gradient elution.
k_0 = retention factor of eluite at the beginning of gradient elution.
$\bar{k}$ = median retention value of a band in gradient elution; $\bar{k} = 1/1.15b$.
t_{g_z} = time of gradient separation, as measured by the elution time of the last component.
k_f = instantaneous retention factor at the column outlet in gradient elution.
G = band compression factor $\left[\dfrac{1 + P + (P^{2/3})}{(1 + P)^2} \right]^{1/2}$, where $P \approx 2.3b$.
t_z = retention time of last component.

Parameter	Isocratic	Gradient
Retention time	$t_R = t_0(1 + k)$	$t_g = (t_0/b) \log(2.31k_0 b + 1) + t_0$
Retention factor	$k = (t_R - t_0)/t_0$	$k_g = (1/b) \log(2.3k_0 b + 1)$
Separation time	$t_z = t_0(1 + k_z)$	$t_{g_z} = (t_0/b) \log(2.3k_{0z} b + 1) + t_0 = t_G + t_0$
Retention term in equation resolution $[R_s / \frac{1}{4} N(\alpha - 1)]$	$k/(1 + k)$	$\bar{k}/(1 + \bar{k})$
k at column outlet, k_f	k	$k_f = 1/(2.3b + 1/k_0)$
Bandwidth (4σ)	$w = (4/\sqrt{N})t_0(1 + k)$	$w = (4/\sqrt{N})t_0(1 + k_f)G$
Relative peak height	$1/w$	$1/w$
Optimum mobile phase	$2 \leqslant k \leqslant 5$	$0.1 \leqslant b \leqslant 0.3$

continuously and, when the earliest peak of the mixture reaches the slowest zone, recycling is terminated.

In planar chromatography, sequences of alternating development and drying have been used in order to increase the effective development length of the plate [219]. This technique has been dubbed unidimensional multiple chromatography and has received appropriate theoretical treatment [220].

3.9.3.2. Two-dimensional development

Resolution of the sample components in planar chromatography can be enhanced by a second development in the direction perpendicular to that of flow during the first development [221]. The technique is referred to as two-dimensional TLC or PC. The forte of this approach is that different eluents can be used in the two developments and, thus, the selectivity of separation can be different in the two cases. The technique is a simple, yet very powerful approach to the separation of complex biological mixtures.

3.9.3.3. Multicolumn chromatography; column switching

In both GC and LC, columns can be coupled in a suitable flow arrangement in order to enhance the efficacy of separation. Such multicolumn schemes are designed to serve a particular purpose in routine analytical work with automated or semi-auto-

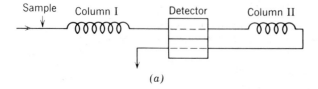

(a)

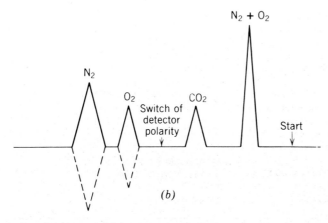

(b)

Fig. 3.42. Flow sheet of (a) a dual-column system in GC for the separation of O_2, N_2, and CO_2, and (b) the resulting chromatogram. Column I, silica gel. Column II, Molecular Sieve 5A. (Reproduced from *Introduction to Modern Liquid Chromatography*, 2nd Edn., Wiley-Interscience, New York, 1979, with permission [216].)

mated instrumentation, such as that associated with process control and clinical analyses.

A rather simple GC system which employs two columns and two detectors for the separation of the major components of air [222] is shown in Fig. 3.42. Column I is packed with silica gel and separates CO_2 from N_2 and O_2, as shown in the chromatogram. After passing through the detector, the eluites enter Column II, which is packed with Molecular Sieve 5A and separates N_2 from O_2 while CO_2 is irreversibly adsorbed. The effluent of Column II passes through the reference cell of the detector. By reversing the polarity of the detector, the otherwise negative N_2 and O_2 peaks appear to be in the usual form on the chromatogram (Fig. 3.42b).

In LC, multicolumn systems are used in various configurations for diverse purposes. In the simplest example, columns are connected in series. In size exclusion, for instance, chromatography columns packed with porous particles having different exclusion limits allow a convenient separation of sample components over a wide molecular weight range.

Among the various multicolumn schemes employed in LC the system shown in Fig. 3.43 offers the possibility of either "stationary-phase programing" or "selectivity switching" [216]. In the first case, Columns A and B are of equal length, but the

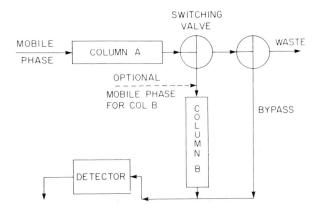

Fig. 3.43. Flow sheet of an experimental arrangement used in multicolumn chromatography. A part of the effluent from Column A, containing unresolved bands, is introduced into Column B in order to bring about the separation, while the rest of the effluent from Column A passes through the detector. (Reproduced from *Introduction to Modern Liquid Chromatography*, 2nd Edn., Wiley-Interscience, New York, 1979, with permission [216].)

phase ratio of Column B is much greater than that of Column A. Such an arrangement is conveniently made by packing A with a pellicular support and B with a totally porous column material of the same chemical nature. After a multicomponent sample is introduced, Column A separates the late peaks well, but the early peaks are poorly resolved. The switching valve is turned so that the tail end of the chromatogram from Column A is directed to the detector, while the front end passes into Column B. After the last peak has emerged from Column A, the valve is switched to elute the peaks from Column B. In this way, considerable improvement can be obtained in analytical sensitivity, and separation time can be reduced. The essence of "stationary-phase programing" is that the weakly and strongly retarded components are eluted with close-to-optimal retention factors by using columns having high and low phase ratios, respectively.

In the "selectivity switching" arrangement, Columns A and B contain stationary phases that have widely different selectivities toward the sample components but allow elution with the same mobile phase. If different mobile phases are used, the fractions from Column A must be compatible with the chromatographic system in Column B. When a complex sample is chromatographed on Column A, which does not have enough peak capacity to resolve certain solute pairs, the unresolved fractions can be "cut out" from the effluent and diverted to Column B, which is more selective for these eluites and where their separation is accomplished. This technique can be used to resolve a few desired components of a complex mixture with considerable saving of time [223]. Of course, such systems are designed especially for a particular separation problem, and they require a careful balancing of conditions and timing of the switching operations.

References on p. A130

3.10. LIST OF SYMBOLS

a	activity (eqns. 3.77, 3.78)
a	absolute value of charge on Ion A (eqns. 3.130–3.132, 3.134, 3.135, 3.137–3.140)
a	forward half-width at 10% of peak height (eqn. 3.44)
a	constant in average plate height equation (eqns. 3.204, 3.205)
a'	forward half-width of peak base (eqn. 3.45)
a^*	forward half-width at 0.134 of C_{max} (eqn. 3.46)
a_i	substituent contribution to molecular area (eqn. 3.129)
a_S, a_M	activity in stationary (S) or mobile (M) phases (eqn. 3.90)
a_1, a_2	parameters in linear free energy relationships (eqn. 3.156)
$a_{\pm}$	activity of a salt (eqn. 3.90)
b	rear half-width at 10% of peak height (eqn. 3.44)
b	gradient steepness parameter (eqns. 3.208, 3.209)
b	absolute value of charge on Ion B (eqns. 3.130–3.132, 3.134)
b	constant in average plate height equation (eqns. 3.204, 3.206)
b'	rear half-width of peak base (eqn. 3.45)
b^*	rear half-width at 0.134 of C_{max} (eqn. 3.46)
c	constant in average plate height equation (eqn. 3.204)
d	characteristic distance in a flow system (eqns. 3.164, 3.168)
d_f	average stationary phase film thickness (eqn. 3.185)
d_p	particle diameter
d_t	tube diameter (eqn. 3.180)
f	fugacity
f	adsorption isotherm of a gas (eqn. 3.116)
h	reduced plate height (eqns. 3.194, 3.198)
j	gas compressibility factor
k	retention (capacity) factor
k_a	rate constant for sorption (eqns. 3.70, 3.189, 3.190)
k_d	rate constant for desorption (eqns. 3.70, 3.189, 3.190, 3.197)
k_0	retention factor with water as mobile phase or in the absence of hetaeron (eqn. 3.108)
k_0	ratio of total to interstitial void volumes (eqns. 3.186, 3.187, 3.190, 3.197)
k_C	retention factor of complexed eluite (eqn. 3.103)
k_A or k_B	isocratic retention factor in Eluent A or B (eqns. 3.103, 3.209)
k_1, k_2	retention factor of Components 1 and 2 (eqns. 3.61, 3.66, 3.67)
k_i	retention factor of i (eqn. 3.104)
$\bar{k}$	average retention factor (eqn. 3.65)
l	(subscript) liquid phase
m	molality
m_i	molality of i (eqn. 3.92)
m_+, m_-	molality of cation and anion (eqn. 3.90)

$m_{i,S}$, $m_{i,M}$	mass of eluite in mobile or stationary phase (eqn. 3.102)
n	peak capacity (eqn. 3.54)
n_{SEC}	peak capacity in size exclusion chromatography (eqn. 3.55)
n_C	number of carbon atoms in reference paraffin (eqn. 3.158)
n_1, n_2	number of moles of 1 and 2 (eqn. 3.82)
n_i	number of moles of i (eqns. 3.74–3.76)
n_j	number of moles of components other than i (eqn. 3.75)
n_i	number of substituents i in a molecule (eqns. 3.150, 3.161)
n_A, n_B	molecular areas of A and B (eqn. 3.127)
n_g, n_h	molecular areas of the most strongly adsorbed components (eqn. 3.128)
r	charge at ion-exchange site (eqn. 3.139)
r	radial position in tube cross-section (eqn. 3.162)
r_i	ratio of stoichiometric coefficients (eqns. 3.103, 3.105–3.107)
t	time
t_D	extracolumn hold-up time (eqn. 3.9)
t_e	residence time of excluded solute (eqns. 3.27–3.29)
t_0	elution time of unretained eluite
t_g	time of gradient development (eqn. 3.209)
t_R	retention time
t_R'	adjusted retention time
$t_{R,1}$, $t_{R,2}$	retention times of components 1 and 2 (eqn. 3.64)
$t_{R,1}'$, $t_{R,2}'$	adjusted retention times of 1 and 2 (eqn. 3.61)
t_R^*	break-through time of a front (eqn. 3.35)
Δt_R	difference in retention time of two substances (eqn. 3.64)
$t_{R,i}^S$	retention time of solvent component i (eqn. 3.10)
u	chromatographic velocity, linear flow velocity
u_b	band velocity (eqns. 3.56, 3.58, 3.60)
u_D	velocity of displacer front (eqn. 3.5)
u_e	interstitial velocity
u_f	solvent front velocity in planar chromatography (eqn. 3.168)
u_0	mobile phase velocity (eqn. 3.5)
u_{opt}	optimum velocity (eqn. 3.192)
u_s	superficial velocity (eqns. 3.24, 3.25, 3.29, 3.30, 3.165)
v	laminar flow velocity (eqn. 3.162)
v_i	atomic diffusion volume of atom i (eqn. 3.178)
v_{max}	maximum flow velocity in tube (eqn. 3.162)
v	(subscript) vaporization (eqns. 3.85, 3.86)
v_{AB}	partial molar volume of solute in A–B binary (eqn. 3.95)
v_S, v_M	partial molar volume of stationary (S) or mobile (M) phase
w	peak base width (eqn. 3.51)
w	spot width in planar chromatography (eqns. 3.199, 3.200)
w_1, w_2	band widths of Peaks 1 and 2 (eqn. 3.64)
$\overline{w}$	average base width of two peaks (eqn. 3.64)
w_h	width at peak half height (eqn. 3.51)

w_i	peak width at inflection points (eqn. 3.51)
w_{in}	sample spot width (eqns. 3.199, 3.202)
x	mole fraction
x_A, x_B	mole fractions of A and B (eqn. 3.127)
x_g, x_h	mole fractions of most strongly adsorbed components (eqn. 3.128)
x_1	mole fraction of eluite in liquid phase (eqns. 3.83, 3.84)
$y_{A,S}$	mass of A bound to surface (eqns. 3.97, 3.98)
y_{max}	maximum mass of A that can be bound to surface (eqns. 3.97, 3.98)
A	first term of Van Deemter equation (eqns. 3.191, 3.193)
$\mathcal{A}$	constant in reduced plate height equation (eqns. 3.194, 3.195, 3.203, 3.205)
A	area of a peak (eqns. 3.36–3.40, 3.42, 3.43)
A, A'	constants (eqns. 3.87, 3.88, 3.113)
A_1, A_2, A_3	parameters of eqns. 3.160, 3.161
A_E	size of the eluite (eqns. 3.121, 3.122, 3.125, 3.126, 3.129)
A_S	area of stationary phase (eqn. 3.109)
A_S, A_M	concentrations of Solute A in stationary and mobile phases (eqn. 3.96)
A_s, A_s'	peak asymmetry measures (eqns. 3.44, 3.45)
A_s^*	peak triangle asymmetry (eqn. 3.46)
A_t	cross-sectional area of tube lumen (eqn. 3.24)
A_{tr}	area bounded by inflection-point-tangent lines and peak base (eqn. 3.41)
B, B'	constants (eqns. 3.87, 3.88, 3.113, 3.114)
B	constant in Van Deemter equation (eqns. 3.191–3.193)
$\mathcal{B}$	constant in reduced plate height equation (eqns. 3.194, 3.196)
B_S, B_M	concentration of Solvent B in stationary and mobile phases (eqn. 3.96)
B^0	permeability (eqns. 3.165–3.167, 3.170)
C, C'	constants (eqns. 3.87, 3.88, 3.114)
C	concentration
C	constant in Van Deemter equation (eqns. 3.191–3.193)
$\mathcal{C}$	constant in reduced plate height equation (eqns. 3.194, 3.197, 3.198, 3.203, 3.207)
$C_{M,D}$	mobile phase concentration of displacer (eqn. 3.5)
C_{max}	concentration at peak apex (eqns. 3.39–3.41)
C_0	front concentration (eqn. 3.35)
$C_{S,D}$	surface concentration of displacer (eqn. 3.5)
D	diffusivity
$\mathcal{D}$	axial dispersion coefficient (eqns. 3.56–3.60)
D_M	eluite diffusivity in mobile phase
$D_{M,eff}$	effective diffusivity in the mobile phase (eqns. 3.174–3.176, 3.182)
D_S	diffusivity in the stationary phase (eqns. 3.185, 3.188)
$D_{S,eff}$	effective diffusivity in the stationary phase (eqn. 3.179)

E	separation impedance (eqn. 3.170)
E	peak excess (eqn. 3.43)
F_c	gas flowrate
F	volumetric flowrate
$G, \Delta G$	Gibbs free energy, change in Gibbs free energy
ΔG^0	standard Gibbs free energy change
$\Delta G_{S,S}, \Delta G_{S,M}$	partial molal free energy of solvent in stationary or mobile phases (eqns. 3.124a, 3.124b)
$\Delta G_{E,S}, \Delta G_{E,M}$	partial molal free energy of eluite in stationary or mobile phases (eqn. 3.124a)
H	plate height
H_{eff}	effective plate height (eqn. 3.53)
H_f	plate height contribution due to film transport (eqns. 3.172, 3.180, 3.183, 3.184)
$H_{f,e.d.}$	plate height contribution due to eddy diffusion (eqns. 3.181, 3.183)
$H_{f,diff}$	plate height contribution due to diffusional resistances within mobile phase (eqns. 3.182, 3.183)
H_{kin}	kinetic contribution to plate height (eqns. 3.172, 3.190)
H_{loc}	local plate height (eqn. 3.203)
$H_{l.d.}$	plate height contribution due to longitudinal diffusion (eqn. 3.172)
H_{min}	minimum plate height (eqn. 3.193)
$H_{M,l.d.}$	plate height contribution due to longitudinal diffusion in the mobile phase (eqn. 3.175)
$H_{m.tr.}$	plate height contribution due to mass transfer resistance (eqn. 3.172)
$H_{m.tr.e.}$	plate height contribution due to external mass transfer resistance (eqn. 3.186)
$H_{m.tr.i.}$	plate height contribution due to internal mass transfer resistance (eqns. 3.187, 3.188)
$H_{S,l.d.}$	plate height contribution due to longitudinal diffusion in the stationary phase (eqn. 3.179)
$H_{S,m.tr.}$	plate height contribution due to mass transfer resistance in stationary phase (eqn. 3.185)
$\overline{H}$	average plate height (eqn. 3.204)
$H, \Delta H^0$	enthalpy, standard enthalpy change
$\Delta H_1^0, \Delta H_2^0$	retention enthalpies of 1 and 2 (eqn. 3.157)
ΔH_v^0	enthalpy of vaporization (eqns. 3.85, 3.86, 3.111, 3.112)
ΔH_a^0	adsorption enthalpy (eqn. 3.115)
ΔH_e^0	differential heat of vaporization (eqn. 3.112)
ΔH_m^0	mixing enthalpy (eqns. 3.111, 3.112)
I	ionic strength (eqns. 3.91–3.93)
I_i	Kováts index of species i (eqn. 3.158)
ΔI	change in Kováts index relative to a reference stationary phase (eqn. 3.159)
K	partition coefficient

K_1	partition coefficient of Component 1 (eqn. 3.63)
K_2	partition coefficient of Component 2 (eqn. 3.63)
K_a	binding constant to surface (eqn. 3.109)
K_d	thermodynamic selectivity (exchange) coefficient (eqns. 3.132, 3.134)
K_f	concentration ratio (eqns. 3.103, 3.105, 3.106)
K_A, K_B	binding constants to surface (eqns. 3.97, 3.98)
K_A, K_B	partition coefficient with neat Solvent A or B (eqn. 3.94)
K_{AB}	partition coefficient with solvent mixture (eqn. 3.94)
K_H	Henry's law coefficient (eqns. 3.84, 3.89)
L	tube or packed column length
L_{req}	required column length (eqn. 3.69)
L_0, L_1	characteristic lengths of an ellipsoid of revolution (eqn. 3.147)
M	(subscript) mobile phase
M	total mass injected (eqn. 3.34)
M	aspect ratio of ellipsoid (eqn. 3.147)
M	molecular weight (eqn. 3.148)
$M_A, M_B,$ M_S, M_M	molecular weight of A, B, stationary or mobile phase substances (eqns. 3.117, 3.118, 3.177, 3.178)
N	Avogadro's number
N	number of theoretical plates
N_{eff}	effective number of plates (eqn. 3.52)
N_{req}	required number of plates (eqns. 3.68, 3.69)
Pe	Peclet number
P	pressure
P_i, P_o	inlet and outlet pressure (eqns. 3.163, 3.165)
ΔP	pressure drop across a column (eqn. 3.170)
P^0	standard pressure (eqns. 3.83, 3.86–3.88, 3.110, 3,111, 3.114)
$\bar{P}$	reference pressure (eqn. 3.117)
P_M	probability of eluite in mobile phase (eqn. 3.17)
P_S	probability of eluite in stationary phase (eqn. 3.16)
R	tube radius (eqns. 3.162, 3.163)
R	universal gas constant
R	retardation factor (eqns. 3.18, 3.19)
R_e	radius of an equivalent sphere (eqn. 3.149)
Re	Reynolds number (eqn. 3.164)
R_G	radius of gyration (eqns. 3.148, 3.149)
R_M	logarithmic retention factor in planar chromatography (eqn. 3.23)
R, R_S	ion exchanger binding sites (eqns. 3.139, 3.140)
R_s	resolution (eqns. 3.2, 3.64–3.67)
R_F	retention factor in planar chromatography (eqns. 3.20, 3.23, 3.200–3.202)
S	(subscript) stationary phase
$S, \Delta S^0$	entropy
S	peak skew (eqn. 3.42)

S^0	standard energy of adsorption (eqns. 3.121, 3.125)
S^0	adsorption energy on fully activated adsorbent (eqn. 3.121)
Sc	Schmidt number
$\Delta S_1^0, \Delta S_2^0$	retention entropy of 1 and 2 (eqn. 3.157)
ΔS_a^0	adsorption entropy (eqn. 3.121)
ΔS_m^0	entropy of mixing (eqn. 3.111)
ΔS_v^0	entropy of vaporization (eqn. 3.111)
T	absolute temperature
T_b	boiling point
T_c	compensation temperature (eqns. 3.157, 3.160)
V	volume
$\overline{V}_A$	molar volume of Solute A (eqn. 3.177)
V_A	pore volume invaded by eluite in SEC (eqns. 3.141, 3.142)
V_N, V_{N+1}	retention volume of standards with N, N + 1 methylenes (eqn. 3.158)
V_e	interstitial volume in packed bed
V_g	specific retention volume (eqns. 3.109, 3.114, 3.117, 3.118)
V_i	internal particle pore volume (eqns. 3.31, 3.142–3.145)
V_i	retention volume of solute i (eqn. 3.158)
V_1, V_v	molar volume in liquid (l) or vapor (v) phase (eqn. 3.85)
V_M	total mobile phase volume in column (eqns. 3.6, 3.13, 3.14, 3.209)
V_N	net retention volume (eqns. 3.110, 3.111, 3.113, 3.115)
$V_{N,1}$	net retention volume of Component 1 (eqn. 3.62)
$V_{N,2}$	net retention volume of Component 2 (eqn. 3.62)
V_N^0	corrected net retention volume (eqn. 3.114)
V_R	retention volume (eqns. 3.13, 3.14, 3.144–3.146)
V_R'	adjusted retention volume
V_S	volume of stationary phase (eqns. 3.6, 3.14, 3.109, 3.121, 3.126)
V_t	inner volume of tube confining packed bed (eqns. 3.26, 3.29, 3.31, 3.146)
V_α	elution volume of first eluite in a chromatogram (eqn. 3.54)
V_ω	elution volume of last eluite in a chromatogram (eqn. 3.54)
$\overline{V}_M, \overline{V}_S$	partial molar volume in the mobile and stationary phases (eqn. 3.117)
Z_i	charge on Species i (eqn. 3.92)
Z_-	charge on anion (eqns. 3.91, 3.93)
Z_+	charge on cation (eqns. 3.91, 3.93)
Z	distance traveled by a peak center (eqns. 3.1, 3.3, 3.4, 3.206)
ΔZ	distance between peak centers (eqns. 3.1, 3.2)
Z_f	distance traveled by solvent front in planar chromatography (eqns. 3.168, 3.169, 3.200–3.202, 3.204)
Z_0	sampling height in planar chromatography (eqn. 3.204)
α	degree of surface activation (eqns. 3.121, 3.127, 3.128)
α	relative retention (selectivity) (eqns. 3.65–3.69)

$\alpha_{2,1}$	retention of Component 2 relative to that of 1 (eqns. 3.61–3.63, 3.119, 3.155)
$\alpha_{i,j}$	contribution of Substituent j to parameter i of eqn. 3.161
β	interaction coefficient (eqn. 3.95)
β	parameter of eqn. 3.120
γ	surface tension (eqn. 3.168)
γ	obstruction factor for diffusion in a packed column (eqns. 3.195, 3.199, 3.203)
γ	activity coefficient (eqn. 3.78)
γ_S, γ_M	activity coefficient of eluite in stationary or mobile phase (eqns. 3.81, 3.117, 3.118)
$\gamma_A, \gamma_B, \gamma_{AB}$	activity coefficient in Phase A, B, or A–B binary (eqn. 3.95)
$\gamma_{AM}, \gamma_{AS},$	activity coefficients of Ions A and B
γ_{BM}, γ_{BS}	in the mobile and stationary phases (eqns. 3.132, 3.134, 3.135)
$\gamma_{1M}, \gamma_{1S},$	activity coefficients of 1 and 2
γ_{2M}, γ_{2S}	in the mobile and stationary phases (eqn. 3.119)
$\gamma_{\pm}$	mean ionic activity coefficient (eqns. 3.90, 3.91, 3.93, 3.137, 3.140)
$\gamma_{\pm M}, \gamma_{\pm S}$	mean ionic activity coefficient in mobile and stationary phases (eqns. 3.137, 3.140)
Δ	correction for solvent–eluite interactions (eqn. 3.126)
ϵ^0	solvent strength (eqns. 3.121, 3.122, 3.125, 3.126, 3.128)
ϵ	dielectric constant of mobile phase (eqn. 3.91)
ϵ^0_{AB}	solvent strength of a binary mixture (eqn. 3.127)
ϵ_e	interstitial porosity (eqns. 3.25, 3.26, 3.29, 3.31, 3.166, 3.167)
ϵ_A, ϵ_B	solvent strengths of A and B (eqn. 3.127)
ϵ_g, ϵ_h	solvent strengths of strongly adsorbed components (eqn. 3.128)
ϵ_i	internal particle porosity (eqn. 3.31)
ϵ_T	total porosity of packed bed (eqns. 3.30, 3.31)
η	viscosity (eqns. 3.163–3.166, 3.168, 3.170, 3.177)
$[\eta]$	intrinsic viscosity (eqn. 3.148)
η	retention modulus (eqn. 3.106)
θ	fraction coverage of surface (eqn. 3.116)
θ	tortuosity factor of particle (eqns. 3.187, 3.197, 3.206)
κ	decimal logarithm of retention factor (eqns. 3.21, 3.160, 3.208)
κ	front migration factor (eqns. 3.169, 3.202)
κ_0	logarithmic retention factor in plain water (eqn. 3.120)
κ_0	front migration constant (eqns. 3.168, 3.169, 3.205–3.207)
κ_0	decimal logarithm of retention factor at starting composition in gradient (eqn. 3.208)
κ_e	natural logarithm of retention factor (eqn. 3.22)
κ_r	logarithmic retention factor with pentane as eluent (eqn. 3.122)
λ	measure of flow inequality in packed columns (eqns. 3.181, 3.184, 3.196, 3.198)
μ, μ^0	chemical potential, standard chemical potential (eqn. 3.77)
μ^0_i	standard chemical potential of i (eqn. 3.150)

μ_S, μ_M	chemical potential in stationary and mobile phases (eqn. 3.79)
μ_S^0, μ_M^0	standard chemical potential in stationary and mobile phases (eqns. 3.80, 3.81)
$\mu_{i,j}$	chemical potential of i in Phase j
$\Delta\mu^0$, $\Delta\mu_i^0$	chemical potential of retention for a molecule and its fragment, i (eqn. 3.150)
$\Delta\mu_X^0$	chemical potential of molecular fragment X (eqns. 3.152, 3.155)
ν	stoichiometric coefficient (eqns. 3.89, 3.96, 3.100, 3.101)
ν_i	stoichiometric coefficient of Species i (eqns. 3.96, 3.99)
ν^+, ν^-	stoichiometric coefficient of cation or anion (eqn. 3.90)
ν	reduced velocity (eqns. 3.33, 3.194, 3.198)
ξ	proportionality constant (eqn. 3.1)
ξ	conversion factor (eqns. 3.148, 3.149)
π	osmotic pressure (eqn. 3.135); 3.14159 elsewhere
ρ	density (eqn. 3.164)
ρ_M	mobile phase density (eqns. 3.117, 3.118)
ρ_0	density of mobile phase (eqn. 3.91)
σ	standard deviation of an eluite zone (eqns. 3.171, 3.199)
σ_{col}	standard deviation contribution of column (eqn. 3.171)
σ_{conn}	standard deviation contribution of connecting tubing (eqn. 3.171)
σ_{det}	standard deviation contribution of detector (eqn. 3.171)
σ_{inj}	standard deviation contribution of injector (eqn. 3.171)
σ_L	standard deviation expressed in distance units
$\sigma_{l.d.}$	standard deviation contribution of longitudinal diffusion (eqn. 3.173)
$\sigma_{M,l.d.}$	standard deviation contribution of longitudinal diffusion in the mobile phase (eqn. 3.174)
σ_t	standard deviation expressed in time units
Φ	logarithm of phase ratio (eqns. 3.111, 3.135, 3.153, 3.154)
ϕ_i	volume fraction of Component i (eqn. 3.10)
ϕ	volume fraction of organic cosolvent in hydro-organic mixture (eqns. 3.120, 3.160)
ϕ	phase ratio (eqns. 3.5, 3.6, 3.15, 3.98, 3.104, 3.189)
ϕ	constant in capillary flow velocity equation (eqn. 3.168)
ϕ_A, ϕ_B	volume fraction of eluent components A and B (eqns. 3.94, 3.95)
ψ_B	association factor in Wilke-Chang equation
ω	column packing parameter (eqns. 3.182, 3.184, 3.196)

3.11. ACKNOWLEDGEMENTS

The authors wish to thank John Frenz for his aid in the preparation of this chapter. The authors gratefully acknowledge support of their research on the subject treated in this chapter by grants No. CA 21948 and GM 20993 from the National

Cancer Institute and National Institute for General Medical Sciences, U.S. Public Health Service, Department of Health and Human Services.

REFERENCES

1 J.C. Giddings, *Dynamics of Chromatography, Part I, Principles and Theory*, Dekker, New York, 1965.
2 G. Schay, *Theoretische Grundlagen der Gaschromatographie*, Deutscher Verlag der Wissenschaften, Berlin, 1960.
3 F. Helfferich and G. Klein, *Multicomponent Chromatography*, Dekker, New York, 1970.
4 L.R. Snyder, *Principles of Adsorption Chromatography*, Dekker, New York, 1968.
5 B.L. Karger, L.R. Snyder and Cs. Horváth, *An Introduction to Separation Science*, Wiley, New York, 1973.
6 G. Guiochon, in C.S. Horváth (Editor), *High Performance Liquid Chromatography. Advances and Perspectives*, Vol. 2, Academic Press, New York, 1980, p. 1.
7 J.R. Conder and C.L. Young, *Physicochemical Measurement by Gas Chromatography*, Wiley, New York, 1979.
8 H. Purnell, *Gas Chromatography*, Wiley, New York, 1962.
9 S. Claesson, *Ark. Kemi, Mineral. Geol.*, 23A (1947) 1.
10 A. Tiselius, *Ark. Kemi*, 164 (1943) 1.
11 A. Tiselius and L. Hagdahl, *Acta Chem. Scand.*, 3 (1950) 394.
12 Cs. Horváth, A. Nahum and J.H. Frenz, *J. Chromatogr.*, 218 (1981) 365.
13 H. Kalász and Cs. Horváth, *J. Chromatogr.*, 215 (1981) 295.
14 C.R. Lowe and P.D.G. Dean, *Affinity Chromatography*, Wiley, Chichester, 1974.
15 M.S. Wainwright and J.K. Haken, *J. Chromatogr.*, 184 (1980) 1.
16 C.J.O.R. Morris and P. Morris, *Separation Methods in Biochemistry*, Wiley, New York, 1976.
17 R.M. McCormick and B.L. Karger, *Anal. Chem.*, 52 (1980) 2249.
18 G.E. Berendsen, P.J. Schoenmakers, L. de Galan, G. Vigh, Z. Varga-Puhony and J. Inczédy, *J. Liquid Chromatogr.*, 3 (1980) 1669.
19 F. Riedo and E. sz. Kováts, *J. Chromatogr.*, in press.
20 W.K. Al-Thamir, J.H. Purnell, C.A. Wellington and R.J. Laub, *J. Chromatogr.*, 173 (1979) 388.
21 J.C. Giddings, G.H. Stewart and A.L. Ruoff, *J. Chromatogr.*, 3 (1960) 239.
22 Cs. Horváth and H.-J. Lin, *J. Chromatogr.*, 126 (1976) 401.
23 J.F.K. Huber, A.M. van Urk-Schoen and G.B. Sieswerda, *Z. Anal. Chem.*, 264 (1973) 257.
24 R.B. Bird, W.E. Stewart and E.N. Lightfoot, *Transport Phenomena*, Wiley, New York, 1960.
25 O. Grubner, in A. Zlatkis (Editor), *Advances in Chromatography 1971*, Chromatography Symposium, Houston, TX, 1971, p. 13.
26 A.J.P. Martin and R.L.M. Synge, *Biochem. J.*, 35 (1941) 1358.
27 B.L. Karger, J.N. LePage and N. Tanaka, in Cs. Horváth (Editor), *High Performance Liquid Chromatography: Advances and Perspectives*, Vol. 1, Academic Press, New York, 1980, p. 113.
28 J. Villermaux, *J. Chromatogr. Sci.*, 12 (1974) 822.
29 I. Amdur and G.G. Hammes, *Chemical Kinetics*, McGraw-Hill, New York, 1966.
30 W.R. Melander, A. Nahum and Cs. Horváth, *J. Chromatogr.*, 185 (1979) 129.
31 W.R. Melander, Cs. Horváth and J. Jacobson, *J. Chromatogr.*, in press.
32 R.C. Reid, J.M. Prausnitz and T.K. Sherwood, *The Properties of Gases and Liquids*, McGraw-Hill, New York, 1977.
33 J.H. Perry, C.H. Chilton and S.D. Kirkpatrick, *Chemical Engineers' Handbook*, 4th Edn., McGraw-Hill, New York, 1963.
34 D.H. Everett and C.T.H. Stoddard, *Trans. Faraday Soc.*, 57 (1961) 746.
35 D.H. Desty, A. Goldup, G.R. Luckhurst and W.T. Swanton, in M. van Swaay (Editor), *Gas Chromatography 1962*, Butterworths, London, 1962, p. 204.

36 D.C. Locke, in J.C. Giddings, E. Grushka, J. Cazes and P.R. Brown (Editors), *Advances in Chromatography,* Vol. 14, Dekker, 1976, p. 87.

37 C.W. Davies, *Ion Association,* Butterworths, Washington, DC, 1962.

38 H.S. Owen and B.B. Owen, *The Physical Chemistry of Electrolyte Solutions,* Reinhold, New York, 1943.

39 R.A. Robinson and R.H. Stokes, *Electrolyte Solution,* Butterworths, London, 1955.

40 E.A. Guggenheim, *Mixtures,* Oxford Univ. Press, Oxford, 1952.

41 J.H. Hildebrand, J.M. Prausnitz and R.L. Scott, *Regular and Related Solution,* Van Nostrand-Reinhold, New York, 1970.

42 A.R. Miller, *Theory of Solutions of High Polymers,* Oxford Univ. Press, Oxford, 1948.

43 P.J. Flory, *Principles of Polymer Chemistry,* Cornell Univ. Press, Ithaca, 1953.

44 O. Sinanoğlu, in J.O. Hirschfelder (Editor), *Advances in Chemical Physics,* Vol. 12, Wiley, New York, 1967, p. 283.

45 O. Sinanoğlu, in B. Pullman (Editor), *Molecular Associations in Biology,* Academic Press, New York, 1968, p. 427.

46 T. Halicioğlu and O.Sinanoğlu, *Ann. N.Y. Acad. Sci.,* 158 (1969) 308.

47 O. Sinanoğlu, personal communication.

48 W.R. Melander and Cs. Horváth, in Cs. Horváth (Editor), *High Performance Liquid Chromatography,* Vol. 2, Academic Press, New York, 1980, p. 114.

49 R.J. Laub and J.H. Purnell, *J. Amer. Chem. Soc.,* 98 (1975) 30.

50 M. McCann, H. Purnell and C.A. Wellington, *Faraday Soc. Symp.,* 15 (1980) 83.

51 J.F.K. Huber, E. Kenndler and H. Markens, *J. Chromatogr.,* 167 (1978) 291.

52 R.J. Laub and R.L. Pecsok, *Physicochemical Applications of Gas Chromatography,* Wiley, New York, 1978.

53 K.-G. Wahlund and I. Beijersten, *Anal. Chem.,* 54 (1982) 128.

54 L.R. Snyder and H. Poppe, *J. Chromatogr.,* 184 (1980) 363.

55 C. Eon, C. Pommier and G. Guiochon, *Chromatographia,* 4 (1971) 241.

56 Cs. Horváth, W. Melander and A. Nahum, *J. Chromatogr.,* 186 (1979) 371.

57 G.K. Ackers, *Biochemistry,* 3 (1964) 724.

58 J.R. Cann, *Interacting Macromolecules,* Academic Press, New York, 1970.

59 Cs. Horváth, W. Melander, I. Molnár and P. Molnár, *Anal. Chem.,* 49 (1977) 2295.

60 M.T.W. Hearn, in J.C. Giddings, E. Grushka, J. Cazes and P.R. Brown (Editors), *Advances in Chromatography,* Vol. 18, Dekker, New York, 1980, p. 59.

61 W.R. Melander, J. Stoveken and Cs. Horváth, *J. Chromatogr.,* 185 (1979) 111.

62 R.L. Martin, *Anal. Chem.,* 33 (1961) 244.

63 J.H. Purnell, *Ann. Rev. Phys. Chem.,* 18 (1967) 81.

64 A. Nahum and Cs. Horváth, *J. Chromatogr.,* 203 (1981) 53.

65 A.K. Hilmi, *J. Chromatogr.,* 17 (1965) 407.

66 H.W. Patton, J.S. Lewis and W.I. Kaye, *Anal. Chem.,* 27 (1955) 170.

67 M.R. Hoare and J.H. Purnell, *Trans. Faraday Soc.,* 52 (1956) 222.

68 S.T. Sie, J.P.A. Bleumer and G.W.A. Rijnders, *Separ. Sci.,* 1 (1966) 41.

69 A. Rose and V.N. Schrodt, *J. Chem. Eng. Data,* 8 (1963) 9.

70 D.E. Martire and L.Z. Pollara, *Advan. Chromatogr.,* 1 (1963) 335.

71 A.J.B. Cruickshank, M.L. Windsor and C.L. Young, *Proc. Roy. Soc. A,* 295 (1966) 271.

72 D.E. Martire and L.Z. Pollara, *J. Chem. Eng. Data,* 10 (1965) 40.

73 T.M. Letcher, *Faraday Soc. Symp.,* 15 (1980) 103.

74 N.C. Saha and D.S. Mathur, *J. Chromatogr.,* 81 (1973) 207.

75 D.C. Locke, in J.C. Giddings and R.A. Keller (Editors), *Advances in Chromatography,* Vol. 8, Dekker, New York, 1970, p. 47.

76 D.C. Locke, *J. Chromatogr.,* 35 (1968) 24.

77 D.C. Locke, *J. Gas Chromatogr.,* 5 (1967) 202.

78 D.E. Martire and D.C. Locke, *Anal. Chem.,* 43 (1971) 68.

79 Cs. Horváth, in C.F. Simpson (Editor), *Practical High Performance Liquid Chromatography,* 2nd Edn., Heyden, London, 1982, in press.

80 H. Colin, C. Eon and G. Guiochon, *J. Chromatogr.*, 122 (1976) 223.

81 K.K. Unger, *Porous Silica,* Elsevier, Amsterdam, 1979.

82 W. Melander, J. Stoveken and Cs. Horváth, *J. Chromatogr.*, 199 (1980) 35.

83 Cs. Horváth and W. Melander, *J. Chromatogr. Sci.*, 15 (1977) 393.

84 L.R. Snyder, *J. Chromatogr.*, 63 (1971) 15.

85 Cs. Horváth, W. Melander and I. Molnár, *J. Chromatogr.*, 125 (1976) 129.

86 J. Timmermans, *The Physico-Chemical Constants in Binary Systems in Binary Solution,* Vol. 4, Wiley-Interscience, New York, 1973.

87 C. Carr and J.A. Riddick, *J. Eng. Chem.*, 43 (1951) 692.

88 G. Åkerlof, *J. Amer. Chem. Soc.*, 54 (1932) 4125.

89 G. Douheret and M. Morenas, *C.R. Acad. Sci. Paris,* 264 (1967) 729.

90 P.J. Schoenmakers, H.A.H. Billiet and L. de Galan, *J. Chromatogr.*, 185 (1979) 179.

91 J.W. Dolan, J.R. Gant and L.R. Snyder, *J. Chromatogr.*, 165 (1978) 31.

92 S.R. Abbott, J.R. Berg, P. Achener and R.L. Stevenson, *J. Chromatogr.*, 126 (1976) 421.

93 S.R. Bakalyar, R. McIlwrick and E. Roggendorf, *J. Chromatogr.*, 142 (1977) 353.

94 N. Tanaka, H. Goodell and B.L. Karger, *J. Chromatogr.*, 158 (1978) 233.

95 R.M. McCormick and B.L. Karger, *J. Chromatogr.*, 199 (1980) 259.

96 W.R. Melander and Cs. Horváth, in M.T.W. Hearn (Editor), *Ion-Pair Chromatography,* Dekker, New York, 1982, in press.

97 M.T.W. Hearn (Editor), *Ion-Pair Chromatography,* Dekker, New York, 1982.

98 J.H. Hildebrand and R.L. Scott, *Regular Solutions,* Prentice-Hall, Engelwood Cliffs, NJ, 1962.

99 J.H. Hildebrand and R.L. Scott, *Solubility of Nonelectrolytes,* Dover, New York, 1964.

100 C.M. Hanson, *Ind. Eng. Chem. Prod. Dev.*, 8 (1969) 2.

101 H.A. Mottola and H. Freiser, *Talanta,* 13 (1966) 55.

102 W. Melander and Cs. Horváth, in M.J. McGuire and I.H. Suffet (Editors), *Activated Carbon Adsorption from the Aqueous Phase,* Ann Arbor Sci. Publ., Ann Arbor, MI, 1980, p. 65.

103 W. Melander and Cs. Horváth, *Arch. Biochem. Biophys.*, 183 (1977) 200.

104 C.M. Riley, E. Tomlinson and T.M. Jefferies, *J. Chromatogr.*, 185 (1979) 197.

105 D.C. Locke, *J. Chromatogr. Sci.*, 12 (1974) 433.

106 R. Majors, in Cs. Horváth (Editor), *High Performance Liquid Chromatography. Advances and Perspectives,* Vol. 1, Academic Press, New York, 1980, p. 76.

107 H. Englehardt and H. Elgass, in Cs Horváth (Editor), *High Performance Liquid Chromatography. Advances and Perspectives,* Vol. 2, Academic Press, New York, 1980, p. 57.

108 R.P.W. Scott and C.F. Simpson, *Faraday Soc. Symp.*, 15 (1980) 69.

109 L.R. Snyder, in Cs. Horváth (Editor), *High Performance Liquid Chromatography. Advances and Perspectives,* Vol. 1, Academic Press, New York, 1980, p. 208.

110 L.R. Snyder, *J. Chromatogr. Sci.*, 16 (1978) 223.

111 G.E. Boyd, S. Lindenbaum and G.E. Myers, *J. Phys. Chem.*, 65 (1961) 577.

112 H.F. Walton, in E. Heftmann (Editor), *Chromatography,* 2nd. Edn., Reinhold, New York, 1967, p. 287.

113 E. Glueckauf, *Proc. Roy. Soc. A,* 214 (1952) 207.

114 R.M. Diamond and D.C. Whitney, in J.A. Marinsky (Editor), *Ion Exchange,* Vol. 1, Dekker, New York, 1966, p. 277.

115 D. Reichenberg, in J.A. Marinsky (Editor), *Ion Exchange,* Vol. 1, Dekker, New York, 1966, p. 227.

116 M.G.T. Shone, *Trans. Faraday Soc.*, 58 (1962) 805.

117 C. Jensen and R.M. Diamond, *J. Phys. Chem.*, 75 (1971) 79.

118 M.A. Curtis and L.B. Rogers, *Anal. Chem.*, 53 (1981) 2349.

119 Cs. Horváth, in D. Glick (Editor), *Methods of Biochemical Analysis,* Vol. 21, Wiley, New York, 1973, p. 79.

120 F. Helfferich, in J.C. Giddings and R.A. Keller (Editors), *Advances in Chromatography,* Vol. 1, Dekker, New York, 1965, p. 3.

121 H. Determann, in J.C. Giddings and R.A. Keller (Editors), *Advances in Chromatography,* Vol. 8, Dekker, New York, 1970, p. 3.

122 W.W. Yau, J.J. Kirkland and D.D. Bly, *Modern Size Exclusion Liquid Chromatography,* Wiley, New York, 1979.

123 J.C. Giddings, E. Kucera, C.P. Russell and M.N. Myers, *J. Phys. Chem.*, 72 (1968) 4397.
124 E.F. Casassa, *Separ. Sci.*, 6 (1971) 305.
125 W.W. Yau, C.P. Malone and S.W. Fleming, *J. Polym. Sci., Part B*, 6 (1968) 803.
126 A.C. Ouano, in J.C. Giddings, E. Grushka, J. Cazes and P.R. Brown (Editors), *Advances in Chromatography*, Vol. 15, Dekker, New York, 1977, p. 233.
127 W. Haller, *J. Chromatogr.*, 32 (1968) 676.
128 N.K. Sabbagh and I.S. Fagerson, *J. Chromatogr.*, 120 (1976) 55.
129 E.F. Casassa, *J. Phys. Chem.*, 75 (1971) 3929.
130 E.E. Brumbaugh and G.K. Ackers, *J. Biol. Chem.*, 243 (1968) 6315.
131 J.V. Dawkins and G. Yeadon, *Faraday Soc. Symp.*, 15 (1980) 126.
132 J.V. Dawkins, *J. Polym. Sci., Polym. Phys. Ed.*, 14 (1976) 569.
133 T. Mizutani and A. Mizutani, *J. Chromatogr.*, 111 (1975) 214.
134 M.J. Frenkel and R.J. Blagrove, *J. Chromatogr.*, 111 (1975) 397.
135 C. Tanford, *Physical Chemistry of Macromolecules*, Wiley, New York, 1961.
136 A.L. Spatorico, *J. Appl. Polym. Sci.*, 19 (1974) 1601.
137 A.L. Spatorico and G.L. Beyer, *J. Appl. Polym. Sci.*, 19 (1973) 2933.
138 E.P. Otocka and M.Y. Hellman, *J. Polym. Sci., Part B*, 12 (1974) 331.
139 A. Dondos, P. Rempp and H. Benoit, *Makromol. Chem.*, 175 (1974) 1659.
140 J. Schechter, *Anal. Biochem.*, 58 (1974) 30.
141 Yu. A. Eltekov and A.S. Nazansky, *J. Chromatogr.*, 116 (1976) 99.
142 H. Determann, *Gel Chromatography*, 2nd Edn., Springer-Verlag, New York, 1969.
143 H. Determann and J.E. Brewer, in E. Heftmann (Editor), *Chromatography*, 3rd, Edn., Van Nostrand-Reinhold, New York, 1975, p. 362.
144 N. Friis and A. Hamiclec, in J.C. Giddings, E. Grushka, R.A. Keller and J. Cazes (Editors), *Advances in Chromatography*, Vol. 13, Dekker, New York, 1975, p. 41.
145 A.J.P. Martin, *Biochem. Soc. Symp.*, 3 (1949) 4.
146 J. Green and S. Marcinkiewicz, *J. Chromatogr.*, 10 (1963) 35.
147 D.H. Desty and B.H.F. Whyman, *Anal. Chem.*, 29 (1957) 320.
148 M. Lederer, *Proc. 2nd Intern. Congr. Surface Activity*, Butterworths, London, 1957.
149 W.R. Melander, B.-K. Chen and Cs. Horváth, *J. Chromatogr.*, 185 (1979) 99.
150 I. Molnár and Cs. Horváth, *J. Chromatogr.*, 142 (1977) 623.
151 B.T. Bush, J.H. Frenz, W.R. Melander, Cs. Horváth, A.R. Cashmore, R.N. Dryer, J.O. Knipe, J.K. Coward and J.R. Bertino, *J. Chromatogr.*, 168 (1979) 343.
152 E.P. Kroeff and D.J. Pietrzyk, *Anal. Chem.*, 50 (1978) 1353.
153 B.-K. Chen and Cs. Horváth, *J. Chromatogr.*, 171 (1979) 15.
154 T.B. Moore and C.G. Baker, *J. Chromatogr.*, 1 (1958) 513.
155 J. Leffler and G. Grunwald, *Rates and Equilibria of Organic Reactions*, Wiley, New York, 1963.
156 J. Grzybowski, H. Lamparczyk, A. Nasal and A. Radecki, *J. Chromatogr.*, 196 (1980) 217.
157 A.H. Sporer and K.N. Trueblood, *J. Chromatogr.*, 2 (1959) 499.
158 C. Hansch, *Acc. Chem. Res.*, 2 (1962) 232.
159 J. Gasparič, *J. Chromatogr.*, 196 (1980) 391.
160 R.F. Rekker, *The Hydrophobic Fragmental Constant*, Elsevier, Amsterdam, 1977.
161 E. Tomlinson, *J. Chromatogr.*, 113 (1975) 1.
162 R. Kaliszan, *J. Chromatogr.*, 220 (1981) 71.
163 R. Lumry and S. Rajender, *Biopolymers*, 9 (1970) 1125.
164 R.R. Krug, W.G. Hunter and Z.A. Grieger, *J. Phys. Chem.*, 80 (1976) 2235.
165 W. Melander, D.E. Campbell and Cs. Horváth, *J. Chromatogr.*, 158 (1978) 215.
166 W.R. Melander, C.A. Mannan and Cs. Horváth, in preparation.
167 L.R. Snyder, *J. Chromatogr.*, 179 (1979) 167.
168 H. Colin, J.C. Diez-Masa, G. Guiochon, T. Czajkowska and I. Miedziak, *J. Chromatogr.*, 167 (1978) 41.
169 W. Melander, B.-K. Chen and Cs. Horváth, in preparation.
170 E. sz. Kováts, *Helv. Chim. Acta*, 41 (1958) 1915.
171 J.K. Haken, *J. Chromatogr. Sci.*, 11 (1973) 144.

172 G. Schomburg, in J.C. Giddings and R.A. Keller (Editors), *Advances in Chromatography*, Vol. 6, Dekker, New York, 1968, p. 211.

173 F.P. Woodford and C.M. van Gent, *J. Lipid Res.*, 1 (1960) 188.

174 M.L. Lee, D.L. Vassilaros, C.M. White and M. Novotny, *Anal. Chem.*, 51 (1979) 758.

175 W.J.A. VandenHeuvel, W.L. Gardiner and E.C. Horning, *Anal. Chem.*, 36 (1964) 1450.

176 H. van den Dool and P.D. Kratz, *J. Chromatogr.*, 11 (1963) 463.

177 G.D. Mitra, G. Mohan and A. Sinha, *J. Chromatogr.*, 99 (1974) 215.

178 R. Pecsok and J. Apffel, *Anal. Chem.*, 51 (1979) 594.

179 L. Rohrschneider, *J. Chromatogr.*, 22 (1966) 6.

180 W.O. McReynolds, *J. Chromatogr. Sci.*, 8 (1970) 685.

181 W.R. Supina and L.P. Rose, *J. Chromatogr. Sci.*, 8 (1970) 214.

182 J.K. Haken and D. Srisukh, *J. Chromatogr.*, 199 (1980) 199.

183 J.K. Baker and C.-Y. Ma, *J. Chromatogr.*, 169 (1979) 107.

184 G. Guiochon and A. Siouffi, *J. Chromatogr. Sci.*, 16 (1978) 598.

185 J.M. Engasser and Cs. Horváth, *Ind. Eng. Chem. Fundam.*, 14 (1975) 107.

186 M. Golay, in D.H. Desty (Editor), *Gas Chromatography 1958*, Butterworths, London, 1958, p. 36.

187 P.A. Bristow and J.H. Knox, *Chromatographia*, 10 (1977) 279.

188 J.C. Sternberg, in J.C. Giddings and R.A. Keller (Editors), *Advances in Chromatography*, Vol. 2, New York, 1966, p. 205.

189 J.G. Atwood and M.J.E. Golay, *J. Chromatogr.*, 218 (1981) 97.

190 E.N. Fuller, P.D. Schettler and J.C. Giddings, *Ind. Eng. Chem.*, 58 (5) (1966) 19.

191 J.A. Koutsky and R.J. Adler, *Can. J. Chem. Eng.*, 43 (1964) 239.

192 R. Tijssen, J.P.A. Bleumer, A.L.C. Smit and M.E. van Kreveld, *J. Chromatogr.*, 218 (1981) 137.

193 A. Klinkenberg and F. Sjenitzer, *Chem. Eng. Sci.*, 5 (1956) 258.

194 J.C. Giddings, *Anal. Chem.*, 35 (1963) 1338.

195 J.F.K. Huber, *J. Chromatogr. Sci.*, 7 (1969) 305.

196 I. Halász and Cs. Horváth, *Anal. Chem.*, 35 (1963) 499.

197 Cs. Horváth and H.-J. Lin, *J. Chromatogr.*, 149 (1978) 43.

198 Cs. Horváth, B.A. Preiss and S.R. Lipsky, *Anal. Chem.*, 39 (1967) 1422.

199 Cs. Horváth and S.R. Lipsky, *J. Chromatogr. Sci.*, 7 (1969) 109.

200 R.A. Keller and J.C. Giddings, *J. Chromatogr.*, 3 (1960) 205.

201 J.J. van Deemter, F.J. Zuiderweg and A. Klinkenberg, *Chem. Eng. Sci.*, 5 (1956) 271.

202 H.-J. Lin and Cs. Horváth, *Chem. Eng. Sci.*, 36 (1981) 47.

203 J.N. Done, G.J. Kennedy and J.H. Knox, in S.G. Perry and E.R. Adlard (Editors), *Gas Chromatography 1972*, Appl. Sci. Publ., Barking, 1973, p. 145.

204 I. Halász, R. Endele and J. Asshauer, *J. Chromatogr.*, 112 (1975) 37.

205 G. Guiochon, A. Siouffi, H. Engelhardt and I. Halász, *J. Chromatogr. Sci.*, 16 (1978) 152.

206 G. Guiochon and A. Siouffi, *J. Chromatogr. Sci.*, 16 (1978) 470.

207 G. Guiochon, F. Bressolle and A. Siouffi, *J. Chromatogr. Sci.*, 17 (1979) 368.

208 G. Guiochon, G. Korosi and A. Siouffi, *J. Chromatogr. Sci.*, 18 (1980) 324.

209 L.R. Snyder, *J. Chromatogr. Sci.*, 8 (1970) 692.

210 Cs. Horváth and S. Lipsky, *Anal. Chem.*, 39 (1967) 1893.

211 B.L. Karger, L.R. Snyder and Cs. Horváth, *An Introduction to Separation Science*, Wiley-Interscience, New York, 1973.

212 W.E. Harris and H.W. Habgood, *Programmed Temperature Gas Chromatography*, Wiley, New York, 1966.

213 J.C. Giddings, *J. Chem. Educ.*, 39 (1962) 569.

214 G. Guiochon, *Anal. Chem.*, 36 (1964) 661.

215 R.W. Ohline and D.D. Deford, *Anal. Chem.*, 35 (1963) 227.

216 L.R. Snyder and J.J. Kirkland, *Introduction to Modern Liquid Chromatography*, 2nd Edn., Wiley-Interscience, New York, 1979.

217 H. Kalász, J. Nagy and J. Knoll, *J. Chromatogr.*, 107 (1975) 35.

218 M. Martin, F. Verillon, C. Eon and G. Guiochon, *J. Chromatogr.*, 125 (1976) 17.

219 J.A. Thoma, *J. Chromatogr.*, 12 (1963) 441.

220 G. Goldstein, *Anal. Chem.,* 42 (1970) 140.
221 R. Consden, A.H. Gordon, A.J.P. Martin and R.L.M. Synge, *Biochem. J.,* 37 (1943) 86.
222 B.W. Taylor, *Pittsburgh Conf. Anal. Chem. Appl. Spectr., 7th,* Pittsburgh, PA, 1959.
223 E.L. Johnson, R. Gloor and R.E. Majors, *J. Chromatogr.,* 149 (1978) 571.

Chapter 4

Column chromatography

R.P.W. SCOTT

CONTENTS

4.1. INTRODUCTION

Column chromatography was the original form of chromatography invented by Tsvet in the latter part of the last century. This invention was virtually ignored for nearly fifty years, and it was not until 1931, when Kuhn and Lederer repeated some of Tsvet's original experiments, that the technique began to be seriously investigated. Even then, the development of CC was not smooth and continuous but was eclipsed at various stages by the invention of PC, TLC, and, more recently, by GC. It was not until the mid-sixties that the renaissance of CC really began, modern LC starting with the introduction of pellicular packings, by Horváth and Lipsky [1], soon followed by the work of Majors [2] and Kirkland [3], who developed procedures for packing microparticulate silica gel. Today, CC is a well-developed technique, which is widely used. However, progress continues, and as yet there is no indication that the rate of development of the technique is slowing down.

The classical definition of chromatography states that a chromatographic separa-

References on p. A160

tion is achieved by distributing substances in a mixture between two phases: a moving phase and a stationary phase. Those substances in the mixture which interact more strongly with the stationary phase will remain within the chromatographic system longer than those that interact more strongly with the mobile phase. Thus, individual components will be discretely eluted from the end of the column. The first will be those that interact weakly with the stationary phase but strongly with the mobile phase, and the last will be those which interact strongly with the stationary phase but weakly with the mobile phase. Although the classical definition correctly defines chromatographic separations, it does not help too much in understanding the mechanism by which the distribution of a solute between the two phases occurs.

4.2. SELECTIVITY

4.2.1. Basis of chromatographic selectivity

The distribution of a solute between two stationary phases takes place because the individual solute molecules interact with the molecules of each phase to different extents, and these interactions arise basically from three kinds of intermolecular forces: ionic, polar, and dispersive forces.

Ionic forces result from the interaction between net charges on the solute molecule itself and the molecule of the phase concerned. The interactions will, therefore, occur between ions of opposite charge. Thus, to separate anionic materials and maintain selectivity and retention by the stationary phase, cationic substances should be present in the stationary phase. Conversely, if it is required to separate cationic materials, anionic substances must be present in the stationary phase.

Polar forces also result from electrical interactions between molecules, but in the case of polar interactions there is no net charge on the molecules concerned. A molecule can be polarized to acquire equal but opposite charges by an external field, due to its proximity to another molecule carrying a charge, or in fact it can carry permanently displaced charges on different parts, which constitute dipoles. Examples of substances having permanent dipoles are: alcohols, ketones, and aldehydes. Conversely, examples of substances that are polarizable but have no permanent dipoles are: benzene, toluene, and naphthalene. Thus, to separate a mixture of substances of different polarity, polar materials are employed as the stationary phase so that polar interactions can take place between the solutes and the stationary phase during development and a separation is effected. It should be pointed out, however, that molecules having permanent dipoles can still be polarized by a local external field; thus, their polarity will be further enhanced.

Dispersive interactions are much more difficult to describe within the terms of reference of this book. It is sufficient to say that dispersive interactions are still electrical in nature, but do not result from net or displaced electrical charges on the molecule. Dispersive interactions are characterized by the interactions between hydrocarbons or between the hydrocarbon chains of polar materials. It follows that if substances of similar polarity but of different molecular weight are to be separated and it is necessary to exploit dispersive interactions between the solute and the stationary phase, a nonpolar or dispersive stationary phase would be required. It should also be pointed out that dispersive interactions are the only molecular interactions that can proceed in isolation from other types of forces. Interactions involving aliphatic hydrocarbons can be only dispersive, but interactions between molecules such as ethyl acetate will include both polar and dispersive interactions, and interactions involving substances such as toluenesulfonic acid can include all three types of molecular forces: ionic, polar, and dispersive.

4.2.2. Selectivity in practice

In general, to separate ionic substances by chromatography, ion-exchange materials, either bonded to a silica gel surface or consisting of an ion-exchange resin, are used as a stationary phase with an appropriately buffered mobile phase. An alternative would be to use an adsorbed ion exchanger, and this has been successfully carried out with alkyl sulfonates and alkyl quaternary ammonium salts at low concentrations in the mobile phase in conjunction with a nonpolar stationary phase. The nonpolar stationary phase adsorbs a layer of the alkyl ion exchanger on its surface, which thus exhibits ion-exchange properties. This chromatography on adsorbed ion exchangers has unfortunately been given the name "ion-pair" chromatography. This is a misnomer, as only under rare and extreme conditions ion pairs (neutral salts) are exchanged between the two phases. The vast majority of separations obtained by "ion-pair" chromatography has, in fact, been achieved by ion-exchange chromatography in which the ion exchanger is adsorbed on the surface of the stationary phase.

To separate polar substances, the obvious stationary phase to use is silica gel, because its surface is covered with hydrated hydroxyl groups, which are strongly polar and will interact with the dipoles of polar solutes. The charge field associated with the hydrated hydroxyl groups on the silica gel can also produce induced dipoles in solutes by polarization, and thus silica will retain polarizable materials. In fact, normally there are no free silanol groups on the surface of silica gel, each hydroxyl group having a molecule of water hydrogen-bonded to it. Solute interactions with hydrated hydroxyl groups on the silica gel will only occur if a nonpolar solvent, such as heptane, is employed as the mobile phase. There are also "bonded phases" available for separating polar materials. For instance, organic molecules containing cyano groups, bonded to an appropriate silica surface, provide a stationary phase with a polarity intermediate between silica gel and a nonpolar stationary phase. However, the use of these specially bonded polar phases is very specific, as most of their characteristics are obtained by either modifying the surface of silica gel, which can be achieved by employing a mobile phase containing an appropriate polar solvent at a low concentration in a nonpolar solvent or, alternatively, by similarly modifying nonpolar stationary phases with aliphatic acids or alcohols in aqueous solutions. In both cases, the interacting surface of the stationary phase is covered with the adsorbed modifier, thus changing both the type and magnitude of the

References on p. A160

solute/stationary phase interactions in a predictable manner.

Finally, to separate substances of similar polarity but different molecular weight, a dispersive stationary phase is employed, such as a silica gel bonded with a C_8- or C_{18}-hydrocarbon chain, in conjunction with methanol–water or acetonitrile–water mixtures as the mobile phase. In this case, partition takes place between a polar mobile and nonpolar stationary phase, which is the reverse of ordinary partition chromatography and has become known as reversed-phase partition. Reversed-phase sorbents (loosely referred to as "reversed phases") bonded to silica gel can vary in two ways: the bonded phase can be made to have different hydrocarbon chain lengths and also they can be either of the "brush" type or the "bulk" ("polymeric") type. The "brush"-type stationary phases are prepared by allowing a monofunctional silane, such as octyldimethylchlorosilane, to react with the silica. Thus, to a first approximation, each molecule of the silane reacts with one silanol group to produce one hydrocarbon chain per original silanol group. The "bulk" modified material is prepared from silica, usually in the presence of excess water adsorbed on the silica surface, by using a trifunctional silane, such as trichloro-octylsilane. After one of the functional groups has reacted with the silanol group on the silica surface, the remaining two functional groups react with water to form more silanol groups. These new silanol groups react in turn with more reagent, forming a cross-linked polymeric structure. In general, the longer the hydrocarbon chain (or the higher the carbon content) of the reversed-phase sorbent, the greater will be the retention or selectivity of the bonded phase [4]. The "brush" type of bonded phase tends to be somewhat easier to pack and provides columns of greater efficiency, whereas the "bulk" type of bonded phase equilibrates more rapidly with extreme changes of solvent [5].

4.3. COLUMNS

4.3.1. Column systems

In the early days of liquid chromatography, solute bands spread very significantly in the columns used so that difficult separations of multicomponent mixtures could not be achieved. The factors that effect band dispersion in the chromatographic column are dealt with more extensively in Chap. 3, but those variables in the chromatographic system that effect band broadening from a practical point of view will be discussed. The renaissance of CC commenced with the improvement of column efficiency that resulted from the pellicular packings introduced by Horváth and Lipsky [1]. The pellicular packings consisted of glass spheres carrying a thin film of adsorbent material on their surface. This allowed rapid transfer of the solute between the stationary and mobile phases, and thus resulted in reduced band dispersion and, consequently, higher efficiency. However, the particles employed were fairly large, and thus the interstices between the particles had a relatively large volume, which resulted in significant residual dispersion due to slow transfer of solute across the pockets of mobile phase. Ideally, small particles of silica gel or nonpolar sorbent are best for chromatographic systems, as the transfer of the solute to and from the particle is rapid and the interparticulate volume is small. Such materials were not employed earlier due to the problem of packing these small particles, and it was not until Majors [2] and Kirkland [3] developed a slurry method of packing chromatographic columns with microparticulate stationary phases that really high efficiencies were obtained. Efficiencies rose from a few hundred to several thousand theoretical plates. As the packing was made up entirely of silica gel or silica gel bonded to a suitable organic moiety, acceptable loading capacities were obtained, as opposed to the low load capacities of the pellicular packings.

Basically, two methods of slurry packing have evolved. The balanced-density packing procedure utilizes, e.g., a mixture of tetrabromoethane and tetrachloroethane having the same density as the packing material to prevent settling of the particles during packing. The packing material is suspended in this mixture (usually 5%, w/v) and the suspension is pumped rapidly through the chromatography tube (terminated by a suitable fritted steel disc) at pressures ranging from 5000 to 12,000 psi. In this way a firm column is formed which permits minimum dispersion of the solute bands and has a high efficiency. Alternatively, mixtures of methyl iodide and pentane can be used for balanced-density packing, but methyl iodide is more toxic.

The second method of slurry packing is the so-called viscosity method, which was developed by Asshauer and Halász [6]. A typical example of this procedure is in the use of a 20% solution of glycerol in methanol as the packing fluid. When particles are suspended in this liquid, they will remain suspended for some period of time, due to the relatively high viscosity of the solvent mixture. A 5% (w/v) slurry made in this manner is forced through the chromatography tube (also containing a terminating disc), but a somewhat higher pressure is required than in the balanced-density method to compensate for the higher viscosity of the packing fluid. Both methods have been used for silica gel and reversed-phase packing materials, and both have produced very satisfactory columns.

Some skill is necessary for packing good columns, and in the hands of the amateur the procedure may not be very repeatable. However, efficiencies of 6000 or 7000 theoretical plates are fairly readily obtainable from 25-cm long columns when particles 10 μm in diameter are used, and if the mean particle size is reduced to 5 μm, columns of 14,000 or 15,000 plates can be prepared. With the presently available detectors and connecting tubes, which have significant volumes, columns having diameters of about 4.6 mm ID are generally used for analytical work. For preparative work, of course, column diameters may be as large as 4 or 5 cm, or even more. In the past, columns less than 4.6 mm ID ($\frac{1}{4}$ in. OD) have tended to give lower efficiencies, but the lower efficiencies were largely due to extra-column band dispersion effects and not to the inherent properties of the columns.

4.3.2. Microbore columns

Band dispersion occurs not only within the column but also in the void volumes between the column and the injection system and between the column and the detector. Furthermore, the absolute volume injected and the absolute volume of the detector cell can also cause significant band dispersion if they are large enough.

Dispersion of bands in extra-column volumes can result from two factors. Firstly, due to the parabolic velocity profile of the mobile phase in a tube, solute in the center of the tube moves more rapidly through the tube than solute situated initially at the wall of the tube. Thus, during passage through the open tube, the band of solute is elongated and the resulting dispersion constitutes significant band spreading and consequently loss of efficiency.

The second effect is the so-called "wash-out" effect, more commonly known as the "logarithmic dilution effect". Solute contained in a dead volume between injector and column or between column and detector is not cleanly displaced by the mobile phase but is eluted at a solute concentration which falls logarithmically with time. Thus, such volumes increase the band width and result in a loss of efficiency or significant tailing of peaks. It follows that injection devices for sample volumes of a fraction of a microliter and having a minimum connecting tube capacity need to be designed, and that detector cells and connecting tubes need to be reduced in volume until their effect on column performance is negligible. The spreading of bands in open tubes has been treated extensively by Golay [7,8]. It is sufficient to say at this point that the smaller these volumes and the smaller the diameter of the connecting tubes, the less will be the dispersion resulting from extra-column volumes. The columns most commonly used today (4.6 mm ID) have sufficiently large peak volumes (i.e. the volume of mobile phase in which the peak is contained) to make the extra-column volume contributions to band dispersion relatively unimportant. However, as the column radius is reduced, the peak volume is also reduced, and under these circumstances extra-column volumes become of paramount importance.

One of the sources of band dispersion in packed columns of larger diameter is the inhomogeneity of column permeability across its diameter. This inhomogeneity of permeability can be very significant at the column wall. A sample centrally injected onto the column can spread sideways across the column and move more rapidly down the wall than down the center with the net result that significant band dispersion is produced and column efficiency is lowered. This wall effect can often be seen in an exaggerated form in a poorly packed preparative column when a single solute injected onto the column produces two discernable peaks. The first peak is due to that part of the injected sample that was eluted rapidly down the wall of the column, whereas the second peak is due to that part of the sample that stayed in the center of the column and was eluted subsequently. To reduce the wall effect, the diameter of the column may be reduced so that the walls are brought closer together and, consequently, the inhomogeneity in radial permeability in such a microbore column is almost eliminated. Reducing the diameter of the column also permits rapid dispersion of any heat generated as a result of the column resistance to flow. This heat loss may become important when the columns employed are very long and, as a result of the large pressure drop across the column, considerable heat may be evolved. By employing small-diameter columns with apparatus of appropriately low extra-column volume, very high column efficiencies can be obtained, as it is possible to connect columns in sequence to produce a linear increase in efficiency with column length.

Microbore columns have other advantages. For a given linear mobile phase

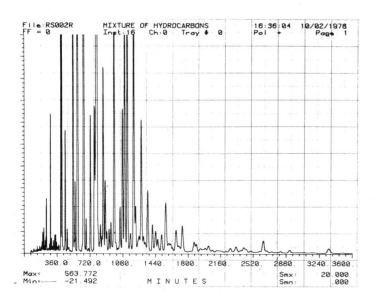

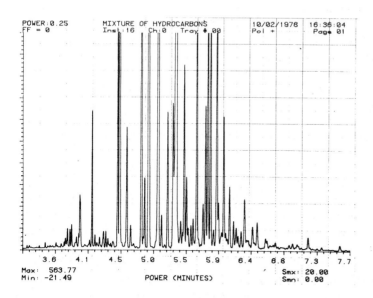

Fig. 4.1. Separation of the polynuclear aromatic hydrocarbons from coal by a reversed-phase microbore column. The same chromatogram is recorded with a normal time scale (top) and a power-function time scale (bottom). Column length, 2 m; column diameter, 1 mm; stationary phase, RP-18; mobile phase, acetonitrile–water; flowrate, 10 μl/min.

References on p. A160

velocity they reduce the consumption of solvent by over one order of magnitude. If many chromatographs are employed, the cost of solvents for their operation can be very significant and, thus, the smaller columns can provide considerable economic advantages. Microbore columns can be used to provide extremely high efficiencies by joining them in series, as previously demonstrated [9]. Owing to their low cross-sectional area, very high linear mobile phase velocities can be used without unreasonable solvent consumption, thus producing rapid separations under economical conditions [10].

Microbore columns also provide very high mass sensitivity [11]. If a detector has a given sensitivity of 10^{-6} g/ml and the band width of a solute eluted from a conventional column with an ID of 4.6 mm is 2 ml, then (as the mass concentration at the peak height is roughly twice the average concentration in the peak) the minimum detectable mass will be 1 μg. If the column is replaced by a microbore column having the same efficiency, the volume of the peak due to the reduced diameter will be only 20 μl. Therefore, if the detector has the same sensitivity, the minimum mass detectable will be 10 ng. Thus, microbore columns permit the analysis of complex mixtures of substances present at concentrations one to two orders of magnitude below the level necessary for the satisfactory operation of the conventional 4.6-mm ID analytical columns.

Fig. 4.1 shows two chromatograms of the same mixture of aromatic hydro-carbons obtained with a reversed-phase microbore column. In the upper chromato-gram the normal time scale is used, and over 150 peaks are discernible. It should be noted that this chromatogram took nearly three days. Resolution in any chromato-graphic system can only be obtained at the expense of load and/or time. Microbore columns are at present the only method of producing very high efficiencies in CC, but such columns may require a development time of many hours. In the lower chromatogram the same separation is recorded with a power-function time scale, which expands the early part of the chromatogram and thus shows the integrity of the early peaks, not apparent in the upper chromatogram.

Fig. 4.2 [10] shows two chromatograms, developed under high-speed conditions, again by using microbore columns. Fig. 4.2.1 represents the separation of benzene and benzyl acetate in about 2.5 sec. The separation is academic in the sense that it is unlikely that anyone would wish to separate benzene and benzyl acetate in 2.5 sec, but it demonstrates that very rapid separations can be obtained while at the same time maintaining the integrity of the Gaussian-shaped peaks. It should also be noted that the separations demonstrate that linear velocities of 12 or 13 cm/sec can be employed in CC; these velocities are high, even for GC. Fig. 4.2.2 represents a more practical separation of a seven-component mixture in 30 sec. Such separations could be extremely useful for plant monitoring and control, as an analysis time of 30 sec is well within the time constants of most chemical plant operations.

Fig. 4.3 is a chromatogram showing the separation of trace components in a 200-μl sample of serum [11]. Here, the high mass sensitivity of the microbore column system is clearly demonstrated. Offering sufficient resolution and speed, this tech-nique could possibly be used for diagnostic purposes.

Today, almost all LC analyses are carried out with the larger columns because

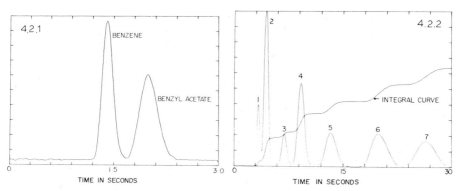

Fig. 4.2. High-speed chromatograms. Fig. 4.2.1, separation of benzene and benzyl acetate on a microbore column in 2.5 sec. Column length, 25 cm; column ID, 1 mm; column packing, Partisil 20; solvent, 3% methanol in pentane–hexane (1:1); flowrate, 12 cm/sec. Fig. 4.2.2, separation of a seven-component mixture on a microbore column in 30 sec. Column length, 25 cm; column ID, 1 mm; column packing, Partisil 20; solvent, 3% methanol in pentane–hexane (1:1); flowrate, 8 cm/sec. Peaks: 1 = 1-phenylundecane, 2 = benzene, 3 = benzyl acetate, 4 = acetophenone, 5 = dimethylphenylcarbinol, 6 = α-phenylethyl alcohol, 7 = benzyl alcohol. (Reproduced from *J. Chromatogr.*, 186 (1979) 475, with permission [10].)

small-volume injectors and detectors are not yet available, but from the chromatograms shown it is fairly obvious that the microbore columns are the columns of the future. In due course, manufacturers will provide detectors and auxiliary equipment appropriate for their use, and it is likely that by the time this book is published LC detectors employing microbore columns will be commercially available. Small-volume

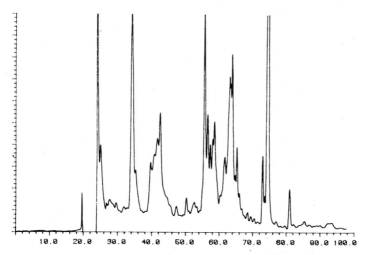

Fig. 4.3. Chromatogram of serum on a microbore column. Sample volume, 400 μl; column length, 1 m, column ID, 1 mm; column packing, RP-18, 10 μm; flowrate, 40 μl/min; linear gradient for 1 h from methanol–water (1:1) to methanol. (Reproduced from *J. Chromatogr.*, 185 (1979) 27, with permission [11].)

References on p. A160

detectors will also provide greater efficiency for the macrocolumns, because the band dispersion of the extra-column volumes may contribute, in some instances and to some extent, to the width of the bands eluted early from high-efficiency macrocolumns.

4.4. MOBILE-PHASE SUPPLY SYSTEMS

The simplest mobile-phase supply consists of a solvent reservoir and a pump, connected directly to the injection device. However, such a system can only be used for isocratic development, i.e., a mobile phase of constant composition. A more complete solvent-supply system is depicted in Fig. 4.4. It consists of two reciprocating pumps, driven by stepping motors and supplied with solvents from two solvent reservoirs. The stepping motor of each pump is driven by its respective square-wave generator and drive unit. The frequency of both, or either, square-wave generator can be controlled by a digital programer which can either control the relative speeds of each pump in a predictable manner and thus provide gradient elution development or control the speed of one pump with respect to time and thus provide flow programming. The outlet from each pump passes through a pulse damper, two flows are mixed in an appropriate mixer, and the mobile phase then passes to the sample valve and column.

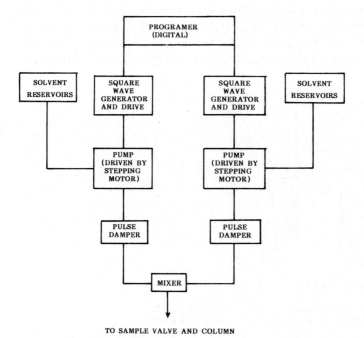

Fig. 4.4. Solvent-supply system for column chromatography. (Reproduced from *J. Chromatogr.*, 185 (1979) 27, with permission [11].)

The early pumps used in LC were syringe-type pumps, driven by an appropriate motor and screw thread to provide the desired flowrate; when gradient elution was needed, it was necessary to employ two such pumps. Syringe pumps have several disadvantages, one of which results from the compressibility of the mobile phase. These disadvantages have been discussed extensively by Martin et al. [12]. Modern LC pumps are usually reciprocating pumps where the piston or diaphragm is driven by cams so designed that when two are used in parallel, the output from the pump is virtually pulseless. Although some pumps are still fitted with normal induction or direct current (DC) motors, the most effective ones are now fitted with stepping motors. The advantages of the stepping motor is that, with relatively simple digital electronics, accurate complex gradients can be developed and flow programing can be carried out over a wide range of flowrates. For example, the Waters Assoc. (Milford, MA, USA) Model 6000A pump, driven by an appropriate frequency generator can cover a range of flowrates from about $2\,\mu l/min$ to 20 ml/min, providing a dynamic range of four orders of magnitude. In many instances, despite the careful design of the cams for piston-type pumps, some pressure pulses still persist in the output; these can be eliminated by appropriate pulse dampers. When pulse dampers are used, it should be remembered that they have considerable capacity and, therefore, when solvents are changed, they must be carefully purged of the previous solvents. Present-day mobile-phase supply systems should deliver solvents at inlet pressures of at least 6000 psi. With the advent of microbore columns, which can have lengths of 10 m or more, pressures in excess of this could be desirable in the future. Various methods for determining the appropriate gradients for the separation of a given mixture have been suggested [13,14], but the theory behind the prediction of gradients for a particular separation is still complex; the basic approach still remains trial and error. However, even when the separation of a very complex mixture is attempted, a satisfactory elution program can usually be devised with the aid of three or four trial gradients.

4.5. INJECTION DEVICES

Samples are introduced into conventional "open" columns by application to the surface of the packing prior to development. When the high-efficiency columns, requiring higher pressures to produce an adequate flow, made their appearance, a septum-type injection system was introduced. This system was actually borrowed from the GC method of injection, suitable precautions being taken to prevent the septum from being affected by solvents. The septum system has several disadvantages: It cannot be used at high pressures for any significant length of time without leaking, nor to inject the sample centrally into the packing, which is critical for good efficiency. A study of the effect of different methods of sample injection on efficiency was carried out by Kirkland et al. [15], who showed that the method of injection, the positions of injection, and the nature of the sample diffuser, all significantly affect column efficiency. The more reliable method of injection now commonly used is the sample valve with either an internal or external loop. A number of valves presently available operate at pressures of 7000 to 8000 psi and provide sample volumes ranging from 0.2 to 100 μl or more. Because the valve must sustain high pressures, the valve seats must be carefully fitted. Therefore, it is important to ensure that no abrasive material enters the valve from the mobile phase or sample loop. A fritted disc at the column inlet ensures that packing is not forced back into the valve. As was previously noted, extra-column volumes can seriously affect column efficiency. Therefore, the tubing volume between valve and column should be kept to a minimum, preferably by using short 0.01-in. ID or, even better, 0.005-in. ID tubing.

4.6. THERMOSTATS

In order to obtain precise retention data, the temperature must be kept under precise control. The retention volume of a substance is directly proportional to the distribution coefficient of that substance between the mobile and stationary phases and is, therefore, proportional to the exponent of the excess free energy of that substance between the two phases. As the excess free energy varies inversely with temperature, the distribution coefficient and thus the retention volume will also be dependent on temperature. The precision of chromatographic measurements will be discussed in Sec. 4.8, but at this point it should be stressed that for high precision in retention data measurements a temperature control of less than 0.1°C may be necessary.

In most modern chromatographic ovens air is used as the heat exchange medium. Air ovens can maintain column temperatures only within perhaps ±0.5°C, unless a very carefully designed thermostating system is employed, because the thermal capacity of a gas is relatively small. Therefore, air baths are inadequate for thermostating columns when retention data need to be measured with high precision. The advantages of air baths are that columns can be easily changed, there are no spillage problems, and the system is cleaner than a liquid bath. However, for adequate thermostating only liquids are a thermostating medium with sufficient heat capacity to maintain the column at a given temperature within the required limits. For most LC analyses, temperatures maintained at about 25°C are satisfactory and, so far, there is no indication that temperature programing is useful for LC [16]. Thus, water can often be used as the thermostating medium. However, in exclusion chromatography, temperatures of up to 200°C may be employed, and appropriate, high-boiling thermostating fluids are needed. The majority of presently available liquid chromatographs are equipped with air baths, but for high-precision measurements thermostats employing liquid heat exchangers are essential to provide the necessary control over column temperature. It is hoped that in the future either instruments will be fitted with liquid thermostat systems or alternative systems will be devised so that the maximum precision can be obtained from the chromatographic apparatus.

4.7. DETECTORS

A LC detector is a device that locates, in the dimensions of space or time, the positions of the components of a mixture that has been subjected to a chromatographic process and thus permits the senses to appreciate the nature of the separation that has been obtained [17]. Basically, there are two principal methods of detection: bulk property detection and solute property detection. Bulk property detectors measure the overall physical property of the effluent, such as density, refractive index, thermal conductivity, which is modified by the presence of the solute. In most instances, the modification of the physical properties of the eluent by the solute is small, and therefore the change in signal measured as the peak is eluted is also relatively small. Furthermore, the sensitivity of bulk detectors is limited, as normal ambient changes, e.g., temperature and pressure of the mobile phase, will produce changes in the detection system that are commensurate with that of the signal from the solute. Even for the detection of substances present at a level of a 10^{-6} g/ml, the temperature control of the detector and column effluent may have to be be better than $0.001°C$ [18]. However, the group of bulk property detectors includes the RI detector, which is probably the most general type of detecting system presently available in LC. RI detectors with appropriate optical system, sensing device, and electronics are capable of giving a linear response and exhibiting reasonable sensitivity. They are used extensively in gel permeation and exclusion chromatography and for the detection of substances that have no UV chromophore, are not fluorescent, and cannot be made to form fluorescent derivatives. The RI detector finds particular use in the quantitative analysis of polymers by exclusion chromatography (Chap. 8.3.3). The RI of a given series of polymers is constant when the number of monomers present is large. Thus, accurate quantitative results can be obtained without calibration by the normalization of peak heights or peak areas. At present the RI detector is the only really effective bulk property detector available, although other practical systems involving the measurement of dielectric constants have also been devised.

The second class of detectors, solute property detectors, function on the principle of measuring some property of the solute, either absent from the mobile phase or present to a much lesser extent. A typical example is the UV-absorption detector, probably the most commonly used detector in LC. As the detecting principle is far more independent of the properties of the mobile phase, it can have much higher sensitivity than a bulk property detector. Substances having a significant extinction coefficient in the UV can be detected at levels of 10^{-8} to 10^{-9} g/ml, and if an appropriate optical system, sensing device, and electronics are available, the response of the UV detector can be linear. The second most common solute property detector is the fluorescence detector, which responds to either the natural fluorescence of the analyte or to a derivative formed by an appropriate fluorescing reagent. In practice, the eluate from the column passes either directly or after mixing with the fluorescing reagent to a cell, where it is irradiated with UV light of the proper wavelength. The resulting fluorescence is freed from the incident radiation by the use of appropriate filters, detected by a photocell, and the output is amplified and fed to a suitable recorder. The fluorescence detector, under ideal circumstances, is probably the most sensitive detector available in LC. Sensitivities in excess of 10^{-12} g/ml have been achieved, and it is obviously more selective and more specific than even the UV detector. However, it has therefore a more limited range of application.

The UV, RI, and fluorescence detectors are the three most commonly used detectors in CC today. A detector that functions on an entirely different principle and which has had significant use in the past is the wire-transport detector. The principle of this detector has formed the basis of a satisfactory interface for LC–MS [19,20], which is the only interface that can provide electron-impact spectra of CC effluents. The wire-transport detector was designed to eliminate the effect of different solvents on the detecting system, thus permitting the use of complex gradients with a wide range of solvents to be employed without affecting the output of the detector. Basically, the transport detector consists of a wire or ribbon passing through the effluent from the column. The wire with a coating of the eluate on the surface moves through a small evaporation chamber, where the solvent is removed and the deposit of solute, forming a fine coating on the wire, passes through a furnace heated to a temperature of about 800°C. As the wire is in contact with oxygen, the solute burns and all the carbon is converted to CO_2. A small Venturi pump sucks the CO_2 into a stream of H_2, which passes over a Ni catalyst, heated at 350°C. This converts the CO_2 to methane which then passes to a normal FID, where it is burned and the methane is detected from the ion current in the usual way. This detector has a linear response and a sensitivity of about 10^{-6} g/ml. The wire-transport detector is, therefore, a universal detector for all substances containing carbon and has a predictable response that is approximately proportional to the carbon content of the substance. The output of the detector is completely independent of the solvents used for chromatography, provided they are volatile. This detector has been employed with incremental gradient elution [13], and with this gradient system it has been applied successfully to the monitoring of cosmetic products.

4.7.1. Detector specifications

Detector specifications must be available to permit any given detector to be compared with other detectors and to be chosen on a rational basis for a particular task. Performance data must, therefore, be consistent even though different detectors may function on different principles. The pertinent properties of an LC detector that should be provided by the manufacturers are therefore as follows.

4.7.1.1. Dynamic range

The dynamic range of a detector is the concentration range over which the detector will give a response; it should be given in g/ml.

4.7.1.2. Linear dynamic range

The linear dynamic range may be defined as that concentration range over which the response of the detector is described by the equation

$$Y = Ac^r$$

where Y is the detector output, c is the concentration of the solute in g/ml, A is a constant, and r is the response index ($0.98 < r < 1.02$).

4.7.1.3. Sensitivity

The detector sensitivity (minimum detectability) is defined as that concentration of solute in g/ml that will provide a signal equivalent to twice the noise level. When the response of the detector varies with different substances, the response must be taken into account. For example, the sensitivity of a UV detector must be stated for a substance having a given extinction coefficient at the wavelength of the UV source employed.

These three detector specifications are the most important, but other properties of the detector, such as cell volume, connecting tube volume, and electronic or amplifier time constant are also important, as their properties may seriously and adversely affect the performance of the column which the detector monitors.

4.8. QUALITATIVE ANALYSIS

The parameters of a chromatogram that permit the identification of a given solute are: the corrected retention time (t'), the corrected retention volume (V'), and the separation ratio (α) of the solute relative to a standard. The basic retention volume equation is

$$V_R = V_0 + V' \tag{4.1}$$

where V_R is the total volume of mobile phase that has passed through the column from the point of injection to the peak maximum and is called the retention volume, V_0 is the retention volume of a completely unretained solute and is called the column dead volume, and V' is the corrected retention volume of the solute. If a constant flowrate is employed, eqn. 4.1 can be expressed in units of time

$$t_R = t_0 + t' \tag{4.2}$$

where t_R is the retention time of the solute, t_0 is the dead time of the column, and t' is the corrected retention time.

The separation ratio α_{AB} of solute A relative to standard B is given by

$$\alpha_{AB} = V'_A / V'_B = t'_A / t'_B \tag{4.3}$$

For a given solute, V' will be constant when it is chromatographed on a given column with a given solvent system, and if the flowrate is kept constant, t' will also remain constant for the given solute. However, V' and t' are of little value if a different column is employed, as both parameters depend on the amount of stationary phase in the column. However, α_{AB} for a given solute A and standard B will be constant and independent of the column, providing the solvent and stationary phase are the same. Therefore, α values are to be preferred for identification purposes. However, even the α value of a substance relative to a known standard is not unique for that substance and cannot provide unambiguous identification. Retention ratios obtained with two or more different stationary phases and different solvent systems increase the probability of correct identification, but it must be remembered that identification by retention measurements alone can never be absolute.

Retention data can be obtained with very high precision [21], but only by carefully controlling the operating conditions. The composition of the solvent used as the mobile phase can have a profound effect on solute retention. It follows that, if retention times are to have a precision of 0.1%, the solvent composition must be maintained sufficiently constant to maintain the required precision. When the corrected retention times of three solutes were determined at various solvent compositions, the results in Table 4.1 were obtained. It is seen that, to achieve a precision of 0.1%, the solvent concentration must be maintained to within 0.02% (w/v). This level of constancy of solvent composition is fairly easy to maintain, providing a closed solvent system is employed, but it is extremely difficult, if not impossible, to make up a solution to this accuracy using volatile solvents. It is, therefore, recommended that large batches of eluent be made up, if precise results are required, and that each new eluent be checked by chromatographing a standard solute.

It is also well known that the retention volume and retention time of a solute vary considerably with temperature. The relationship is logarithmic, but over a small range of temperatures it is approximately linear. Therefore, a linear function was force-fitted to the results for the same three solutes by regression analysis. The data in Table 4.2 show that, to attain a precision of 0.1%, the temperature of the solvent and column must be maintained to within $\pm 0.04°C$. It is not difficult to maintain this level of temperature control with a thermostat bath, but it is extremely difficult to return to a given temperature to within $\pm 0.04°C$ after it has been changed. It should also be pointed out that column temperature control to $\pm 0.04°C$ would be

TABLE 4.1

SOLVENT CONCENTRATION TOLERANCES FOR RETENTION TIME PRECISION

Solvent	Retention time at 44% of butyl chloride in heptane (min)	Concentration tolerance for 1% precision (%, w/v)	Concentration tolerance for 0.1% precision (%, w/v)
p-Chlorophenetol	2.85	± 0.14	± 0.014
2-Ethoxynaphthalene	5.01	± 0.10	± 0.010
o-Dinitrobenzene	17.27	± 0.10	± 0.010

TABLE 4.2

TEMPERATURE TOLERANCES FOR RETENTION VOLUME PRECISION

Solute	V' at 238 nm (ml)	k'	Temperature control for 1% precision (°C)	Temperature control for 0.1% precision (°C)
p-Chlorophenetol	3.072	0.945	±0.35	±0.04
2-Ethylnaphthalene	4.925	1.519	±0.35	±0.04
o-Dintrobenzene	17.185	5.301	±0.33	±0.03

extremely difficult, if not impossible, to maintain if an air bath was employed. For example, due to the relatively low thermal capacity and specific heat of air, local variations of 1°C can usually be measured in GC hot-air ovens.

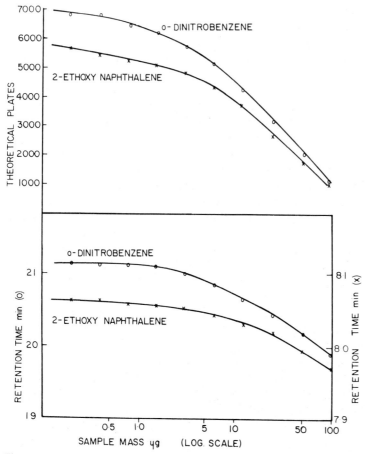

Fig. 4.5. Graphs of retention time and column efficiency against sample mass for two different solutes. (Reproduced from *J. Chromatogr.*, 138 (1977) 283, with permission [21].)

References on p. A160

The mass of the sample injected into a LC column can also significantly affect the solute retention time. In Fig. 4.5 the retention times for two solutes are shown plotted against mass of solute injected. It is seen that, for precise comparative work, either the mass of sample injected must be kept constant or the total mass of each solute must be maintained at a level below 0.1 μg. Replicate analyses have shown that retention time measurements can be made with a standard deviation of 0.25% or less, even by manual measurement.

4.9. QUANTITATIVE ANALYSIS

Quantitative analysis places much greater demands on the performance of the detector than qualitative analysis. As qualitative analysis only depends on the accurate measurement of retention time, the detector does not have to be linear. Even the time constant of the detector does not have to be small, as long as the position of the center of peak maximum can be accurately determined. For quantitative analysis, on the other hand, the detector must have a linear response over a wide concentration range and be stable and noise-free. Quantitative analysis in LC is usually achieved by measuring the peak height or area of the substance concerned under the assumption that these values are linearly related to the mass of material corresponding to each peak. However, none of the presently used LC detectors provides the same or similar response to all compounds. It follows that the normalization procedure common in GC, where the percent composition of a mixture is obtained by expressing the area of a given peak as a percentage of the total area of all the peaks, cannot be employed in LC. Each peak area or peak height must be corrected for the relative response of that particular component and, therefore, calibration procedures have to be used.

A possible exception to this is the wire detector, which has a predictable response depending on the carbon content of the materials chromatographed. Therefore, if their carbon content is known, their prior calibration may not be necessary. Another instance where peak area or height normalization can be used is in the analysis of polymers by exclusion chromatography with the RI detector. Providing the degree of polymerization exceeds 5, the RI of the polymer is a constant. Under these conditions the response of the detector will be the same for all solutes, and analysis can be achieved by a normalization procedure.

It has been shown that, in general, measurements of peak heights give greater precision in quantitative analysis than peak areas. The reason for this is not completely certain at this time.

A simple form of the procedure used for quantitative analysis in CC is given as follows. A known weight, m_A, of the solute A to be determined in a given mixture is chromatographed together with a known weight m_S of a standard S that must be well separated from solute A and from all other components present in the mixture. Let the peak heights of solute A and standard S be h_A and h_S, respectively. Then

$$\frac{m_A}{m_S} = \frac{\phi h_A}{h_S} \text{ or } \phi = \frac{m_A h_S}{m_S h} \tag{4.4}$$

where ϕ is the calibration constant for the solute A and the standard S. A known weight m'_S of the standard is now added to the mixture containing an unknown weight of solute A equal to m'_A, and the mixture is chromatographed under the same conditions. Now, if the peak heights of the solute and standard in the resulting chromatogram are h'_A and h'_S, respectively, then

$$\frac{m'_A}{m'_S} = \phi \frac{h'_A}{h'_S} \tag{4.5}$$

and, thus, substituting for ϕ from eqn. 4.4 in eqn. 4.5 and simplifying

$$m'_A = \frac{m_A h_S}{m_S h_A} \frac{m'_S h'_A}{h'_S} \tag{4.6}$$

If it is considered appropriate, peak areas can be employed as an alternative to peak heights for a given analysis, and then the respective peak areas are substituted for peak heights in eqn. 4.6.

4.10. COMBINATION OF COLUMN CHROMATOGRAPHY WITH SPECTRO-SCOPIC TECHNIQUES

The linking of identification techniques with separation techniques started with the introduction of the GC–MS system in the early 1960s. It was a direct result of the development of high-efficiency packed columns and capillary columns capable of separating very complex mixtures. To identify the separated substances effectively it was necessary to link the gas chromatograph with an on-line identification technique, and as the mass spectrometer lent itself to interfacing with a gas chromatograph, the GC–MS system was developed. Similarly, as the efficiency of LC columns improved and more complex mixtures were separated, the need for an identification technique directly linked to the liquid chromatograph became apparent. Two effective LC spectroscopic systems evolved: the liquid chromatograph–UV spectrometer (LC–UV) system and the liquid chromatograph–mass spectrometer (LC–MS) system.

4.10.1. The LC–UV system

Interfacing of the liquid chromatograph with the UV spectrometer was the first combination to be successfully achieved. This was largely because interfacing was simple and actually only an extension of the already well-established UV detector. The normal fixed-wavelength light source was replaced with a deuterium lamp and a suitable optical system. This includes a grating or prism inserted so that the wavelength of the light passing through the detector can be selected or, if required, continuously varied in a predictable manner to produce an absorption spectrum, which is then traced on the recorder. Such systems are now commercially available, and they are very sensitive and capable of producing excellent UV spectra from microgram amounts of sample. A diagram of the optical system of the Perkin-Elmer

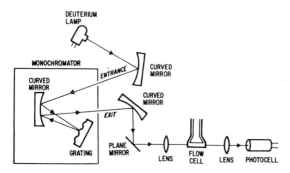

Fig. 4.6. Variable-wavelength detector.

Model LC75 scanning UV detector is shown in Fig. 4.6. Light from a deuterium lamp is focused by means of two curved mirrors onto a diffraction grating. The grating is rotatable, either manually or by a scanning motor, so that either light of a specific wavelength can be selected or a section of the UV spectrum is automatically and continually scanned. The diffracted light from the grating is focused by the second curved mirror, an exit curved mirror, and a lens through the flow-cell of the detector. The transmitted light from the flow-cell is focused by means of a second lens onto a photocell, and the output of the photocell is amplified and fed to a recorder.

The LC–UV system can be used in two ways. One is to choose a specific wavelength or series of wavelengths to monitor a particular sample. This permits the analysis of specific compounds, even if they are not separated from other compounds which do not absorb at the wavelength selected. The second method of using the LC–UV combination is to obtain UV spectra of individual peaks as they are eluted from the column as an aid in identification. This is achieved by a stop-flow procedure, in which a peak is eluted and the flow of mobile phase is stopped at the peak maximum, as monitored by the detector. Owing to the relatively low compressibility of the mobile phase and low diffusivity of the solute, the solute peak remains at its maximum inside the detector cell after the flow has stopped and the pressure has been allowed to fall. The UV wavelength is then adjusted to the starting value of the scan, and the spectrum is obtained by scanning a selected wavelength range. Rapid-scanning spectrometers with integrating array detectors such as Vidicons or solid-state diode arrays, are an alternative approach to LC–UV systems, one of which was described by Milano et al. [22]. In the latter, the radiation is focused onto a diode array and the output from the diodes is interfaced with a 16K core memory computer. Data are stored continuously during the development of the chromatogram and processed on completion. The total spectrum can be scanned over a period of 2.6 msec every 14 msec, and 70 spectra can be averaged every second, but significantly lower scan speeds and scan frequencies are used in practice. Although useful, UV spectra generally do not provide enough information for structure elucidation.

4.10.2. The LC–MS system

The development of a satisfactory LC–MS system presented far greater problems than the development of the GC–MS system. When the mobile phase is a gas, it can be led straight into the mass spectrometer, and with the aid of a suitable splitting device low pressures can be maintained in the ion source. However, when the mobile phase is a liquid, a large volume change takes place when it is vaporized in a mass spectrometer. Therefore, only very small quantities of eluate can be permitted, otherwise the ion source pressure would be increased to a level at which the mass spectrometer could no longer function. Two practical interfaces have been developed, both of which are now commercially available and link the liquid chromatograph directly with the mass spectrometer without requiring too great a compromise in the operating conditions of either instrument.

The first interface was developed by Argino et al. [23] and is called the direct inlet system. It passes the eluate from the chromatographic column through a splitter so that only a small quantity of liquid (a few microliters) enters the mass spectrometer by means of a capillary tube from which the solvent and sample are vaporized. The vapor is used for chemical ionization to yield a mass spectrum of the dissolved solute. This device works satisfactorily, but certain problems result from the blockage of the capillary by deposited solute and from electrical breakdown due to the high concentration of solvent vapor in the ion source. However, when carefully controlled operating conditions are adhered to, the system is capable of producing

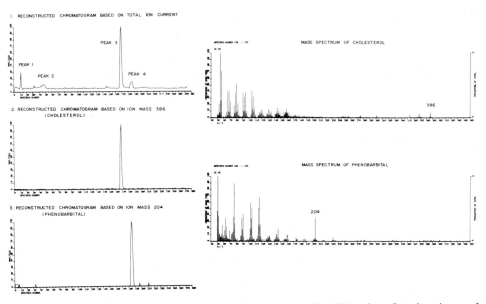

Fig. 4.7. Analysis of a synthetic mixture with the moving-wire LC–MS interface. Sample, mixture of triacontane, cholesteryl laurate, cholesterol, and phenobarbitone; column, 250×4.6 mm ID; Partisil, 10 μm; incremental gradient elution; flowrate, 2 ml/min. (Reproduced from *Ciba Found. Symp.*, 26 (1974) 155, with permission [19].)

References on p. A160

useful mass spectra from LC eluates. One of the disadvantages of the direct inlet system is that it can normally only provide chemical ionization spectra. Chemical ionization spectra are very helpful in structure elucidation, because they often give information that can furnish the molecular weight of the solute, but electron-impact spectra give more structural information and therefore are more desirable. For this reason a second type of interface was developed, which involves a wire-transport system.

The wire-transport interface was developed by Scott et al. [20], and consists of a moving wire that passes through two vacuum ports, then through the ion source of the mass spectrometer, and through two further vacuum ports onto a spool. The eluate from the column wets the wire, and the thin film of liquid is passed through the vacuum ports where the solvent is evaporated; the residual solute then goes through the ion source. The wire is heated by passing a current through it, so that in the ion source under conditions of high vacuum the sample is vaporized directly into the electron beam to produce satisfactory electron-impact spectra. The interface, in fact, functions as a continuous probe sampling device. Fig. 4.7 shows a total ion current chromatogram obtained with this device from a synthetic mixture, together with two chromatograms obtained by single-ion monitoring, and an example of spectra obtained from two of the eluted solutes. The chromatogram shown as Curve 1 in Fig. 4.7 is based on the total ion current. The first peak is the n-alkane, the second cholesteryl laurate, the third cholesterol, and the fourth phenobarbitone. Curve 2 was plotted from the data collected during the run by using only the intensities for the molecular ion of cholesterol (m/z 386). This chromatogram indicates that the third component is cholesterol. Similarly, Curve 3, reconstructed on m/z 204, indicates that the fourth component is phenobarbitone. Mass spectra taken from these two peaks are included in Fig. 4.7. The disadvantages of this system lie in the fact that only a small proportion of the eluate passes through the mass spectrometer owing to the low capacity of the wire; therefore, its sensitivity is limited. Modern microbore columns, having a low flowrate would pose no serious problem, because the wire could take virtually all of the effluent from the column whereas insufficient sample from the macrobore column is taken into the mass spectrometer by the wire-transport system.

McFadden [24] has developed an alternative interface, based on a ribbon instead

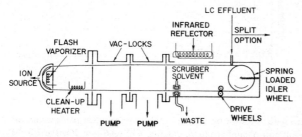

Fig. 4.8. Diagram of the belt LC–MS interface. (Reproduced from *J. Chromatogr. Sci.*, 18 (1980) 97, with permission [24].)

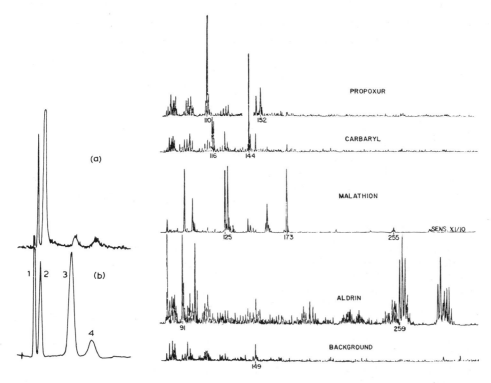

Fig. 4.9. Analysis of a herbicide mixture with the belt LC–MS interface. (a) Total ion-current chromatogram; (b) UV detector recording; (c) mass spectra. (Reproduced from *Liquid Chromatography Detectors*, Elsevier, Amsterdam, 1977, p. 243, with permission [17].)

of a wire. The ribbon takes the form of an endless belt and has a capacity of about 1.5 ml/min under normal conditions. A diagram of this belt LC–MS interface is shown in Fig. 4.8. It is similar in form to the system developed by Scott, but the material is vaporized by a heater situated close to the band where the transport system enters the ion source instead of heating the band itself. Furthermore, after the solute is vaporized, the band passes by another heater, which removes the last traces of solute before the band is recycled, and this eliminates repetitive spectra or "ghosting". An example of some mass spectra from the belt interface system obtained during the separation of a mixture of herbicides is shown in Fig. 4.9 together with the total ion-current chromatograms (a) and the recording obtained simultaneously from an on-line UV detector (b). Excellent mass spectra are obtained, which are completely adequate for identification purposes.

The LC–MS system is still somewhat in its infancy. Practical and effective LC–MS systems are commercially available, featuring both the direct inlet system and the transport method. There are still some problems associated with the technique, involving mainly stability, sensitivity, and the vaporization of solutes.

References on p. A160

Some development work is yet required before the performance of the LC–MS system can be considered equivalent to that of the GC–MS system.

REFERENCES

1 Cs. Horváth and S.R. Lipsky, *Anal. Chem.,* 41 (1964) 1227.
2 R.E. Majors, *Anal. Chem.,* 44 (1972) 1722.
3 J.J. Kirkland, *J. Chromatogr. Sci.,* 9 (1971) 206.
4 R.P.W. Scott and P. Kucera, *J. Chromatogr.,* 142 (1977) 213.
5 R.P.W. Scott and C.F. Simpson, *J. Chromatogr.,* 197 (1980) 11.
6 J. Asshauer and I. Halász, *J. Chromatogr. Sci.,* 12 (1974) 139.
7 M.J.E. Golay, in D.H. Desty (Editor), *Gas Chromatography 1958,* Butterworths, London, 1958, p. 36.
8 M.J.E. Golay, *J. Chromatogr.,* 186 (1979) 357.
9 R.P.W. Scott and P. Kucera, *J. Chromatogr.,* 169 (1979) 51.
10 R.P.W. Scott, P. Kucera and M. Munroe, *J. Chromatogr.,* 186 (1979) 475.
11 R.P.W. Scott and P. Kucera, *J. Chromatogr.,* 185 (1979) 27.
12 M. Martin, G. Blu, C. Eon and G. Guiochon, *J. Chromatogr.,* 112 (1975) 399.
13 R.P.W. Scott and P. Kucera, *Anal. Chem.,* 45 (1973) 749.
14 L.R. Snyder, J.W. Dolan and J.R. Grant, *J. Chromatogr.,* 165 (1979) 3.
15 J.J. Kirkland, W.W. Yau, K.S. Stoklosa and C.H. Dilks, Jr., *J. Chromatogr. Sci.,* 15 (1977) 303.
16 L.R. Snyder, in A. Zlatkis (Editor), *6th Intern. Symp. on Advances in Chromatography, Adv. Chromatogr.,* Preston, Evanston, IL, 1970, p. 355.
17 R.P.W. Scott, *Liquid Chromatography Detectors,* J. Chromatogr. Library Series, Vol. 11, Elsevier, Amsterdam, 1977, p. 1.
18 R.P.W. Scott, *Liquid Chromatography Detectors,* J. Chromatogr. Library Series, Vol. 11, Elsevier, Amsterdam, 1977, p. 36.
19 R.P.W. Scott, C.G. Scott, M. Munroe and J. Hess, Jr., *The Poisoned Patient: The Role of the Laboratory,* Ciba Found. Symp. 26 (New Series), Elsevier, Amsterdam, 1974, p. 155.
20 R.P.W. Scott, C.G. Scott, M. Munroe and J. Hess, Jr., *J. Chromatogr.,* 99 (1974) 398.
21 R.P.W. Scott and C.E. Reese, *J. Chromatogr.,* 138 (1977) 283.
22 M.J. Milano, S. Lam and E. Grushka, *J. Chromatogr.,* 125 (1976) 315.
23 P. Argino, B.G. Dawkins and F.W. McLafferty, *J. Chromatogr. Sci.,* 12 (1974) 574.
24 W. McFadden, *J. Chromatogr. Sci.,* 18 (1980) 97.

Chapter 5

Planar chromatography

KAREL MACEK

CONTENTS

5.1. INTRODUCTION

Thin-layer chromatography (TLC) and paper chromatography (PC) differ from other chromatographic techniques in the planar arrangement of the stationary phase. Otherwise, practically all the chromatographic principles and, in TLC, all the types of sorbents are similar to those used in column chromatography. The planar (flat-bed) arrangement has several advantages, such as simplicity, flexibility, parallel analysis of a large number of samples, two-dimensional development, and applicability of selective or specific chemical and biological detection methods directly to the chromatogram. Disadvantages are that automation is difficult and that the sensitivity and accuray of the quantitative analysis are slightly lower than for other methods.

Both TLC and PC are very closely related in their technical aspects. The techniques of sample application, development, and detection are analogous, as are the techniques of qualitative and quantitative analysis. The two methods differ fundamentally in the nature of the stationary phase. In PC, the stationary phase is in most cases anchored to a carrier in sheet form, i.e., on the paper. In TLC, on the other hand, separation ordinarily occurs on a sorbent that is either loosely spread on, or, more often, fixed on a rigid support, usually a glass plate or a foil. The borderline between the two methods is beginning to become blurred, and perhaps the differences will be completely obliterated as further progress is being made in both methods.

The position of PC and TLC among other chromatographic techniques is evident from Fig. 5.1, which shows the relative use of individual chromatographic techniques between 1970 and 1979. The graph traces a vast increase of liquid column tech-

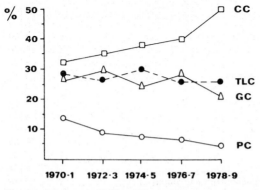

Fig. 5.1. Percentage of all publications in chromatography contributed by PC, TLC and other chromatographic procedures.

niques, which is mainly due to the introduction of HPLC, and it shows a simultaneous decrease of PC. The proportions of TLC and GC are about constant.

In analogy to LCC, in TLC the HPTLC procedures have lately attracted much attention. Their goals are: shortening the analysis time, increasing the sensitivity of detection, and increasing the separation efficiency. Because HPTLC is basically not a new technique and because it is difficult to find a sharp borderline between conventional TLC and HPTLC, both techniques are discussed in this chapter side by side.

A number of monographs on TLC [1–7], PC [8–10], TLC and PC [11–15], review articles [16–25], and tape cassettes [26] contain detailed information on the techniques of planar chromatography. The bibliography of papers published on PC and TLC is compiled in some books [27–35], and a current listing, together with indexes, has appeared regularly since 1974 in the Bibliography Section of the *Journal of Chromatography*.

5.2. SAMPLE PREPARATION

Sample preparation, the first step preliminary to chromatography, is identical for both TLC and PC.

5.2.1. Dissolving

An amount of solid sample containing a sufficient quantity of the substance to be analyzed is dissolved in a suitable solvent (preferably an organic solvent with a low boiling point). The concentration of the solution (usually 0.1–0.01%) depends on the amount to be applied to the layer or paper (preferably 1–5 μl, in HPTLC 0.02–0.2 μl).

5.2.2. Extracting and concentrating

In the analysis of biological materials or pharmaceutical preparations containing the test substances in low concentration, an extraction and concentration of the sample must be performed. This usually involves repeated extractions and adsorption or ion-exchange chromatography. Recently, disposable columns have been introduced in the market: these columns speed up and simplify extraction and sample preparation for subsequent chromatography (Extrelut, Sep-Pak, ClinElut, ToxElut, etc.) [36].

5.2.3. Removing ballast material

Extracts from biological material frequently contain substances which, when present in large amounts, may have an unfavorable effect on chromatography. Such ballast substances, particularly proteins, lipids, and inorganic ions, must therefore be removed from the extract. In addition to the classical procedures (removal of proteins by precipitation, ultrafiltration, or extraction; removal of lipids by extraction; and removal of inorganic substances by ion exchange) some more recent procedures should be mentioned that were specially designed for TLC. For the preparation of samples from plant material, the so-called TAS (thermomicro-transfer –application–separation) technique [37] was developed, which combines extraction with ballast removal. The sample material is transferred to an ampoule with a nozzle and heated in an oven to a suitable temperature. Components which are volatile or capable of sublimation issue from the nozzle and condense on the starting line of the thin-layer chromatogram. An improvement of this technique is thermofractography (TFG), in which the temperature of the oven is gradually raised (e.g., from 50 to 450°C) and the substances are prefractioned according to their volatility before reaching the layer [38]. The use of supercritical gases for extraction also belongs in this category [39].

5.2.4. Preparing derivatives

It is advantageous to chromatograph the substances after conversion to derivatives [40] if, e.g.,

(a) a volatile substance (alcohol, aldehyde, etc.) is chromatographed in the form of a nonvolatile derivative;

(b) a substance cannot be detected on layers or paper, but its derivative can be detected;

(c) the sensitivity of detection can be increased (e.g., fluorescence labeling);

(d) the derivatives are easier ot separate than the original substances;

(e) the removal of ballast material is facilitated;

(f) the derivatization contributes to the identification.

5.3. SAMPLE APPLICATION

The first step in actual TLC and PC, sample application, is of fundamental importance for both resolution and accurate quantitative analysis. For this purpose, the point of application, the origin (or start), is usually marked with an ordinary pencil. The samples can be applied in the form of spots (diameter 1–4 mm in TLC, 5–10 mm in PC) or streaks. The solution (1–10 μl) is usually applied with the aid of micropipettes, but for quantitative analysis it is necessary to use some type of constriction pipette (disposable Microcaps, Camag automatic pipettes, etc.) or some special sample applicator (Camag Chromatocharger or Linomat III, Desaga Auto-liner 75 or Microdotter 80). If larger volumes (more than 10 μl) are to be applied, the spots must be dried between successive applications to the same spot. In this case, evaporation of the solvents may be accelerated by a hair drier, draft hood, etc.

In HPTLC, the sample application is very important. Theoretically, optimum results are obtained by applying 2 nl over an area of 0.1 mm diameter [41], but in practice considerably larger volumes are spotted (20–200 nl). Special spotting devices (e.g., Camag Nanomat) are necessary with Pt–Ir capillaries as essential

Fig. 5.2. EVA-Chrom applicator (with permission of W&W Electronic, Basle, Switzerland).

components. For everyday use the EVA-Chrom apparatus (Fig. 5.2) appears to be handier. Both devices can also be used with Microcaps capillaries, especially when they are used for conventional TLC.

The application of samples is the most time-consuming manipulation in planar chromatography. Therefore, the search continues for methods capable of accelerating or automating the sample application (e.g., Desaga Impulsomat and Autosampler and Camag Linomat III). Among the large number of ideas [21–23,42–44] a new principle must be reported in which the regularity of the starting zone in TLC is achieved in a purely chromatographic process. A plate with two adjacent layers (twin layers) is used. After the dilute sample solution is applied to a layer of weak sorbent, solvent development carries it to the edge of a layer of strong sorbent where it forms a narrow initial zone [45,46]. This principle is used in ready-for-use plates with a concentrating ("preadsorbent") zone (Merck, Whatman).

Also worth mentioning are the so-called transfer techniques in which a sample that has already been subjected to another chromatographic technique is applied to a thin layer or on paper. This sample may be the effluent from a GC column, applied to the starting line of a TLC plate in gaseous form [47]. More frequently, this technique is practiced when transferring a zone from the electrophoretic medium to TLC (so-called homochromatography; see Chap. 5.4.4.1.4) [48–51]. An interesting technique in trace analysis of biological fluids, e.g., blood, is the direct application to the origin of the chromatogram, where some compounds, e.g., proteins, precipitate and thus cause no interference with the chromatographic analysis [52,53]. A transfer technique *sui generis* is also the so-called contact spotting for HPTLC, where samples solution up to 50 μl are deposited in depressions formed on a nonwetting polymer film, the solvents are evaporated, and the residues are transferred to the adsorbent layer by bringing them into contact [54].

5.4. THIN-LAYER CHROMATOGRAPHY

According to the number of publications between 1970 and 1979, TLC holds second place among the chromatographic techniques: 27% of them were devoted to this technique (see Fig. 5.1). This certainly attests to the popularity of TLC, which it owes not only to the modest demands on instrumentation, but also to its sensitivity, general applicability, and, last but not least, its flexibility.

5.4.1. Sorbents for thin-layer chromatography

One of the most important factors in TLC is the composition and condition of the stationary phase. In TLC, the stationary phase consists of a fine-grained sorbent on a supporting glass or metal plate or on a plastic sheet.

Sorbents may be classified, e.g., according to their chemical nature into organic and inorganic ones. Alternatively, according to the binding forces that prevail during chromatographic separation, we may distinguish sorbents suitable for

(a) adsorption chromatography (silica gel, alumina, etc.);
(b) partition chromatography (cellulose, silica gel, kieselguhr, etc.);
(c) ion-exchange chromatography (cellulose or resin ion exchangers);
(d) gel chromatography (Sephadex, Bio-Gels, etc.).

In addition, there are some other types of sorbents which do not fit into these classifications of sorbents (polyamides, porous organic polymers, such as Porapak, etc.).

Though a great deal of attention has been paid to sorbents from the very beginning of TLC [55], many authors have not realized their importance until recently. It has been shown that the size and shape of sorbent particles can substantially influence the efficiency of a particular type of chromatography [56], HPLC and HPTLC being poignant examples.

The emphasis in research on sorbents for TLC continues to be on silica gel. For its application to different types of separations not only its skeletal structure, but also its pore system and activity are of prime importance [57,58]. However, it has been shown that secondary features, like particle size [59] and particle size distribution are equally important. Belenkii et al. [60] have determined that the optimum particle size of silica gel for TLC lies between 2 and 7 μm, i.e. in a much narrower range than commonly used.

Currently, over 150 different types of silica gel are commercially available, differing substantially in their physico-chemical properties. The particle size of these products varies from 1 to 50 μm, the porosity ranges between 0.4 and 1.1 ml/g, the pore diameter is between 3 and 13 nm, and the surface area usually lies within 120 to 720 m^2/g. Silica gel is very hygroscopic; at relative humidities of 45–75% it takes up 7–20% of water. This water content appears to be optimal for most chromatographic separations.

There are several forms in which silica gel is available on the market: silica gel without a binder (usually designated as H or N), silica gel with a binder, mostly calcium sulfate (designated as G), silica gel with a fluorescent indicator (F or F$_{254}$), silica gel with chemically bonded alkyl residues for reversed-phase separations (RP-2, RP-8, or RP-18), silica gel extra pure (HR), silica gel for preparative purposes (P), and silica gel for HPTLC (e.g., Merck's Silica Gel 60 for nanogram-scale TLC).

After silica gel, cellulose is the most frequently used sorbent. Cellulose for TLC has properties which are analogous to those of chromatographic paper. The difference is mainly in the fiber length, which is much less for the cellulose powder used in TLC. Cellulose for TLC is available as native fibrous cellulose and as microcrystalline cellulose (e.g., Avicel) [61]. For some separations—mainly for the combination of chromatography with electrophoresis—cellulose acetate film is frequently used.

For chromatography of high-molecular substances and nucleic acid components, cellulose ion exchangers have become very popular. The principal ones are PEI-cellulose, DEAE-cellulose, ECTEOLA-cellulose, CM-cellulose and P-cellulose. In contrast, resin ion exchangers are used for the separation of low-molecular compounds [62] and of inorganic ions.

Among other sorbents, polyamides also find occasional use [63,64]. Polycaprolactam is the only one in this category of sorbents which is of practical importance.

During the past few years a considerable amount of work has been done on the application of gel chromatography to TLC [65]. Most authors are using Sephadex-like materials [66,67] although other types, like porous glass beads [68], Styragels [69], or polystyrene–divinylbenzene copolymers [70] are also employed. Technical differences from the common TLC are due to the fact that layers of organic gels of the Sephadex type cannot be taken to dryness. Layers of organic copolymers, which may also serve as carriers of the stationary phase in reversed-phase separations, can only be stabilized by adding considerable amounts of binders (10–25%), such as gypsum or cellulose [70]. Mechanical instability and difficulties in sample application to a small area are among the main disadvantages of gel layers, but many of these sorbents have the useful property of permitting a separation of substances according to their molecular size.

Among other inorganic sorbents that are employed with relative frequency in TLC we should at least mention alumina and kieselguhr. Calcium sulfate, magnesium silicate, hydroxylapatite, charcoal, and, in the category of organic sorbents, Porapak and alginic acid are only occasionally encountered in the literature.

5.4.2. Preparation of layers

Although all commonly needed types of layers are marketed today in ready-for-use form [71] and although the application of these layers offers better separations and more reproducible results, many laboratories still prepare their own layers, and in special situation the laboratory preparation of layers is unavoidable.

5.4.2.1. Supports

Ordinary glass plates are still the most popular supports. The sizes commonly used are 20×20, 20×10, and 20×5 cm. For rapid exploratory tests 7.5×2.5-cm microscope slides are convenient, and for preparative purposes plates of larger dimensions, up to 20×100 cm, may be used. For some purposes (mainly for use with the FID, see Chap. 5.4.5.1) rod-shaped layers are needed [72,73].

Foils made of plastic [mostly poly(ethylene) terephthalate] or aluminum are often preferred to glass plates, mainly with ready-for-use layers [74]. The advantages of foils are: simpler manipulation, abrasion resistance, and easier storage and documentation. If the foil is strong enough, there is no need for a support: self-supporting layers prepared by fusing a suitable sorbent with polyolefin binders may serve as an example [75]. Whether polyamide films [76] are considered thin layers of sheets, like paper, is a matter of definition.

Quartz plates or tubes and some plastics are transparent in the UV region. This facilitates both detection and quantitative analysis based on the absorption of the transmitted UV radiation. In addition, quartz tubes allow use of the FID at high temperatures.

5.4.2.2. Binders

Binders are necessary for the preparation of stable layers. However, they may cause problems in the separation process and in the detection reaction. Gypsum (Merck's Silica Gel G) and diverse types of polymers, like polyvinyl alcohol, polymethacrylates, and polyolefins are the most common binders. Sometimes, the use of sorbent mixtures may improve the mechanical stability of the layer. Only a few special silica gels, mainly those with small particle size [59], and cellulose do not require the addition of a binder.

Lately, considerable progress has been achieved by Okumura [77] in substituting sintered glass for the binder. The layers are prepared by mixing silica gel or other suitable sorbents with glass powder. After spreading the layers on glass plates, they are heated briefly to 450–750°C. Highly porous glass does not affect the sorption processes; the layers can be exposed to corrosive detection reagents, and they can be regenerated by heating. For these reasons, such layers are referred to as permanent layers [78]. Another version are the layers that are prepared by heating sorbents with polyethylene or polypropylene.

5.4.2.3. Layer formation

The layers are prepared from a slurry of the mixture of sorbent and binder in a suitable solvent, occasionally with added binder, by shaking it in a stoppered flask or by homogenizing it in a mortar. When gypsum, used as a binder, is mixed with water, the spreading of the layer must follow in the next 60 sec. The sorbent-to-water ratio depends on the origin of the sorbents and is usually specified by the manufacturer. For preparing slurries of cellulose or cellulose ion exchangers an electric stirrer is needed. In some cases slurries are prepared in organic solvents; e.g., methanol is used for poyamide, and for the layers by the dipping technique silica gel is slurried in either chloroform or in a mixture of chloroform–methanol (2 : 1).

Layers may be prepared by pouring, dipping, or spraying, but the most frequently used procedure is spreading. A whole series of devices have been constructed for spreading, but the following two types are most commonly used:

(a) the reservoir containing the sorbent suspension is fixed, while the plates underneath are moved past it (Fig. 5.3) [79];

(b) the plates are stationary on a mounting board and the sorbent is applied by means of a movable metal block with two gates at opposite sides. A hollow cylinder with a wide longitudinal slot fits into this block (Fig. 5.4). The cylinder containing the slurry can be rotated by a lever to release the slurry on the glass plate [80].

In both types of devices the layer thickness can be adjusted. In order to obtain high-quality layers, it is necessary to prepare the slurry precisely, to have glass plates of equal thickness, and to apply the slurry with appropriate and constant speed. Glass plates of differing thickness can be used in an adjustable mounting board

Fig. 5.3. Camag spreader (with permission of Camag, Muttenz, Switzerland).

References on p. A190

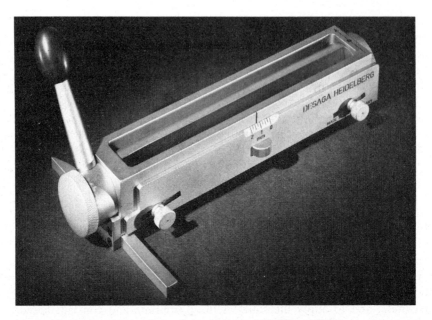

Fig. 5.4. Desaga spreader (with permission of Desaga, Heidelberg, GFR).

(Shandon Unoplan leveller). For laboratories using a large number of plates daily, partly or fully automated apparatus is recommended [80,81].

Twin layers (adjacent layers) and gradient layers require special spreading techniques. Twin layers in most cases consist of two layers, one of which is made of a more active and the other one of a less active sorbent (cf. Chap. 5.3). Such layers are rather easily prepared by inserting a barrier into the applicator. The applicator for gradient layers, as described by Stahl [82], is a little more complicated. Using this device, it is possible to prepare layers with an activity gradient either parallel or perpendicular to the direction of the development. In addition to gradients made from two sorbents, it can also be used to prepare pH gradients.

Among other methods of layer preparation, dipping of the support into a suspension of sorbents, usually in organic solvents, should be mentioned. This technique is very useful for the coating of small plates, such as microscope slides [83] or of glass rods [84]. The spraying [85,86] and pouring [87] techniques, and the spreading of dry sorbents (for nonadhering layers [88]) are now more rarely employed.

Layers prepared by any of these methods are air-dried. For silica gel layers, heating to 100°C for about 1 h is recommended. The properties of the layers are considerably influenced by the relative humidity, not only during the development, but also during storage [89].

5.4.2.4. Impregnation

Although chemically bonded stationary phases are now generally preferred, the impregnation of sorbents is still widely practiced. Sorbent impregnation serves mainly to modify sorption properties. This includes impregnation with ion-exchanging materials and liquid stationary phases. Not only hydrophilic or hydrophobic organic solvents may be held stationary, but also salts or buffers that modify the pH of the stationary phase. The impregnation is usually carried out by adding the appropriate compound to the sorbent during slurry preparation. Alternatively, layers may be impregnated by chromatographic development with the appropriate liquid medium or by exposure to vapors [90].

Soap chromatography [91], involving the addition of a detergent to silanized or reversed-phase silica gel, is said to improve the separation of, e.g., organic bases. In ion-pair chromatography, counterions, e.g., in the form of tetraalkylammonium salts, are incorporated in the sorbent. Various other compounds that interact with some components of the sample may be incorporated in the stationary phase. Most popular in this respect are silver nitrate (argentation chromatography) [93] or urea. Also, certain detection reagents may be added to the stationary phase to facilitate quantitative analysis (sulfates, phosphomolybdate, etc.). Finally, compounds may be incorporated that bind impurities in either the sorbent or in the sample, which would otherwise interfere with the chromatographic analysis (complex-forming reagents, antioxidants, etc.) [94].

5.4.3. Solvent systems

The choice of a suitable mobile phase is dictated by the stationary phase. After having selected the sorbent for adsorption chromatography (silica gel, alumina, etc.), the criteria for mobile phase selection are analogous to those applied in column adsorption chromatography. All organic compounds, including solvents, may be

TABLE 5.1

ELUOTROPIC SOLVENT SERIES

Water	Phenol
Formamide	n-Butanol
Methanol	n-Amyl alcohol
Dimethyl sulfoxide	Ethyl acetate
Acetic acid	Diethyl ether
Acetonitrile	n-Butyl acetate
Dimethyl formamide	Chloroform
Ethanol	Benzene
Isopropanol	Toluene
Acetone	Cyclohexane
n-Propanol	Petroleum ether
t-Butanol	Paraffin oil

References on p. A190

classified on the basis of their ability to form hydrogen bonds. Arranged according to this property, solvents from a series which was called the eluotropic series by Trappe (Table 5.1). At the beginning of this series there are solvents that are either donors or acceptors of electron pairs and have the ability to form intermolecular hydrogen bridges (hydrophilic or polar solvents), whereas at the end of the series we find solvents lacking this property (hydrophobic, lipophilic, or nonpolar solvents). Between these two extremes there is a continuous transition formed by solvents of intermediate polarity. The solvents in the first part of Table 5.1 up to t-butanol are miscible with water in all proportions, whereas the remaining solvents form two layers with water.

The mobility of the ionizable substances is influenced not only by the nature of the above solvents or their combinations, but also by the pH value of the system. In most cases, it is necessary to select a multicomponent mobile phase for development. In planar chromatography (in contrast to column chromatography) mobile-phase gradients are formed during development, as hydrophilic solvents are preferentially sorbed by hydrophilic sorbents [95]. This is detrimental to the reproducibility of chromatographic separations, but it may be exploited for improving the separations. Deliberately regulated mobile-phase gradients are only rarely used in TLC [96]. Some improvement in achieving a constant composition of the mobile phase can be realized by using azeotropic solvent mixtures [97]. In adsorption chromatography, attention must be paid to the relative humidity during development and to the composition of the vapor phase above the layer [3,98].

When the sorbent mainly serves as the carrier for the stationary phase (cellulose, kieselguhr, and occasionally silica gel), the main types of partition chromatography systems fall into three groups:

(a) Aqueous stationary phase. In this type of system, water is held stationary on the carrier, and the mobile phase, which is usually immiscible with water, passes through. The sorbent holds some of the water from the preparation of the layer and also takes up water from the atmosphere (e.g., silica and cellulose are hygroscopic).

(b) Stationary hydrophilic organic solvent. The stationary solvent is usually a solvent of low volatility, e.g., propylene glycol or formamide. This solvent is diluted with a more volatile organic solvent, e.g., methanol or acetone, and the carrier is impregnated in the manner described in Chap. 5.4.2.4.

(c) Reversed phases. In this type of system a hydrophobic solvent is held stationary by impregnation or, more often, a hydrophobic solvent is chemically bound to the sorbent, usually silica gel [99,100]. A hydrophilic mobile phase then passes over it. In this case, of course, the sequence of chromatographic zones is the reverse of that found in (a) and (b).

A special case of reversed phases is the so-called ion-pair chromatography, which is applied mainly for separating strongly basic compounds. In this process, basic compounds migrate as uncharged ion pairs, if a suitable inorganic (e.g., bromide or chloride) or organic (e.g., heptanesulfonic acid) counterion is present in adequate amounts in the mobile phase [101,102].

When ion exchangers are used as sorbents, the mobile phases consist of acids, bases, or buffer solutions. In gel chromatography, the mobile phases are mainly appropriate buffer solutions. In some cases, the separation of macromolecules is improved by the presence of mild (e.g., sodium deoxycholate) or denaturing (e.g., sodium docecyl sulfate) detergents [103].

5.4.4. Tank and development

The next step in chromatographic practice is the choice of the chamber and direction of development. The mobile phase may either rise in the layer (ascending technique), flow downward (descending technique), or flow horizontally (horizontal and radial techniques). In TLC, ascending chromatography is most frequently used, and development continues to be carried out in the glass tanks originally suggested by Stahl [104], measuring $6 \times 21 \times 21$ cm, with a ground upper edge and a plate glass cover. The mobile phase covers the bottom up to a height of about 0.5 cm. In this arrangement, the so-called normal saturation occurs. Often, authors recommend lining the walls of the jar with filter paper, which is saturated with the mobile phase. Ascending development stops automatically when the mobile phase reaches the

Fig. 5.5. Camag Sandwich chamber (with permission of Camag, Muttenz, Switzerland).

References on p. A190

upper edge of the layer, which may be prescored with a needle or pencil point. There are also tanks allowing parallel chromatography of a large number of plates and chambers for development of two plates in different solvent systems (twin-trough) [105]. For chromatography at fixed temperatures (-50 to $+50°C$), jacketed chambers must be used (Desaga Thermo-chamber) [82].

The so-called sandwich chambers or S-chambers (Fig. 5.5) are formed by the glass plate with the sorbent layer and a parallel cover plate. Either a three-sided frame is inserted between the two plates, separating them by a 2-mm free space, or the cover plate is already supplied with an attached narrow glass frame. Both plates are clamped together by means of bulldog clips and placed, with the open end downward, into a trough containing the mobile phase. The advantages of these small-volume chambers are low solvent consumption and more reproducible saturation.

Chambers for horizontal development are also useful. For fast analysis, a pocket TLC chamber (Scilab, Schaffhausen, Switzerland) has been introduced. Some authors prefer the more or less complicated horizontal chambers, such as the Brenner–Niederwieser (BN-)chamber [106], the Vario-KS-chamber [107], and the VP-chamber [108]. These chambers give more reproducible results and more perfect separations,

Fig. 5.6. U-chamber for HPTLC (with permission of Camag, Muttenz, Switzerland).

mainly by making use of gradients of the mobile phase, stationary phase, or vapors. Lately, these gradients have been supplemented by temperature gradients. The success of HPLC led to the application of high pressure in TLC. This technique is also referred to as over-pressured TLC [109]. Descending development is used only rarely in TLC [71].

In the last few years, chambers for HPTLC have attracted a great deal of attention. Generally speaking, the high performance effect is due mainly to the sorbents used. Conventional chambers for TLC can be used for development, but smaller chambers are preferred. Several types of commercial HPTLC chambers are on the market, both for linear [110] and radial (Camag U-chamber, Fig. 5.6) [5] development. Such chambers offer better reproducibility of R_F values. The separation process is also influenced by the fact that these chambers allow both an equilibration before the development and a choice of flowrates for the mobile phase. Although comparative studies indicate that radial development apparently gives better results, most laboratories prefer linear development for HPTLC [41].

5.4.4.1. Multiple chromatography

Multiple chromatography includes all procedures in which the development is repeated after one development is completed and the sorbent has evaporated.

5.4.4.1.1. Multiple development. The chromatogram is repeatedly developed in the same direction, and thus complete resolution of two or more substances with closely similar R_F values may be obtained. As the mobile phase, one may use either the same solvent system or different solvent systems. A frequently used modification of this technique is a stepwise procedure, in which the first development runs a shorter distance than the second one. The first development with a more polar mobile phase separates the more polar substances, while the less polar substances migrate with the solvent front. The less polar substances are then separated in the second development with a less polar mobile phase. An improvement of multiple development is the so-called programmed multiple development (PMD) [111]. In this technique the plate is automatically cycled through a preset number of developments and subsequent drying periods.

5.4.4.1.2. Two-dimensional chromatography. This method is based on multiple development, analogous to the previous one, but with the difference that a square layer is used, the sample is applied near one corner, and the second development is carried out in a direction at right angles to the first one [14]. The method is suitable mainly for the separation of complex mixtures of compounds. In the usual arrangement, different types of solvent systems are used in each of the two directions: thus, e.g., one may use an acidic mobile phase in the first direction and a basic one in the second; or one may use solvents that are electron acceptors and electron donors; or may even choose to use different separation mechanisms in the two directions (e.g., adsorption and partition) [112,113]. The nature of interactions may be altered by changing the composition of the stationary phase: Vidrine and Nicholas [114]

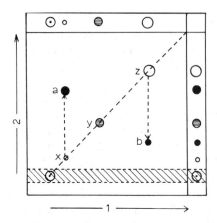

Fig. 5.7. Principle of diagonal chromatography. Reagent is applied to shaded area between two developments. *a* is formed from *x*, *y* does not react (it is situated on the diagonal), *b* is formed from *z* [118].

employed a mixture of silica gel and silanized silica gel for two-dimensional TLC. With an aqueous mobile phase, the reversed-phase partition effect on silanized silica gel was governing the separation, while in a nonaqueous system the predominant mechanism was adsorption on the nonsilanized silica gel. By using twin layers of silica gel and silica gel with silver nitrate in a two-dimensional arrangement, one can distinguish, e.g., lipids according to molecular size in one direction and according to the number of double bonds in the second direction [115].

A special case of two-dimensional chromatography is the diagonal technique [116]. In this technique, the chromatogram is developed with the same solvent system in both dimensions (Fig. 5.7). Substances which do not undergo chemical change during chromatography will be situated on the diagonal of the chromatogram. This method is mainly used for further characterization of spots in the chromatogram by performing certain chemical, biological, or photochemical reactions between the two developments. This method is known as reaction chromatography or SRS (TRT) technique [117,118].

5.4.4.1.3. "Multidimensional" planar chromatography. In this type of development, a spot is repeatedly transferred after development in one dimension by attaching or applying it (e.g., by the dry transfer technique [119]) to the origin of a new chromatogram, and then developed anew.

5.4.4.1.4. Homochromatography. This name is given to TLC combined with electrophoresis. After electrophoresis on a cellulose acetate strip, the band is transferred to a DEAE-cellulose layer and subjected to chromatography in a second dimension. Very good results have been obtained with this technique in the field of nucleic acid components [120–122].

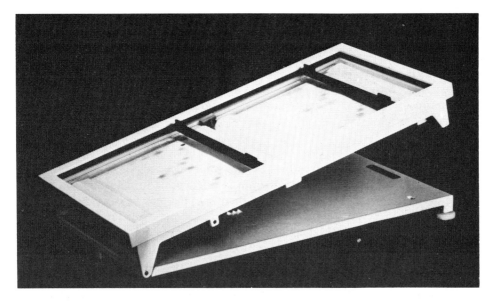

Fig. 5.8. Chamber for gel TLC (with permission of Pharmacia, Uppsala, Sweden).

5.4.4.2. Special procedures

5.4.4.2.1. Overrun development. Solvent overrun is not as widely practiced in TLC as in PC. In order to make the mobile phase overrun after reaching the upper edge of the layer, it is necessary to place an additional amount of sorbent there to soak up the solvents [123] or to make a slit into the tank cover, letting the upper part of the layer protrude from the chamber to ensure evaporation of the solvents [124]. A simpler arrangement, analogous to descending PC, makes use of the ready-made layers in roll form [71].

5.4.4.2.2. Gel thin-layer chromatography. For gel TLC, the classical TLC chamber cannot be used, because the gel layer is kept in loose form and, moreover, it is unable to imbibe the mobile phase. A sloping chamber (Fig. 5.8) for descending development, adjustable to any angle between 10 and 45° from the level position, has been designed for gels. The mobile phase is introduced into the gel through a strip of filter paper [125]. However, for special silica gels, organic copolymers, or sintered gels, the conventional TLC chambers can be used.

5.4.4.2.3. Other techniques. Temperature may influence chromatographic development. Moreover, low temperatures (down to −77°C) [126] will minimize the decomposition of samples during development, and high temperatures (up to 160°C) [127] will increase their solubility in the mobile phase.
  Centrifugal TLC (Chromatotron, Harrison, Palo Alto, CA, USA) not only speeds

up development, but tends to sharpen chromatographic zones, and it can be scaled up for preparative purposes. Conversely, very small amounts of sample (less than ppb) may be concentrated by centripetal chromatography [128,129] in combination with, e.g., GC. When dilute samples are applied to the periphery of a rotated thin-layer disc, the mobile phase evaporates and the sample, which is concentrated at the center of the disc, can be passed into a gas chromatograph.

5.4.5. Detection

Since most substances resolved by TLC are colorless, methods must be found for detecting them. Usually, the chromatogram is dried prior to detection in order to remove the residues of solvents from the sorbent. Drying may be carried out at room temperature or at elevated temperatures in drying cabinets. For the visualization of spots, one can use physical, chemical, or biological detection methods. As far as detection is concerned, TLC offers more possibilities than column chromatography. Thus, for instance, there are hundreds of chemical detection methods, from general to selective and specific reagents, which increase the reliability of the chromatographic identification. The sensitivity of a number of reagents allows the qualitative analysis of compounds in the nanogram and even picogram range. Many TLC detection methods are nondestructive and permit further analysis of the separated substances [130].

5.4.5.1. Physical detection methods

Not only the absorption of visible light (color), but also the absorption of UV light allows nondestructive detection. A large number of organic compounds exhibit absorption at 254 nm (short-wave UV). They will appear as areas of quenching on the fluorescent background of layers prepared with addition of fluorophores. Many organic substances will show a fluorescence after irradiation with UV light from a high-pressure mercury vapor lamp (long-wave UV). Some nonfluorescent substances may also exhibit fluorescence when the layer is cooled to very low temperatures [131,132]. Other substances may show fluorescence after heating the chromatogram to high temperatures.

Derivatization reactions, resulting in the formation of fluorescent compounds, increase the sensitivity by several orders of magnitude and also increase the selectivity of the detection reactions. Derivatization may be performed either before applying the sample to the layer, or, more expeditiously, directly on the start of the chromatogram. This procedure is called fluorescence labeling [133,134]. With some reagents, derivatization is carried out after the chromatographic separation, as in other chemical detection methods. The best-known labeling reagent is 1-dimethylaminonaphthalene-5-sulfonyl chloride (dansyl chloride), which is relatively nonspecific. It reacts not only with primary and secondary amino groups, but also with phenolic hydroxyl and, in some cases, also with alcoholic hydroxyl groups. Direct fluorometry permits the determination of picomole amounts of dansyl-amides, making the sensitivity in TLC comparable to the sensitivity of GC detectors. A more selective reagent is fluorescamine, which gives a positive reaction only with primary amines [135]. This reagent is in most cases applied after the chromatographic development. An analogous reagent is o-phthalaldehyde, which, in the presence of a strong reducing reagent, such as 2-mercaptoethanol, produces highly fluorescent compounds [136].

The application of lasers for fluorescence excitation is also worth mentioning. During laser scanning of a chromatogram, some compounds exhibit fluorescence at very low levels (in the subnanogram range), and the emission may be viewed by a photomultiplier [137].

Scattered reports on the use of the FID [84] have gained importance after the Iatroscan TH-10 apparatus was introduced [138]. In this method, a layer is deposited on a glass rod with the aid of sintered glass. After development and thorough evaporation of the mobile phase, the layer is moved at constant speed through the flame of a FID. Similarly, layers in tubular form may be heated in the presence of oxygen, expecially if CuO has been incorporated into the layer. In the presence of CuO, the products of pyrolysis and oxidation are completely oxidized to CO_2, which is reduced to methane by hydrogen and determined by means of a FID, in analogy to Scott's moving wire detector (see Chap. 4.10.2) [139,140]. One of the most sensitive physical methods is based on conductivity measurements, which permit the detection of inorganic compounds on ultra-thin layers at subnanogram levels [141].

Compounds labeled with radioactive isotopes are detectable on layers by either autoradiography or scanning methods [142].

5.4.5.2. Chemical detection methods

Depending on the reaction of the substances with the reagents, the chemical detection methods give black, colored, or fluorescent (see above) zones. The reagent is usually applied by spraying and, occasionally, by exposing the chromatogram to vapors or by drawing it through a solution of the reagent. For spraying, atomizers of various types or aerosol sprays (Shandon Spray Gun) are used. After the application of the reagent, the chromatogram is dried in a draft hood or drying cabinet, or warmed in an incubator or chromatography oven or on a hot-plate.

A great number of detection reagents has been described, and recipes for their preparation can be found in various texts [1,7,9,11]. Among the general reagents, we must at least mention charring with sulfuric acid at elevated temperature when inorganic sorbents are used. Alternatively, sulfates, incorporated directly into the layer, will liberate sulfuric acid on heating [143]. Sulfuric acid detects all but the volatile organic compounds. Iodine vapors also detect many organic compounds, but in contrast, they are usually not destroyed by the reagent. Among the group reagents, ninhydrin is used to reveal the presence of the primary amino groups; chlorination, potassium iodide, and starch for secondary amines; Dragendorff's reagent or iodoplatinate for tertiary or quaternary amino groups; p-dimethylamino-benzaldehyde for aromatic amino groups or indole rings; 2,4-dinitrophenylhydrazine for oxo compounds, etc.

5.4.5.3. Enzymatic and biological detection methods

Enzymatic methods are employed either for the detection of enzymes or for the detection of substrates. In the first case, the procedure is carried out in such a way that, e.g., for the detection of amylases, the layer is sprayed with a starch solution, incubated for a suitable period, and then sprayed with an iodine solution. The amylases will appear as white spots on a blue background. As an example of the second type, pesticides may be detected by enzymatic inhibition [144,145]. They are resolved by TLC, sprayed with an enzyme solution, and then sprayed with an enzyme substrate solution. The sensitivity of such procedures lies in the nanogram range.

In bioautography [146,147] based on growth inhibition, the chromatogram is, e.g., sprayed with an agar medium, and another agar medium, seeded with test organisms, is poured over the surface of the prepared plate. The plate is then incubated at a suitable temperature. Microorganisms that are sensitive to the substance analyzed grow all over the plate, with the exception of areas containing the test substances. In the variant which, by contrast, is based on growth promotion, the chromatogram is placed on a seeded agar medium that is complete, except for the factor to be determined. After incubation, the plate is examined for areas of growth.

Detection methods based on certain biological effects on higher organisms (e.g., insects) are used only in exceptional cases (e.g., pheromones).

5.4.6. Quantitative analysis

In contrast to the column techniques, where quantitative determinations are performed outside the chromatographic system, in TLC the analysis is usually carried out in situ. Older methods of quantitative analysis after elution are now used more rarely, because elution from the layer is more laborious and may be less accurate. Several monographs [6,15,148] and reviews [140,149–154] have been devoted to quantitative analysis.

5.4.6.1. In situ methods

The most commonly used methods utilize the relation between concentration and the area, length, color intensity, fluorescence, or UV absorption of zones. The simplest in situ method is the visual comparison of the spot size and intensity with a standard or with a standard series of known concentrations which, in practice, should be done for every evaluation of a chromatogram. However, this procedure is only semiquantitative.

For quantitative analysis, color intensity, absorption, fluorescence, and area of zones are evaluated with a densitometer. In this instrument the layer is drawn automatically past a slit, positioned in front of a photocell. Another version makes use of two-dimensional scanning (zig-zag scanning, flying-spot scanning) [155]. For the photometric estimation, either the reflectance (remission) or the transmission are measured.

There is no general agreement about the relative merits of measuring reflected and transmitted light [156,157]. Photometry in transmitted light offers higher sensitivity, but the noise caused by the inhomogeneity of the layer increases the error of the analysis. With transmitted light the response follows Lambert–Beer's law, if the conditions are idealized. With reflected light, the response is described by Kubelka–Munk's equation which, according to Pollak (ref. 6, p. 11), may be approximated by the linear dependence of concentration on the reciprocal of reflectance. Since even in transmitted light the range of linearity of the concentration versus absorbance plot is not very large, the advantage of transmitted light is of little importance in practice. By using computers [158,159] it is possible to transform the signal according to the Kubelka–Munk equation and filter off part of the noise before integration to obtain the concentration. Computers are now also used for some other steps in the quantitative analysis [160].

However, no matter whether transmission or remission measurements are used, a very noisy baseline is always obtained, and this, of course, influences the accuracy of the estimation. Several authors [161,162] have tried to solve this problem by simultaneous detection of the reflected and transmitted radiation and by compensation corrections of the reflectance curve. As a result of these simultaneous measurements, the detection limit is improved by a factor of 10 to 100, so that nanogram amounts can be accurately determined.

Numerous scanners are currently on the market [21–23]. They enable photometric estimation of colored substances, and most of them allow the estimation of UV-absorbing compounds without detection reactions. As TLC is carried out in many cases in a sorbent layer containing a fluorescent indicator, a 254-nm light source, under which the indicator shows a green fluorescence, is used for photometry. Substances that absorb generally in this region will decrease the fluorescence intensity. This measurement is called fluorescence quenching. The UV spectrophotometers are sensitive and selective and give reliable results, but they are relatively expensive. As in HPLC, in TLC incompletely separated substances may also be analyzed by their absorption at two different wavelengths [163,164]. Because it is more sensitive, fluorometry is gaining in popularity. It requires the conversion of nonfluorescent compounds into fluorescent derivatives, either before chromatography or afterwards, directly on the layer (see Chap. 5.4.5.1).

The sensitivity of spectrophotometers and spectrofluorometers is in the nanogram range, rarely in the picogram range. It is thus equivalent to the sensitivity of CC, particularly in HPTLC [165]. The accuracy of the assay depends to a considerable extent on the quality of the sorbent and of the layer. In most cases, better reproducibility is achieved with commercially available plates or films. Equally important for accuracy is the technique of spotting the sample solution on the start line. For proper comparison of the peak areas of analytes and standards, all spots must have an identical shape and relative mass distribution. This is best achieved by applying identical volumes of the analyte and standard samples and by using pipettes with reproducible flowrates. Accuracy in measuring the spotted volume is another requirement for quantitative TLC, especially as internal standards of the type which are often used in GC are not common in TLC. Because a large number

References on p. A190

of samples can be chromatographed side by side, several standards of various concentration may be applied to provide, in essence, a calibration graph for every chromatogram. Under these conditions, the accuracy of the assays is around 1–2%.

Among the nonphotometric procedures, the application of FID to quantitative analysis should be mentioned (cf. Chap. 5.4.5.1). Also, the application of flow-through detectors has been described. Schmid et al. [166] used a continuous photometric detector and Pastuska et al. [167] exploited the temperature effects produced by the adsorption and desorption of compounds during development. None of these methods are commonly used.

For continuous scanning of radioactivity [142], various instruments are available. In most cases, a windowless flow-counter in the proportional range is used. Alternatively, if position-sensitive radiometric sensors are used, the whole radiochromatogram can be counted simultaneously.

5.4.6.2. Quantitative analysis outside the layer

Methods of quantitative analysis outside the layer are essentially the same as the current methods of microanalysis. The only step characteristic for TLC is the transfer of the analyte from the sorbent to the medium in which it is going to be measured. After a nondestructive detection of the compound on the chromatogram (by UV light, iodine, or the so-called hot-line technique [168]), the spot, together with the sorbent, is removed from the layer. The transfer is effected either manually by scraping off the layer or by the application of suction. Because this operation is time-consuming, especially when the number of samples is large, automatic zonal scrapers have been devised [169,170]. These methods are mainly used prior to radiometric estimation of labeled compounds by liquid scintillation counting. The presence of silica gel does not interfere with the measurement, though it is of advantage to use a scintillation cocktail which desorbs the analyte from the silica gel and dissolves it. In some cases, these procedures are also used in the combination of different chromatographic techniques, e.g., in coupling TLC with GC quantitation. Such methods avoid elution from the layer, which is always time-consuming and a source of error. As examples, elution of polar substances with a trimethylsilylating reagent or elution with concomitant methylation may be mentioned [171,172].

5.4.7. Preparative layer chromatography

Preparative layer chromatography (PLC) is a very popular technique for obtaining milligram to gram amounts of substances [173]. Compared to classical column chromatography, PLC is faster and consumes less solvents, the optimum conditions for a particular separation are easier to estimate, it is easier to detect compounds directly on the layer, and in many cases even the resolution is better. Compared to preparative HPLC, by far the main advantage of PLC is economical. Disadvantages are that the separated substances may decompose, owing to the large surface exposed to the atmosphere and that one must ultimately separate the compounds from the layer.

As far as the technique is concerned, there is not much difference between PLC and analytical TLC [174]. The main difference is in the layer thickness. Best results are achieved on layers measuring between 0.5 and 2 mm. Thicker layers are useful only for very rough fractionations of substances differing considerably in their R_F values. The commonly used plate sizes, 20×20 cm or 20×40 cm, are recommended, but for the separation of larger amounts long plates, up to 20×100 cm, appear to be more suitable. A perfect layer is an essential condition for successful separations by PLC. Cracking, which occurs during drying, and lack of binding strength are the most common mishaps. Good results are obtained with ready-for-use plates (Merck PSC-Fertigplatten Kieselgel F_{254}) with a layer thickness of 2 mm.

The sample solution should be as concentrated as possible (2–10%). The samples are applied about 2.5 cm from the lower edge of the plate usually in streak form. The simplest method of sample streaking employs a pipette and a ruler. Usually, up to 10 ml of solution may be thus applied. Commercially available streakers can also be used, or a groove can be made in the layer and filled with sorbent or slurry containing the sample.

If the zones are too broad after a single development, resolution may be improved by repeated development. After development, zones may be detected in UV light, after exposure to iodine vapors, spraying with water, or by applying chemical detection methods to the sides of the chromatographic plate. After the substances are located, the individual bands are scraped off with a spatula or aspirated by means of devices based on the vacuum cleaner principle. For the elution of substances from isolated zones the sorbent is usually transferred to a chromatographic tube, provided with a sintered glass filter and percolated with a suitable solvent.

5.5. PAPER CHROMATOGRAPHY

The major advances in PC occurred in the Fifties. Today this technique is eclipsed by the faster, more efficient, and more sensitive method of TLC. Still, about 4% of all chromatographic publications are devoted to PC. It is applied mainly to compounds of hydrophilic nature, such as oligosaccharides, peptides, nucleotides, phenolic compounds, and inorganic ions.

5.5.1. Paper

Though a large variety of papers, based on both cellulose and fiber glass [9,175] have been marketed for PC in the past, the selection of papers that have withstood the test of time is now very limited. In practice, we encounter in the literature only the so-called standard cellulose papers (Whatman No. 1 and Schleicher and Schüll 2043b), thicker papers for preparative applications (Whatman No. 31 ET and 3 MM), and glass-fiber papers containing silica gel, which are marketed under the misleading name "Instant Thin Layers" [176]. Some other papers are used in exceptional cases, and we shall mention them only briefly. Standard cellulose papers are available mainly in rectangular or circular sheets, wedge-shaped strips, and papers with multiple strips, slots, etc. Standard papers are supplied in smooth form, acid-washed, or free of lipid-soluble substances. For certain applications to the separation of substances with polar character, papers with increased ion-exchange capacity have been introduced (papers containing ion-exchange resins and various cellulose ion-exchange papers) [177]. For the separation of hydrophobic substances, kieselguhr filter papers, acetylated papers, and silicone-treated papers have been recommended. Some other papers contain adsorbents, such as alumina or silica gel. In addition to cellulose papers, glass-fiber papers have been introduced in the market [176]. The application of membrane ultra-filters, which are used mainly as carrier material in the separation of macromolecules, is rather rare [178].

5.5.2. Solvent systems

The selection of solvent systems is, in principle, subject to the same rules as those summarized in Chap. 5.4.3 for partition TLC. Because in PC there is much less opportunity for varying the stationary phase than in TLC and because partition prevails, solvent systems where the stationary phase constitutes a polar organic solvent for normal or nonpolar solvents for reversed-phase partition chromatography are much more extensively used. In contrast to TLC, these solvents are anchored on paper by impregnation.

(a) In the category of solvent systems with stationary aqueous phase, perhaps the most popular is n-butanol–acetic acid–water (BAW) (4:1:5). This and other two-phase systems are prepared by shaking the components together in a separatory funnel. Both phases are used to saturate the atmosphere inside the tank, and the less hydrophilic phase serves for development. The paper is not generally impregnated with the aqueous phase, although this may be recommended in some cases [179]. The paper takes up water from the atmosphere when it is suspended in a closed chamber where the atmosphere is saturated with water vapor. If an aqueous buffer solution or salt solution is to be used as the stationary phase, the paper is drawn through this solution, allowed to dry, and then the same procedure is followed as the one just described. The most frequently used basic system is 2-propanol–ammonia–water (9:1:2).

(b) A very popular category of solvent systems employs polar organic solvents as the stationary phase. While volatile solvents, such as methanol, are no longer used, nonvolatile solvents, such as formamide or propylene glycol (Zaffaroni-type systems) still find application. These solvents are diluted with a volatile organic solvent (methanol, ethanol, or acetone) and the paper is drawn through this solution. It is then allowed to hang in air until the diluent has evaporated. Chromatograms are developed with suitable mobile phases, such as chloroform, benzene, cyclohexane (or their mixtures). This type of system has a number of advantages over aqueous systems. It allows the separation of compounds with a rather broad range of polarities, it has a much higher separating efficiency for both, members of homologous series and analogous compounds, and it produces regular spots in a relatively short time.

(c) In the reversed-phase systems a hydrophobic solvent is held stationary on the paper, and the hydrophilic mobile phase passes over it. The method of impregnation is as described under (b). Kerosene or paraffin oil may serve as stationary phase, while aqueous alcohols may be used as mobile phases.

Among other types of solvent systems, we should mention the impregnation of paper with liquid ion exchangers [180,181], which produces very successful separations of inorganic compounds.

5.5.3. Tank and development

Numerous publications have been devoted to techniques of development in PC. Nevertheless, individual modifications usually have no pronounced effect on the chromatographic separation. Descending chromatography, originally described by the inventors of PC [182], is still the most frequently used technique, in contrast to TLC. The apparatus consists of a well-sealed tank, which is provided with a trough for the mobile phase in its upper section. The troughs are usually made of glass, but may be also made of porcelain, steel, or plastics. The paper, to which the sample has been applied, is inserted with the upper end in the trough, and may be equilibrated with the atmosphere in the tank for a certain period before the mobile phase is introduced into the trough or, more frequently, development is started immediately. For serial determinations, in which from three to eight samples must be simultaneously developed on one paper strip, glass tanks in the form of cylinders or square boxes are used. The trough containing the mobile phase is mounted inside the tank on a stand or on glass rods which may be supported, e.g., in notches. Tanks that are wider above a point about 10 cm below the upper edge are very useful, because the trough can be supported without a stand. For the separation of a large number of samples or for two-dimensional chromatography, large steel cabinets with metal framework and glass walls are used.

The application of ascending development is less frequent. The main advantage of this type of development is that it requires no special apparatus. The same tanks as those for descending development, but without stands and troughs, may be used. The paper with the samples can be suspended from the lid or can be made to stand up on the bottom of the tank in the mobile phase by rolling it into a cylinder, held together by staples, string, or plastic clips. Even stoppered test tubes can be used as chromatographic chambers. For the simultaneous development of several sheets, especially in two-dimensional chromatography, special frames have been constructed [183,184].

Horizontal development requires very little space. The chamber can be easily placed into an incubator or refrigerator. The chamber may be made from a shallow glass, metal, or plastic container, and the chromatogram is laid horizontally on glass rods [185] or synthetic fibers. Horizontal development can also be carried out on paper between two glass [186] or aluminum [187] plates, especially when volatile substances are chromatographed.

A special case of horizontal development is radial development [188]. It is based on the migration of the sample from the center of the paper toward the periphery.

Small tanks may be fashioned from two Petri dishes, one inverted over the other. The filter paper disc with the applied sample is stretched between the two dishes, and the mobile phase is fed in through a wick from the bottom dish to the center of the point of application. For larger chambers, desiccators can be used, in which the paper is stretched between the cover and the lower part. The mobile phase is either applied to the center of the paper through a wick from the bottom of the desiccator, or it is allowed to drip from the top through a microburet. An improvement over the application of the sample in the form of a spot is the chromatography in sectors [189], where the samples are applied around the periphery of a circle about 2 cm in diameter and where the solvent system is admitted to the center of this circle.

5.5.4. Detection

For the detection of compounds on a paper chromatogram all procedures that have been described in the section on TLC (Chap. 5.4.5) are made use of, except for the application of corrosive reagents (e.g., sulfuric acid) to filter paper.

5.5.5. Quantitative analysis

The methods of quantitative analysis are also very similar to those described for TLC (Chap. 5.4.6). In PC, the results of semiquantitative analysis in situ are slightly better than in TLC. In this method the size and color intensity of the sample zones are compared with those of a dilution series of standards. This method gives more accurate results when the samples of standards are applied in decreasing concentration (e.g., $30, 20, 10$ μg) and the test substance alternates with the standards in increasing concentration ($10, 20, 30$ μg).

The methods of eluting compounds from paper are slightly different from those used in TLC. Unless the substance is colored, fluorescent, or UV-absorbing, the usual procedure is as follows. The test substance is applied in three or more places at the origin of the chromatogram, and after development is completed, pilot strips are cut off on both sides and stained. On the basis of the position of the spots in the pilot chromatograms, the corresponding spots on the unstained aper are then cut out and eluted with a suitable solvent. This is usually done by cutting the paper strip to a point and eluting it between two microscope slides [190] or by a method analogous to descending chromatographic development.

5.6. IDENTIFICATION OF SUBSTANCES BY THIN-LAYER AND PAPER CHROMATOGRAPHY

In TLC and PC, substances are identified primarily on the basis of their mobility in suitable solvent systems [7,14,191] and, in addition, on the basis of their reactions with selective or specific detection reagents or on the basis of their absorption or fluorescence in UV light. The mobility is expressed by the R_F values, hR_F ($= 100 \times R_F$) values, or by the relative mobilities, R_X values (distance migrated by the substance over that of a reference compound, X). Though R_F values may be considered constant under strictly defined conditions [192,193], this is hardly the case in ordinary laboratory practice. R_F values are, therefore, to be regarded merely as guides that give information on the approximate mobility of substances under examination.

For actual identification, no reliance should be placed on tables of R_F values, and the mobility of an unknown substance must be compared with that of a reference compound on the same chromatogram. If the mobilities are different, the two compounds must be different. If they are the same, it may be assumed that the two substances are possibly identical. More positive identification may be made after the substance has been compared with the reference compound in two or more systems that are different in character or are based on different principles (e.g., TLC and GC). Furthermore, the relationship between structure and chromatographic behavior of the sample can also be utilized.

The coupling of chromatography with spectrometric methods also confirms identification. In the simplest form, the UV spectra are determined directly on the layer or paper by a spectrophotometric densitometer (e.g., Zeiss Chromatogram Spectralphotometer, KM-3). IR spectroscopy is usually carried out on the eluate, but spectrometry of reflected light is also feasible in situ [194]. For the identification of compounds the combination of TLC with mass spectrometry is very useful. In this case, the technique of transferring the compound to the mass spectrometer is important [195]. For the separation of the sorbent from the eluate, filtration and absorption in potassium bromide may be used [196,197]. Potassium bromide does not interfere with mass spectrometry. Another possibility is to heat the spot of the compound with the sorbent on a quartz plate from beneath by a hydrogen–oxygen flame [198]. The compound is evaporated or sublimed and introduced by an inert gas into the mass spectrometer. Also, instruments usable for compounds with the sorbent have been described [199,200]. The compound is sublimed and enters the ionization chamber of the mass spectrometer directly.

Further confirmation of the identity of a given substance is furnished by various reactions of the substance either before it is applied directly to the layer or paper or at the starting line before or during chromatographic development. When two spots of the same substance are applied to the origin and one of them has been subjected to a chemical reaction, subsequent chromatographic development can give a very simple demonstration of whether or not and in what way a substance has reacted [118]. Also, diagonal chromatography (see Chap. 5.4.4.1.2) may yield information about the reactivity of a compound. Some of the reactions that can be carried out on layers or paper are: oxidation, hydrogenation, acetylation, addition of halogens to double bonds, esterification, opening and closing of lactone rings, photolysis, hydrogenolysis, conversion of amines to fluorescent derivatives (see Chap. 5.4.5.1), and formation of other derivatives.

5.6.1. Systematic analysis

Systematic analysis provides identification of unknown substances within a certain group of substances [7]. Procedures of this kind may be classified into two groups. In one case, a series of data (R_F values in various systems and several detection reactions) are collected for an unknown compound and then compared with the same data for reference compounds, as a rule, with the aid of punched cards and sorting machines. In the second method, a prescribed scheme is followed step by step. The first procedure, which also includes the chromatographic "spectra" (or profiles) [201–204], calls for strict adherence to the analytical in order to obtain reproducible R_F values. Owing to the difficulties involved in this requirement, most authors prefer the second one. The usual procedure [7,205] is to chromatograph the test substance first in a general system and then to classify it according to its behavior on paper or layer as belonging to a certain group. Subsequently, it is identified within that group by comparison with reference substances, further, on the basis of several detection reactions and UV spectra in situ.

The development of diagnostic procedures in various fields related to chromatography may provide further types of computer programs for the identification of substances. The advantage of chromatography, and especially of the planar types, in such diagnostic procedures is the capability of characterizing a substance or a number of substances without first isolating them.

5.7. LIST OF SUPPLIERS

5.7.1. General equipment for thin-layer and paper chromatography

Analabs, Inc., 80 Republic Drive, North Haven, CT 06473, USA
Analtech, Inc., P.O. Box 7558, Newark, DE 19711, USA
Anspec Company, Inc., P.O. Box 7044, 122 Enterprise Drive, Ann Arbor, MI 48107, USA
Applied Science, P.O. Box 440, State College, PA 16801, USA
Applied Science Europe B.V., P.O. Box 1149, 3260 AC Oud-Beijerland, The Netherlands
Brinkman Instruments, Cantiague Road, Westbury, NY 11590, USA
Camag, P.O. Box 34, CH-4132 Muttenz, Switzerland
Chromatronix, Inc., 960 San Antonio Road, Palo Alto, CA 94306, USA
Desaga, GmbH, P.O. Box 407, D-69 Heidelberg 1, GFR
Drummond Scientific Company, 500 Parkway, Broomall, PA 19008, USA
Field Instruments Company, Queens House, Holly Road, Twickenham, Middlesex TW1 4EG, Great Britain
Fisher Scientific Company, 52 Fadem Road, Springfield, NJ 07081, USA
Gelman Sciences, Inc., 600 South Wagner Road, Ann Arbor, MI 48106, USA
Kontron Ltd., Bernerstrasse Süd 169, CH-8048 Zürich, Switzerland
Macherey-Nagel&Co., P.O. Box 307, D-5160 Düren, GFR
Pharmacia Fine Chemicals AB, Box 175, S-75104 Uppsala 1, Sweden
Quickfit Instrumentation, Stone, Staffs. ST15 OBG, Great Britain
Regis Chemical Company, 8210 Austin, Morton Grove, IL 60053, USA
Scilab Co., CH-8200 Schaffhausen, Switzerland

Shandon Southern Products Ltd, Chadwick Road, Astmoor, Runcorn, Cheshire, Great Britain
Supelco, Inc., Supelco Park, Bellefonte, PA 16823, USA

5.7.2. Scanners and related equipment for quantivative analysis

Camag
Desaga
Farrand Optical Co., Inc., 117 Wall Street, Valhalla, NY 10595, USA
Iatron Laboratories, Inc., Tokyo, Japan
Joyce, Loebl and Co., Ltd., Princesway, Team Valley, Gateshead, Co. Durham, Great Britain
Kontes, Spruce Street, Vineland, NJ 08360, USA
Kratos/Schoeffel Instruments, 24 Booker St., Westwood, NJ 07675, USA
Nuclear Chicago-Searle, 200 Nuclear Drive, Des Plaines, IL 60018, USA
Packard Instrument Co., Inc., 2200 Warrenville Road, Downers Grove, IL 60515, USA
Panax Nucleonics, Ltd., Trowers Way, Holme Thorpe Industrial Estate, Redhill, Surrey, Great Britain
Philips N.V., Eindhoven, The Netherlands
Photovolt Corp., 1115 Broadway, New York, NY 10010, USA
Sequoia-Turner, 755 Ravensdale Dr., Mountain View, CA 94043, USA
Shimadzu Corporation, 14-5, Uchikanda 1-chome, Chiyoda-ku, Tokyo 101, Japan
Shimadzu Scientific Instruments, Inc., 9147-H Red Branch Road, Columbia, MD 21045, USA
Vitatron Scientific B.V., P.O. Box 100, 6950 AC Dieren, The Netherlands
Zeiss, Carl, D-7082 Oberkochen, GFR

5.7.3. Sorbents, papers, and ready-for-use plates

Analabs
Applied Science
Baker Chemical Company, 222 Red School Lane, Phillipsburg, NJ 08865, USA
Bio-Rad Laboratories, 2200 Wright Avenue, Richmond, CA 94804, USA
Brinkman Instruments
Camag
Chromatronix
Chrompack Inc., P.O. Box 6795, Bridgewater, NJ 08807, USA
Chrompack Nederland B.V., Kuipersweg 6, Middelburg, The Netherlands
Desaga
Fisher Scientific Company
Gelman Sciences
Johns-Manville Corporation, Ken Caryl Ranch, Denver, CO 80217, USA
Koch-Light Laboratories, Inc., 2 Willow Road, Colnbrook, Slough SL3 OBZ, Great Britain

References on p. A190

Kontes
Macherey-Nagel & Co.
Mallinckrodt, Inc., 675 Brown Road, St. Louis, MO 63134, USA
Merck, E., P.O. Box 4119, 6100 Darmstadt 1, GFR
Pharmacia Fine Chemicals
Schleicher & Schuell AG, D-3354 Dassel, GFR
Serva Feinbiochemica, GmbH, P.O. Box 105260, D-6900 Heidelberg 1, GFR
Supelco
Whatman, Inc., Clifton, NJ 07014, USA
Whatman, Ltd., Springfield Mill, Maidstone, Kent, Great Britain
Woelm, M., D-3440 Eschwege, GFR

REFERENCES

1 E. Stahl (Editor), *Dünnschicht-Chromatographie*, Springer, Berlin, 2nd Edn., 1967.
2 J. Kirchner and E.S. Perry, *Thin-Layer Chromatography*, Wiley, New York, 2nd Edn., 1978.
3 F. Geiss, *Die Parameter der Dünnschichtchromatographie*, Vieweg, Braunschweig, 1972.
4 J.C. Touchstone and M.F. Dobbins, *Practice of Thin-Layer Chromatography*, Wiley, New York, 1978.
5 A. Zlatkis and R.E. Kaiser (Editors), *HPTLC — High Performance Thin-Layer Chromatography*, J. Chromatogr. Library Series, Vol. 9, Elsevier, Amsterdam, 1977.
6 J.C. Touchstone and J. Sherma (Editors), *Densitometry in TLC. Practice and Applications*, Wiley, New York, 1979.
7 K. Macek (Editor), *Pharmaceutical Applications of TLC and PC*, Elsevier, Amsterdam, 1972.
8 F. Cramer, *Papierchromatographie*, Verlag Chemie, Weinheim, 5th Edn., 1962.
9 I.M. Hais and K. Macek (Editors), *Paper Chromatography*, Academic Press, New York, 3rd Edn., 1964.
10 J. Sherma and G. Zweig, *Paper Chromatography*, Academic Press, New York, 1971.
11 G. Zweig and J. Sherma (Editors), *Handbook of Chromatography*, Vols. 1 and 2, CRC Press, Cleveland, OH, 1972.
12 I. Smith and J.W.T. Seakins, *Chromatographic and Electrophoretic Techniques*, Vol. 1, *Paper and Thin-Layer Chromatography*, Heinemann, London, 4th Edn., 1976.
13 J. Gasparič and J. Churaček, *Laboratory Handbook of Paper and Thin-Layer Chromatography*, Wiley, Chichester, 1978.
14 I.M. Hais, M. Lederer and K. Macek (Editors), *Identification of Substances by Paper and Thin-Layer Chromatography*, Elsevier, Amsterdam, 1970.
15 E.J. Shellard (Editor), *Quantitative Paper and Thin-Layer Chromatography*, Academic Press, London, 1968.
16 M. Lederer (Editor), *Chromatogr. Rev.*, Vols. 1–24, Elsevier, Amsterdam, 1959–1980.
17 G. Zweig and J. Sherma, *Anal. Chem.*, 46 (1974) 73R.
18 G. Zweig and J. Sherma, *Anal. Chem.*, 48 (1976) 66R.
19 G. Zweig and J. Sherma, *Anal. Chem.*, 50 (1978) 50R.
20 H.J. Issaq and E.W. Barr, *Anal. Chem.*, 49 (1977) 83A.
21 R.J. Hurtubise, P.F. Lott and J.R. Dias, *J. Chromatogr. Sci*, 11 (1973) 476.
22 P.F. Lott, J.R. Dias and R.J. Hurtubise, *J. Chromatogr. Sci.*, 14 (1976) 488.
23 P.F. Lott, J.R. Dias and S.C. Slahck, *J. Chromatogr. Sci.*, 16 (1978) 571.
24 J.R. Kirchner, *J. Chromatogr. Sci.*, 13 (1975) 558.
25 E. Stahl, *J. Chromatogr.*, 165 (1979) 59.
26 V.W. Rodwell, *Thin-layer Chromatography*, Amer. Chem. Soc., Washington, DC, 1975, 4 tape cassettes.

27 K. Macek and I.M. Hais, *Biobliography of Paper Chromatography 1944–1956*, Publ. House of Czechosl. Acad. Sci., Prague, 1960.

28 K. Macek, I.M. Hais, J. Gasparič, J. Kopecký and V. Rábek, *Bibliography of Paper Chromatography 1957–1960*, Academic Press, London, 1962.

29 K. Macek, I.M. Hais, J. Kopecký and J. Gasparič, *Bibliography of Paper and Thin-layer Chromatography 1961–1965*, Elsevier, Amsterdam, 1968.

30 K. Macek, I.M. Hais, J. Kopecký, J. Gasparič, V. Rábek and J. Churáček, *Bibliography of Paper and Thin-layer Chromatography 1966–1969*, Elsevier, Amsterdam, 1972.

31 K. Macek, I.M. Hais, J. Kopecký, V. Schwarz, J. Gasparič and J. Churáček, *Bibliography of Paper and Thin-layer Chromatography 1970–1973*, Elsevier, Amsterdam, 1975.

32 D. Jänchen (Editor), *Thin-layer Chromatography. Cumulative Biobibliography I (1965–1967)*, Camag, Muttenz, 1967.

33 D. Jänchen (Editor), *Thin-layer Chromatography. Cumulative Bibliography II (1967–1969)*, Camag, Muttenz, 1970.

34 D. Jänchen (Editor), *Thin-layer Chromatography. Cumulative Bibliography III (1969–1973)*, Camag, Muttenz, 1974.

35 D. Jänchen (Editor), *Thin-layer Chromatography. Cumulative Bibliography IV (1973–1977)*, Camag, Muttenz, 1977.

36 J. Breiter, *J. Clin. Chem. Biochem.*, 14 (1976) 46.

37 E. Stahl, *J. Chromatogr.*, 37 (1968) 99.

38 E. Stahl and F. Karig, *Z. Anal. Chem.*, 265 (1973) 81.

39 E. Stahl, *J. Chromatogr.*, 142 (1977) 15.

40 J.F. Lawrence and R.W. Frei, *Chemical Derivatization in Liquid Chromatography*, Elsevier, Amsterdam, 1976.

41 R.E. Kaiser (Editor), *Einführung in die Hochleistungs-Dünnschicht-Chromatographie*, Institut für Chromatographie, Bad Dürkheim, 1976.

42 E. Stahl and E. Dumont, *J. Chromatogr.*, 39 (1969) 157.

43 R.A. de Zeeuw and G.G. Dull, *J. Chromatogr.*, 110 (1975) 279.

44 J.P. Leppard, A.D.R. Harrison and J.D. Nicholas, *J. Chromatogr. Sci.*, 14 (1976) 438.

45 A. Musgrave, *J. Chromatogr.*, 41 (1969) 470.

46 H. Halpaap and K.-F. Krebs, *J. Chromatogr.*, 142 (1977) 823.

47 J. Janák, *J. Chromatogr.*, 15 (1964) 15.

48 G.G. Brownlee and F. Sanger, *Eur. J. Biochem.*, 11 (1969) 395.

49 P.G.N. Jeppesen, *Biochem. J.*, 124 (1971) 357.

50 E.M. Southern, *Anal. Biochem.*, 62 (1974) 317.

51 G. Volckaert, W. Min Jou and W. Fiers, *Anal. Biochem.*, 72 (1976) 433.

52 J. Christiansen, *J. Chromatogr.*, 123 (1976) 57.

53 M. Riechert, *J. Chromatogr.*, 146 (1978) 175.

54 D.C. Fenimore and C.J. Meyer, *J. Chromatogr.*, 186 (1979) 555.

55 E. Stahl, *Pharmazie*, 11 (1956) 633.

56 H.W. Kohlschütter and K. Unger, in E. Stahl (Editor), *Dünnschicht-Chromatographie*, Springer, Berlin, 2nd Edn., 1967, p. 7.

57 H. Halpaap and K. Klatyk, *J. Chromatogr.*, 33 (1968) 80.

59 A. Siouffi and G. Guiochon, *Analusis*, 4 (1976) 147.

60 B.G. Belenkii, E.S. Gankina, S.A. Pryanishnikova and D.P. Erastov, *Mol. Biol.*, 1 (1967) 184.

61 P. Wollenweber, in K. Macek and I.M. Hais (Editors), *Stationary Phase in Paper and Thin-layer Chromatography*, Elsevier, Amsterdam, 1965, p. 98.

62 T. Devenyi, *Kem. Ujabb Eredmenyei*, 37 (1977) 197; *C.A.*, 89 (1978) 19344z.

63 L. Hörhammer, H. Wagner and K. Macek, *Chromatogr. Rev.*, 9 (1967) 103.

64 K.T. Wang, Y.T. Lin and I.S.Y. Wang, *Advan. Chromatogr.*, 11 (1974) 73.

65 J.N. Miller, in R. Epton (Editor), *Chromatography of Synthetic and Biological Polymers*, Vol. 1, Wiley, Chichester, 1978, p. 181.

66 T. Wieland and H. Determann, *J. Chromatogr.*, 28 (1967) 2.

67 C.H. Hung, D.K. Strickland and B.G. Hudson, *Anal. Biochem.*, 80 (1977) 91.

68 A. Waksmundzki, P. Pryke and A. Dawidowicz, *J. Chromatogr.*, 168 (1979) 234.
69 M. Shibukawa, K. Oguma and R. Kuroda, *J. Chromatogr.*, 166 (1978) 245.
70 J. Pietrzyk, T.D. Rotsch and S.W. Ch. Leuthauser, *J. Chromatogr. Sci.*, 17 (1979) 555.
71 H. Halpaap and H. Bausch, *J. Chromatogr.*, 48 (1970) 144.
72 H. Feltkamp, *Deut. Apoth.-Ztg.*, 102 (1962) 1269.
73 W. Gietz, A.A. Boulton and F. Pollak, *J. Chromatogr.*, 107 (1975) 81.
74 H. Halpaap, K. Klatyk and H. Rössler, *J. Chromatogr.*, 48 (1970) 163.
75 T. Okumura, *Bunseki Kagaku*, 24 (1975) 192.
76 Zh.S. Sogomonyants, N.S. Shabanova, N.G. Afanas'eva and B.G. Belenkii, *USSR Pat.* 443, 309 (Cl. GO1n, BO1d), 15 Sep. 1974; *C.A.*, 82 (1975) 118591q.
77 T. Okumura, *J. Chromatogr.*, 184 (1980) 37.
78 V.D. Tsydendambaev, A.V. Zhukov and A.G. Vereshchagin, *J. Chromatogr.*, 132 (1977) 195.
79 J.M. Miller and J.G. Kirchner, *Anal. Chem.*, 26 (1954) 2002.
80 E. Stahl. *Chem. Ztg.*, 82 (1958) 323.
81 S. Takitani and K. Masuda, *Bunseki Kagaku*, 14 (1965) 846.
82 E. Stahl, *Angew. Chem., Int. Ed. Engl.*, 3 (1964) 784.
83 J.J. Peifer, *Mikrochim. Acta*, (1962) 529.
84 F.B. Padley, *J. Chromatogr.*, 39 (1969) 37.
85 L. Bekersky, *Anal. Chem.*, 35 (1963) 261.
86 K. Morita and F. Haruta, *J. Chromatogr.*, 12 (1963) 412.
87 H.H.O. Schmid, L.L. Jones and H.K. Mangold, *J. Lipid Res.*, 8 (1967) 692.
88 E.A. Mistryukov, *Collect. Czech. Chem. Commun.*, 26 (1961) 2071.
89 K. Chmel, *Chem. Listy*, 66 (1972) 1305.
90 E. Stahl, G. Becker and V. Brüderle, *J. Chromatogr.*, 129 (1976) 41.
91 L. Lepri, P.G. Desideri and D. Heimler, *J. Chromatogr.*, 155 (1978) 119.
92 Å. Bergman, R. Göthe and C.A. Wachtmeister, *J. Chromatogr.*, 123 (1976) 231.
93 L.J. Morris, in A.T. James and L.J. Morris (Editors), *New Biochemical Separations*, Van Nostrand, London, 1964, p. 295.
94 S. Frgačić and Z. Kniewald, *J. Chromatogr.*, 94 (1974) 291.
95 M. Brenner, in K. Macek and I.M. Hais (Editors), *Stationary Phase in Paper and Thin-Layer Chromatography*, Elsevier, Amsterdam, 1965, p. 263.
96 T. Wieland, G. Lueben and H. Determann, *Experienta*, 18 (1962) 430.
97 E. Röder, in A. Niederwieser and G. Pataki (Editors), *Progress in Thin-Layer Chromatography and Related Methods*, Vol. 2, Ann Arbor Sci. Publ., Ann Arbor, MI, 1971, p. 93.
98 R.A. de Zeeuw, *Anal. Chem.*, 40 (1968) 915.
99 R.E. Kaiser and R. Rieder, *J. Chromatogr.*, 142 (1977) 411.
100 A.M. Siouffi, T. Wawrzynowicz, F. Bressole and G. Guiochon, *J. Chromatogr.*, 186 (1979) 563.
101 R.A. de Zeeuw, F.J.W. van Mansvelt and J.E. Greving, *J. Chromatogr.*, 148 (1978) 255.
102 D. Volkmann, *J. High Resolut. Chromatogr. Chromatogr. Commun.*, 2 (1979) 729.
103 J.F. Collawn, Jr., D.J. Cox, L.M. Hamlin and W.W. Fish, *J. Chromatogr.*, 157 (1978) 227.
104 E. Stahl, *Chem. Ztg.*, 83 (1958) 323.
105 P. Petrin, *J. Chromatogr.*, 123 (1976) 65.
106 M. Brenner and A. Niederwieser, *Experienta*, 17 (1961) 237.
107 F. Geiss and H. Schlitt, *Chromatographia*, 1 (1968) 392.
108 R.A. de Zeeuw, *Anal. Chem.*, 40 (1968) 2134.
109 E. Tyihák, E. Mincsovics and H. Kalász, *J. Chromatogr.*, 174 (1979) 75.
110 R.E. Kaiser and D. Jänchen, *Labor Praxis*, 4 (1978) 20.
111 J.A. Perry, *J. Chromatogr.*, 113 (1975) 267.
112 H. Wagner, L. Hörhammer and K. Macek, *J. Chromatogr.*, 31 (1967) 455.
113 K. Macek, Z. Deyl and M. Smrž, *J. Chromatogr.*, 193 (1980) 421.
114 D.W. Vidrine and H.J. Nicholas, *J. Chromatogr.*, 89 (1974) 92.
115 H.H.O. Schmid, W.J. Baumann, J.M. Cubero and H.K. Mangold, *Biochem. Biophys. Acta*, 125 (1966) 189.
116 I.M. Hais, *J. Chromatogr.*, 48 (1970) 200.

117 E. Stahl, *Arch. Pharm.*, 293 (1960) 531.
118 M.S.J. Dallas, *J. Chromatogr.*, 48 (1970) 193.
119 G. Székely, *J. Chromatogr.*, 42 (1969) 543.
120 G.G. Brownlee and F. Sanger, *Eur. J. Biochem.*, 11 (1969) 395.
121 E.M. Southern, *Anal. Biochem.*, 62 (1974) 317.
122 C.P.D. Tu, E. Jay, Ch.P. Bahl and R. Wu, *Anal. Biochem.*, 74 (1976) 73.
123 R.D. Bennett and E. Heftmann, *J. Chromatogr.*, 12 (1963) 245.
124 E.V. Truter, *J. Chromatogr.*, 14 (1964) 57.
125 L. Fischer, *An Introduction to Gel Chromatography*, North Holland, Amsterdam, 1971.
126 H.J. Issaq, M.M. Mangino, G.M. Singer, D.J. Wilbur and N.H. Risser, *Anal. Chem.*, 51 (1979) 2157.
127 G. Székely and P. Baumgartner, *J. Chromatogr.*, 186 (1979) 575.
128 J.H. van Dyk, *Chimia*, 24 (1970) 234.
129 V.J.R. De Deyne and A.F. Vetters, *J. Chromatogr.*, 103 (1975) 177.
130 G.C. Barrett, *Advan. Chromatogr.*, 11 (1974) 145.
131 J.S.T. Chou and B.M. Lawrence, *J. Chromatogr.*, 27 (1967) 279.
132 K. Randerath, *Anal. Biochem.*, 21 (1967) 279.
133 J.F. Lawrence and R.W. Frei, *Chemical Derivatization in Liquid Chromatography*, Elsevier, Amsterdam, 1976.
134 N. Seiler and L. Demisch, *Handb. Deriv. Chromatogr.*, (1978) 346; *C.A.*, 89 (1978) 190492v.
135 H. Nakamura and J.J. Pisano, *J. Chromatogr.*, 121 (1976) 79.
136 E.G.G. Lindeberg, *J. Chromatogr.*, 117 (1976) 439.
137 M.R. Bermann and R.N. Zare, *Anal. Chem.*, 47 (1975) 1200.
138 T. Okumura, T. Kadono and A. Iso'o, *J. Chromatogr.*, 108 (1975) 329.
139 K.D. Mukherjee, *J. Chromatogr.*, 96 (1974) 242.
140 H.K. Mangold and K.D. Mukherjee, *J. Chromatogr. Sci.*, 13 (1975) 398.
141 E. Cremer, T. Kraus and H. Nau, *Z. Anal. Chem.*, 245 (1969) 37.
142 T.R. Roberts, *Radiochromatography*, Elsevier, Amsterdam, 1978.
143 J.C. Touchstone, T. Murawec, M. Kasparow and W. Wortmann, *J. Chromatogr.*, 66 (1972) 172.
144 C.E. Mendoza, *J. Chromatogr.*, 78 (1973) 29.
145 C.E. Mendoza, *Res. Rev.*, 50 (1974) 43; *C.A.*, 81 (1974) 164467f.
146 V. Betina, *J. Chromatogr.*, 78 (1973) 41.
147 Z. Ďuračková, V. Betina and P. Nemec, *J. Chromatogr.*, 116 (1976) 155.
148 K. Macek and I.M. Hais (Editors), *Flat-bed Chromatography with Special Reference to Quantitative Analysis*, Elsevier, Amsterdam, 1973.
149 H. Jork, *J. Chromatogr.*, 33 (1968) 297.
150 U. Hezel, *Angew. Chem.*, 85 (1973) 334.
151 J.G. Kirchner, *J. Chromatogr.*, 82 (1973) 101.
152 R.R. Goodall, *J. Chromatogr.*, 123 (1976) 5.
153 V. Pollak, *J. Chromatogr..*, 123 (1976) 11.
154 U. Hezel, *GIT Fachz. Lab.*, (1977) 694.
155 J. Goldman and R.R. Goodall, *J. Chromatogr.*, 40 (1969) 345.
156 T. Aratani and F. Mizui, *J. Chromatogr.*, 79 (1973) 173.
157 V. Pollak, *J. Chromatogr.*, 105 (1975) 279.
158 R.R. Goodall, *J. Chromatogr.*, 78 (1973) 153.
159 J.M. Owen, *J. Chromatogr.*, 79 (1973) 165.
160 S. Ebel and J. Hocke, *J. Chromatogr.*, 126 (1976) 449.
161 L.R. Treiber, R. Nordberg, S. Lindstedt and P. Stöllnberger, *J. Chromatogr.*, 63 (1971) 211.
162 H. Jork, *J. Chromatogr.*, 82 (1973) 85.
163 S. Ebel and G. Herold, *Chromatographia*, 9 (1976) 41.
164 H. Yamamoto, T. Kurita, J. Suzuki, R. Hira, K. Nakano, H. Makabe and K. Shibata, *J. Chromatogr.*, 116 (1976) 29.
165 J. Ripphahn and H. Halpaap, *J. Chromatogr.*, 112 (1975) 81.
166 H.U. Schmid, Y. Cramer and H. Arm, *Chimia*, 30 (1976) 62.
167 G. Pastuska, R. Krüger and V. Lehmann, *J. Chromatogr.*, 84 (1973) 241.

168 J.L. Bloomer and W.R. Eder, *J. Chromatogr.*, 34 (1968) 548.
169 E. Fosslien, F. Musil, D. Domizi, L. Blickenstaff and J. Lumeng, *J. Chromatogr.*, 63 (1971) 131.
170 G. Kasang, G. Göldner and N. Weiss, *J. Chromatogr.*, 59 (1971) 393.
171 M. Donike, H. Suberg and L. Jaenicke, *J. Chromatogr.*, 85 (1973) 9.
172 J.D. Mann, N.G. Porter and J.E. Lancaster, *J. Chromatogr.*, 92 (1974) 177.
173 H. Halpaap, in I. Smith (Editor), *Chromatographic and Electrophoretic Techniques*, Vol. 1, Heinemann, London, 1969, p. 834.
174 H. Halpaap, *Chem. Ing. Tech.*, 35 (1963) 488.
175 K. Macek and H. Becvarova, *Chromatogr. Rev.*, 15 (1971) 1.
176 F.C. Haer, *An Introduction to Chromatography on Impregnated Glass Fiber*, Ann Arbor Sci. Publ., Ann Arbor, MI, 1969.
177 C.S. Knight, *Advan. Chromatogr.*, 4 (1967) 61.
178 T.I. Pristoupil, *Chromatogr. Rev.*, 12 (1970) 109.
179 K. Macek and I.M. Hais (Editors), *Stationary Phase in Paper and Thin-layer Chromatography*, Elsevier, Amsterdam, 1965.
180 G. Alberti, *Chromatogr. Rev.*, 8 (1966) 246.
181 U.A.T. Brinkman and G. de Vries, *J. Chem. Educat.*, 49 (1972) 244.
182 R. Consden, A.H. Gordon and A.J.P. Martin, *Biochem. J.*, 38 (1944) 225.
183 S.P. Datta, C.E. Dent and H. Harris, *Science*, 112 (1950) 621.
184 I.R. Hunter, D.F. Houston and H.S. Owens, *Anal. Chem.*, 28 (1956) 283.
185 H.R. Roberts, *Anal. Chem.*, 29 (1957) 1443.
186 F. Franks, *Analyst (London)*, 81 (1956) 384.
187 J. Green and S. Marcinkiewicz, *J. Chromatogr.*, 10 (1963) 35.
188 L. Peyron, *Bull. Soc. Chim. Fr.*, (1958) 889; (1960) 1243.
189 H. Proom and A.J. Woiwod, *J. Gen. Microbiol.*, 5 (1951) 681.
190 P. Decker, *Naturwissenschaften*, 38 (1951) 287.
191 R. Neher, *J. Chromatogr.*, 48 (1970) 7.
192 P. Decker, *Naturwissenschaften*, 45 (1958) 464.
193 D.S. Galanos and V.M. Kapoulas, *J. Chromatogr.*, 13 (1964) 128.
194 J. Polesuk, *J. Chromatogr. Sci.*, 11 (1973) 226.
195 M. Köhler, *Chromatographia*, 8 (1975) 685.
196 G. Székely, in K. Macek (Editor), *Pharmaceutical Applications of TLC and PC*, Elsevier, Amsterdam, 1972, p. 101.
197 W.E. Court and M.S. Habib, *J. Chromatogr.*, 73 (1972) 274.
198 R. Kaiser, *Chem. Br.*, 5 (1969) 54.
199 C.-A. Nilsson, Å. Norström and K. Andersson, *J. Chromatogr.*, 73 (1972) 270.
200 G.J. Down and S.A. Gwyn, *J. Chromatogr.*, 103 (1975) 208.
201 L. Reio, *J. Chromatogr.*, 1 (1958) 338.
202 L. Reio, *J. Chromatogr.*, 4 (1960) 458.
203 L. Reio, *J. Chromatogr.*, 48 (1970) 11.
204 J. Franc and Z. Stranský, *Collect. Czech. Chem. Commun.*, 24 (1959) 3611.
205 K. Macek and J. Večerková, *Pharmazie*, 20 (1965) 605.

Chapter 6

Gas chromatography

C.A. CRAMERS and H.M. McNAIR

CONTENTS

6.1. INTRODUCTION

Since its introduction almost 30 years ago, gas chromatography has experienced a phenomenal growth. It is accepted today as a routine analytical technique for thousands of laboratories around the world and the instrumentation has been developed to such a level that major changes or improvements are unlikely. Rapid growth in applications is still occurring in industrial hygiene, clinical, biomedical, geological, and toxicological laboratories. Future growth in all areas of applications will depend primarily on the use of capillary columns. Because of the growing interest in fused silica and glass capillary columns, special attention has been given in this chapter to capillary columns and sampling systems for capillary columns.

Fig. 6.1 shows schematically a GC system. An inert carrier gas (e.g., nitrogen) flows continuously from a high-pressure cylinder through the injection device, the column, and the detector. The flowrate of the carrier gas is carefully controlled to ensure reproducible retention times and to minimize detector drift and noise. The sample is injected (usually with a microsyringe) into the heated injection port, where it is vaporized and carried onto the column. The sample may also be placed directly on the column ("on-column injection"), particularly if the compounds are thermolabile.

Packed columns consist of glass or stainless-steel tubes, packed tightly with solid particles (the solid support). The solid support is coated uniformly with a thin film of a high-boiling liquid (the stationary phase). Open tubular or capillary columns consist of long, narrow-bore tubes of glass or, more recently, fused silica, where the stationary phase is deposited as a thin film on the inside wall. In both columns the sample partitions itself between the carrier gas and the stationary phase and is

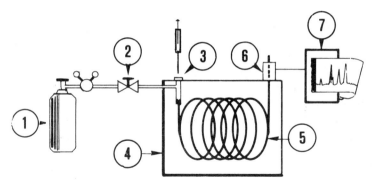

Fig. 6.1. Schematic GC system. 1=Carrier gas supply; 2=flow control valve; 3=sample inlet system; 4=column thermostat; 5=column; 6=detector; 7=recorder or data handling system.

thereby separated into individual components. After the column, the carrier gas and sample pass through a detector. In the presence of a sample component this device generates an electrical signal, which passes to a recorder and generates a chromatogram (the written record of the analysis). In many cases, a data handling device automatically integrates the peak area, measures the retention time, performs calculations, and prints out a final report.

6.2. BASIC CONCEPTS

The signal from the detector, plotted as a function of time (the chromatogram), is illustrated in Fig. 6.2. The time elapsed between the injection of the sample and the emergence of the peak maximum is called the retention time. Retention times or derivatives thereof are used in qualitative analysis, as will be discussed shortly. The area of the peak, or preferably, the integral, A, is proportional to the quantity of a

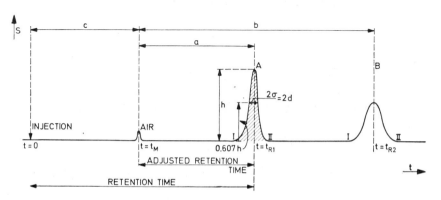

Fig. 6.2. Chromatogram with definition of terms.

component.

$$A = \int_I^{II} S \, dt \tag{6.1}$$

where A is the area of a peak (in cm^2, $A \cdot sec$, or $V \cdot sec$); S is the signal (in cm, A, or V); and I and II are the beginning and end of a peak, respectively. The actual separation of two components is determined by the difference in their retention times and by the peak broadening, which always occurs. A measure of the "goodness" of a column with respect to peak broadening is the plate number, N.

6.2.1. Retention time

The residence time of the peak maximum in the column, the retention time t_R (in sec), is given by

$$t_R = \frac{L}{\bar{u}}(1+k) = t_M(1+k) \tag{6.2}$$

where L is the length of the column (in cm); $\bar{u}$ is the average linear velocity of the mobile phase (in cm/sec); k is the capacity ratio of the stationary and mobile phases for a sample component; $L/\bar{u} = t_M$ is the gas hold-up time (see c in Fig. 6.2) or the retention time of an unretained component (e.g., air or the carrier gas itself); and $t_R - t_M$ is the adjusted retention time (see a in Fig. 6.2).

The capacity ratio, k, is derived from the distribution coefficient, K, by multiplication with the volumetric ratio of the stationary and mobile phases:

$$k = K \frac{V_L}{V_M} = \frac{a}{c} \tag{6.3}$$

where V_L is the volume of stationary phase in the column (in cc) and V_M is the volume of mobile phase in the column (in cc). The phase ratio, $\beta = V_M/V_L$, in packed columns is of the order of 10–20; in open tubular columns it is considerably larger (values of 100–500 are common). It may be concluded that substances with different K values will have different retention times. However, whether a separation occurs is also determined by peak broadening.

6.2.2. Peak width

A narrow and concentrated zone of solute, introduced at the column inlet, broadens in time to form wider zones (compare Peaks A and B in Fig. 6.2). A quantity describing this phenomenon is the plate number, N, of the column given by

$$N = \frac{t_R^2}{\sigma^2} \tag{6.4}$$

where N is the number of plates and σ^2 is the variance (in time units) of the eluted peak.

For symmetrical Gaussian peaks the standard deviation, σ, can be calculated from the chromatogram in the following way:

$$\sigma = \frac{2d}{2} = d \qquad (6.5)$$

where d is the half width at 0.607 height (see Fig. 6.2).

The plate number can be related to the length, L, of the column by introducing the quantity H.

$$H = \frac{L}{N} \qquad (6.6)$$

where H is the height equivalent to a theoretical plate. It is a function of the linear velocity, $\bar{u}$, of the carrier gas and a number of experimental parameters, as expressed in the equations originally derived by Van Deemter et al. for packed columns and by Golay for open tubular columns. The H vs. $\bar{u}$ equation for capillary columns is discussed in Chap. 6.3.4.4. For an analogous discussion of packed columns the reader is referred to Cramers and Rijks [1].

6.2.3. Resolution

The degree of separation of two components leaving the column can be expressed by the resolution, R_s.

$$R_s = \left(\frac{\alpha - 1}{4\alpha} \right) \left(\frac{k_2}{k_2 + 1} \right) \sqrt{N} \qquad (6.7)$$

where α is the relative retention given by (see Fig. 6.2)

$$\alpha = \frac{K_2}{K_1} = \frac{k_2}{k_1} = \frac{b}{a} \qquad (6.8)$$

The separation is essentially complete if $R_s = 1.5$ and just acceptable if $R_s = 1.0$. Packed columns usually operate with relatively large values of k, and therefore the ratio $k/(k+1)$ approaches unity. However, open tubular columns operate with smaller k values, because the volumetric phase ratio V_M/V_L is larger. This implies that a larger number of theoretical plates is needed for capillary columns to obtain a given resolution. Fortunately, a large number of theoretical plates is readily obtainable in open tubular columns, since the columns can be made very long. Moreover, for a given open tubular column, k can easily be increased by lowering the column temperature. Accordingly, for the same separation problem, capillary columns are operated at appreciably lower temperatures than are packed columns (typically at 50°C).

References on p. A223

6.3. COMPONENTS OF GAS CHROMATOGRAPHIC SYSTEMS

6.3.1. Carrier gas

6.3.1.1. Purpose

The purpose of the carrier gas is to carry the sample through the column. The gas should be inert, i.e. it should not react with either the sample or the stationary phase. The choice of carrier gas can affect both the separation and the speed of analysis (see Chap. 6.3.4.4). A secondary but still essential purpose of the carrier gas is to provide a suitable matrix for the detector to measure the sample components. In the case of a thermal conductivity detector (TCD), light gases with high thermal conductivities are required to provide uniform and high sensitivity. Helium and hydrogen are commonly used. However, hydrogen should not be used with thermistor beads, since it reacts with the rare earth oxides present. The flame-ionization detector (FID) is operated with helium or nitrogen. Nitrogen produces about two times the sensitivity of helium in the FID. Hydrogen is sometimes used as carrier gas with capillary columns to provide very fast analyses. Electron-capture detectors (ECD) use very dry nitrogen or a mixture of argon and 5% methane. Special scrubber filters (see Chap. 6.3.1.2) are necessary to remove traces of water and oxygen.

6.3.1.2. Purity

It is important that the carrier gas have a high purity. Impurities can chemically degrade some liquid phases. Polyester, polyglycol, and polyamide columns are prone to degradation by oxygen and water. Trace amounts of water can also desorb contaminants in the column and produce a high detector background or even "ghost peaks". Traces of hydrocarbons in the carrier gas cause a high background with the FID and decrease the detection limits.

Traces of water and hydrocarbons can be easily removed by installing a Molecular Sieve filter between the gas cylinder and the instrument. Such drying tubes are commercially available. The Molecular Sieve should be regenerated by heating it to 300°C for 3 h with a slow flow of nitrogen every time before it is used with the next gas cylinder. Oxygen is more difficult to remove. It requires a special filter, made of a finely divided and active form of copper, produced by reducing copper oxide with hydrogen. Most of the chromatography accessory manufacturers sell such oxygen removers.

6.3.2. Flow control

Accurate control of carrier gas flow is essential both for high column efficiency and for qualitative and quantitative analysis. For qualitative analysis it is essential to have reproducible flowrates so that retention times can be accurately reproduced. Comparison of retention times or related parameters of unknown compounds and standards is the quickest and easiest method for compound identification, but, of course, it should be noted that two or more compounds may have the same retention time. Unequivocal confirmation of peak identity is not possible by GC methods alone, although selective detectors may help. In general, it requires the use of auxiliary analyses, such as MS, NMR, or IR.

6.3.3. Sample inlet systems

6.3.3.1. Sample size

The separation begins after the introduction of gaseous or vaporized liquid or solid samples into the carrier gas stream. Because of the different physical forms of the samples to be analyzed, the wide range of component concentrations, and the great variety of chromatographic conditions (column length and diameter, weight percent of stationary phase, gas velocity), a variety of sampling techniques have to be used.

There is no optimum sample size, but there is a maximum sample size, and some general guidelines are available. For the best peak shape and maximum resolution the sample size must be kept below that which would overload the column. A variety of sample sizes can be accomodated, from nanogram quantities in open tubular columns up to gram quantities in preparative columns (Table 6.1).

6.3.3.2. Gas samples

The preferred method for introducing gas samples is by means of a sample valve (Fig. 6.3). In the sample loading position (Fig. 6.3, left) the gas sample flows continuously through the sample loop until it contains nothing but the sample. The volume of the sample loop is controlled by the length and diameter of the tubing. Sample loops from 1 μl up to 100 ml capacity are available. In the sample introduction position (Fig. 6.3, right) the sample valve is rotated and the carrier gas sweeps the sample through the sample loop and into the column. A sampling valve gives better reproducibility, requires less skill, and can be more easily automated than sample introduction with a syringe.

TABLE 6.1

RANGE OF SAMPLE VOLUMES FOR VARIOUS COLUMN TYPES

Column type	ID	Liquid phase	Gas	Liquid
Preparative	20 mm	20%	0.1–1.0 l	0.01–1.0 ml
Regular analytical	4.6 mm	10%	0.1–10 ml	0.1–10 μl
High efficiency	2 mm	3%	0.1–1.0 ml	0.01–1.0 μl
Capillary	0.25–0.50 mm	0.5 μm film thickness	< 10 μl	0.001–1.0 μl

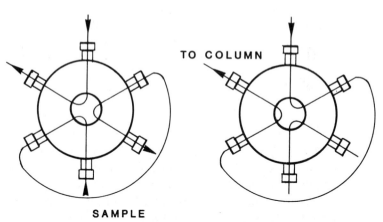

CARRIER GAS

TO COLUMN

SAMPLE

Fig. 6.3. Gas sample valve. Left, sample loading position. Right, sample introduction.

6.3.3.3. Liquid samples

Most of the samples analyzed by GC are liquids. They are vaporized in an inlet system before entering the column. Syringes are used almost universally for liquid sampling; the most common sizes are 1 and 10 μl. Automated syringe samplers are available, and liquid sample valves are used in process gas chromatographs. The major limitations of liquid sample valves are that temperatures above 150°C decrease their life-span and reproducibility and that samples must not contain particulate matter.

6.3.3.4. Solid samples

Solids may be handled by dissolving them in an appropriate solvent and using syringes to inject the solution. Various automatic sampling systems are also available in which sealed ampoules or capsules are used.

6.3.3.5. Inlet systems for packed columns

A diagram of an injection block is shown in Fig. 6.4. The heated inlet block ensures a constant temperature in the vaporization tube. The dead volume is kept to a minimum to ensure rapid introduction of the vaporized sample into the column and to reduce band dispersion. The use of glass inserts is highly desirable for chemically and thermally labile samples. Among these are the derivatives of amino acids, steroids, carbohydrates, pesticides, and many drugs. On-column inlet systems are also available for packed columns.

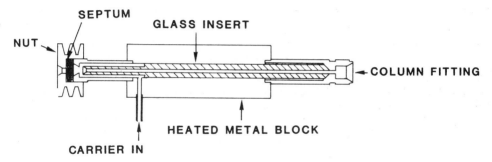

Fig. 6.4. Injection block. (Reproduced through the courtesy of Perkin-Elmer Corp., Norwalk, CT, USA.)

6.3.3.6. Inlet systems for capillary columns

An inlet system as described above can be used with packed columns and in some instances (e.g., flowrates > 5 cc/min) with micropacked, porous-layer open tubular (PLOT) or wide-bore wall-coated open tubular (WCOT) columns (see Chap. 6.3.4.1). However, small-bore open tubular columns, operated under optimum conditions, are characterized by low flowrates (ca. 1 cc/min). Here different sampling techniques have to be used, depending on the operating characteristics of the capillary column and the range of component concentrations in the sample. A complete discussion of different sampling systems for capillary chromatography has been presented by Schomburg [2]. Here we will limit ourselves to the characteristics of the most commonly used injection techniques.

6.3.3.6.1. Split injection

It can be seen from Table 6.1 that the sample capacity of capillary columns is one or two orders of magnitude less than that of conventional packed columns. An indirect sampling procedure is often utilized. A relatively large (0.1–1 µl) liquid sample is injected into the sample inlet. The vaporized sample, mixed with the carrier gas, is divided into two highly unequal parts, the smaller of which goes onto the column, the larger one being discarded. The ratio of these two flows is called the split ratio and typically ranges from 1:10 to 1:100. In order to be effective the stream splitter must be nondiscriminatory, i.e. all sample components (independent of their molecular weight and concentrations) must be divided in the same ratio. Design considerations of split systems are given by Schomburg [2]. Typically, stream splitters are used for WCOT columns (split ratios 1:50 to 1:1500) and PLOT or wide-bore WCOT columns (split ratios 1:10 to 1:50). Sample splitting is not compatible with trace analysis, because the amount of the trace component introduced into the column is very small. Quantitative results by sample splitting are not as good as by splitless and on-column techniques.

6.3.3.6.2. Splitless injection

In trace analysis it is necessary to introduce the entire sample into the column. One way to accomplish this is by the splitless sampling technique, originally described by Grob and Grob [3]. In this technique a relatively large amount of dilute sample (1–5 μl) is introduced and vaporized in an inlet system and carried onto the column. The amount of the components to be determined should be less than 50 ng to prevent column overloading. The large surplus of volatile solvent produces a long solvent tail, obscuring peaks that are eluted early. To minimize this solvent tail, the injection port is backflushed 30–60 sec after injection. In this way the solvent tail is limited without loss of the components to be determined. Splitless injection is only successful if the sample components, initially broadened in the injection port, are again concentrated into narrow bands at the head of the column.

The first method, proposed by Grob and Grob [3], utilizes a "solvent effect" for this reconcentration. The most widely used solvents include dichloromethane and hexane. The initial column temperature should be 10–30°C below the boiling point of the solvent. Another method of reconcentrating the components at the front of the column is to keep the initial column temperature low enough to condense these solutes ("cold trapping"). A general guide is that the initial column temperature

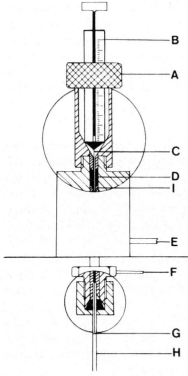

Fig. 6.5. On-column injection port for capillary columns. (Reproduced through the courtesy of Chrom-pack, Middelburg, The Netherlands.) A=Shut-off ring; B=on-column syringe; C=syringe needle; D=silicone seal; E=cooling air inlet; F=carrier gas inlet; G=needle outlet; H=capillary column; I=removable guide.

should be 150°C lower than the boiling points of the components. The splitless technique is well suited for trace analysis and compatible with WCOT columns.

6.3.3.6.3. On-column injection

The introduction of a liquid sample directly into a capillary column was first described by Schomburg et al. [4]. They described macro- and microversions of this technique, in which the sample never encounters temperatures higher than the column temperature. This method proved to be superior to all other sampling techniques for the separation of compounds having low volatility and samples having a wide boiling range. Not only is the precision of the analyses better, but also the discrimination of compounds is much less.

Grob and Grob [5,6] and Galli and coworkers [7,8] have described on-column systems where the sample is introduced by means of a special syringe into narrow-bore capillary columns. Galli and Trestianu [8] include in their sampling technique additional cooling of the column inlet to overcome problems caused by the sudden vaporization of volatiles in the syringe needle. A commercial version of the on-column injector is shown in Fig. 6.5.

6.3.4. Columns

6.3.4.1. Classification of columns

In gas chromatography one can distinguish two main classes of columns:

The first class, capillary or, more properly, open tubular columns, are character-ized by the fact that the tube is open and therefore has a large permeability. The importance of open tubular columns, in particular those made of fused silica, is growing rapidly. Usually two types of open tubular columns are distinguished:

(a) In the wall-coated open tubular (WCOT) column the liquid phase is spread as a thin film on the tubing wall. For polar stationary phases spreading is often assisted by the deposition or formation by reaction of micrometer-size support particles on the column wall. An excellent monograph on WCOT columns has been written by Jennings [9].

(b) Porous-layer open tubular (PLOT) columns have the stationary liquid phase coated onto a relatively thick layer (up to 50 μm) of support material, usually porous in itself, such as diatomaceous earth. Ettre and Purcell [10] have published an extensive review on PLOT columns.

The second class, packed columns, are columns more or less densely packed with solid particles. One may distinguish two groups:

(a) Classical packed columns. Quite arbitrarily, columns of this type are often defined as micro-packed columns if the inside column diameter is about 1 mm or less.

(b) Columns having a packing density substantially less than classical packed columns. An example of the latter is the so-called "packed capillary column" introduced by Halász and Heine [11].

There are two means of attaining high efficiencies from packed columns. One approach is the reduction of the particle size of the solid support [12,13] and the other approach is the increase of the length of columns with larger particles sizes [14,15]. In both cases relatively large pressure drops are necessary for operating these columns. The required inlet pressure for the very fine-grained packings is an order of magnitude higher than that for the normal packed columns, and this causes severe problems with sample introduction. For a detailed treatment of the theory of packed columns the reader is referred to standard text books on gas chromatography and Refs. 1 and 13. In this chapter special attention will be given to the theory of operation of capillary columns.

6.3.4.2. Plate height equation for capillary columns

The plate height, H, of a capillary column can be deduced from the Golay [16] equation, extended to situations of appreciable pressure drop by Giddings [17]:

$$H = \left[\frac{2D_{m,o}}{u_o} + \frac{11k^2 + 6k + 1r^2 u_o}{24(1+k)^2 D_{m,o}} \right] f_1 + \frac{2}{3} \frac{kd_f^2 u_o f_2}{(1+k)^2 D_s} \tag{6.9}$$

where $D_{m,o}$ is the diffusion coefficient of a component in the mobile phase at column outlet pressure; D_s is the diffusion coefficient in the stationary phase; r is the inner radius of the column; d_f is the film thickness of the liquid phase; k is the capacity ratio of a solute; f_1 and f_2 are pressure corrections factors [17]:

$$f_1 = \frac{9}{8} \frac{(P^4 - 1)(P^2 - 1)}{(P^3 - 1)^2} \tag{6.10}$$

$$f_2 = \frac{3}{2} \frac{P^2 - 1}{P^3 - 1} \tag{6.11}$$

where P is the ratio of inlet to outlet pressure, P_i/P_o and u_o is the linear carrier gas velocity at the column outlet or

$$u_o = \frac{\bar{u}}{f_2} = \frac{L}{t_M f_2} \tag{6.12}$$

6.3.4.3. Flow in capillary columns

Under most of the experimental conditions encountered in GC the gas flow can be considered laminar. The gas flow is proportional to the pressure gradient:

$$u(x) = \frac{-\kappa}{\eta} \frac{dp}{dx} \tag{6.13}$$

Eqn. 6.13 is Darcy's equation, κ being the column permeability and η the dynamic viscosity of the carrier gas. As shown by Martire and Locke [18], the carrier gas can be considered as an ideal gas under practically all conditions, and therefore the dynamic viscosity is independent of pressure. With integration the Darcy equation becomes

$$u_o = \frac{\kappa}{2\eta L P_o}(P_o^2 - P_i^2)$$ (6.14)

or

$$u_o = \frac{\kappa P_o}{2\eta L}(P^2 - 1)$$ (6.15)

The average carrier gas velocity $\bar{u}$ is related to u_o by

$$\bar{u} = f_2 u_o = \frac{3}{4}\frac{\kappa}{\eta L}P_o\frac{(P^2 - 1)^2}{(P^3 - 1)}$$ (6.16)

For an open tubular column with an inner diameter d_c the permeability is given by $\kappa = d_c^2/32$.

6.3.4.4. Minimum plate height and optimum carrier gas velocity

By differentiating eqn. 6.9 with respect to u_o the optimum values of H and u_o can be found. A complete treatment of this subject is given by Cramers et al. [19].

In many situations the film of stationary phase is very thin, and thus the third term of eqn. 6.9, describing the resistance to mass transfer in the stationary liquid phase, can be neglected. The differentiation then leads to the following expressions for optimum gas chromatographic conditions:

$$H_{min} = \tfrac{1}{2}d_c f(k)$$ (6.17)

$$u_{o,opt} = \frac{1}{d_c}\frac{8D_{m,o}}{f(k)}$$ (6.18)

or

$$\bar{u}_{opt} = \frac{f_2}{d_c}\frac{8D_{m,o}}{f(k)}$$ (6.19)

where

$$f(k) = \sqrt{\frac{1 + 6k + 11k^2}{3(1 + k)^2}}$$ (6.20)

Under the assumptions made, the following conclusions can be drawn:

(a) The number of plates, N, that can maximally be obtained from a capillary column is independent of the carrier gas used. Also, a decrease in column diameter results in a proportional gain in the number of theoretical plates per unit length.

(b) The optimum carrier gas velocity, $\bar{u}_{opt}$, can be expected to depend heavily on d_c, pressure drop (f_2), and nature of the carrier gas ($D_{m,o}$).

If the pressure drop is low ($f_2 = 1$), the optimum carrier gas velocity is proportional to $1/d_c$ and $D_{m,o}$. Light carrier gases, like hydrogen and helium, will show the

References on p. A223

largest values of $\bar{u}_{opt}$, hydrogen giving the fastest analysis time. Experimental H vs. $\bar{u}$ curves (Fig. 6.6) demonstrate this effect. In the above discussion the contribution of the third term in eqn. 6.9 was assumed to be negligible. Also, it was assumed that f_2 approximated 1. Under these conditions the retention time for a separation requiring N theoretical plates is

$$t_R = t_M(1 + k) = \frac{NH_{min}}{\bar{u}_{opt}}(1 + k) \qquad (6.21)$$

Since t_R is proportional to $1/d_c^2$, a reduction in column diameter by a factor of 5 will yield a gain in analysis time by a factor of 25.

If, however, the number of plates required for a given separation increases, longer columns will be needed, appreciable pressure drops are encountered, and f_2 no longer can be approximated by 1 [20]. At a fixed plate number N, columns of all diameters have considerable inlet to outlet pressure ratios, and $\bar{u}_{opt}$ tends to become independent of the column diameter. This fact can easily be verified from the theory. $(P^2 - 1)$ approximates P^2 at high values of P, and the equations for flow and optimum chromatographic conditions combine to become

$$\bar{u}_{opt} = \frac{3}{4f(k)}\left[\frac{D_m}{\eta N}\right]^{1/2} \qquad (6.22)$$

where D_m is the diffusion coefficient in the mobile phase at 1 bar. Thus, at high

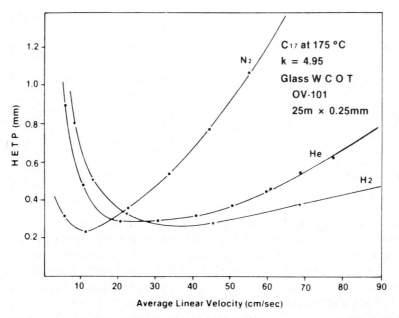

Fig. 6.6. Plot of theoretical plate height versus average carrier gas velocity for different carrier gases ($d_f = 0.4\ \mu$m). (Rproduced through the courtesy of Hewlett-Packard, Avondale, PA, USA.)

values of P the optimum carrier gas velocity $\bar{u}_{opt}$ no longer depends on column diameter. In this situation the retention time, t_R, for a given analysis is proportional to $1/d_c$ and a reduction in column diameter by a factor of 5 results in an analysis that is only 5 times faster.

At intermediate pressure drops the ratio of retention times on columns of differing diameter, a and b, is given by

$$\frac{t_{R,b}}{t_{R,a}} = \frac{d_{c,b}^2}{d_{c,a}^2} \frac{f_{2,a}}{f_{2,b}} \tag{6.23}$$

This means that, depending on the value of $P = P_i/P_o$, a reduction in column diameter by a factor of 5 will result in a gain in analysis time somewhere between 5 and 25; or, stated in another way, a reduction in column diameter yields at least a proportional gain in analysis time [20].

At present, open tubular columns with small diameter can yield large plate numbers in a relatively short time, even with unmodified commercial chromatographic equipment. Table 6.2 summarizes some important column properties for both packed and capillary columns.

6.3.4.5. Liquid phase requirements

It is the liquid phase which must exhibit the differential solubility to affect a separation between components. The relative retention, α, is a thermodynamic property and could be calculated from partition coefficients. Because only limited thermodynamic data are available, it is easier to determine relative retention experimentally by chromatographic techniques.

When a pair of compounds is chromatographed, the adjusted retention times are measured and the ratio of adjusted retention times is calculated, the relative retention, α, is obtained. It measures the differential solubility of that pair of compounds in that liquid phase at the column temperature. Table 6.3 provides a valuable insight into the effect of α on the number of plates required to obtain 98%

TABLE 6.2

TYPICAL PERFORMANCE OF PACKED AND CAPILLARY COLUMNS

	Packed columns		Capillary columns	
ID, mm	2	1	0.25	0.05
Particle size, μm	150	50	–	–
Film thickness, μm	–	–	0.5	0.1
Length, m	2	2	50	8
Pressure drop, bar (helium carrier gas)	1	10	0.5	15
Minimum plate height, μm	500	180	300	60
Optimum carrier gas velocity, cm/sec	2	6	25	30
Maximum sample size per component, ng	1,000,000	100,000	100	1

TABLE 6.3

EFFECT OF RELATIVE RETENTION, α, ON THE NUMBER OF PLATES, N, REQUIRED FOR $R_s = 1.0$

α	N *
1.015	165,000
1.075	7,400
1.157	2,000
1.245	930
1.345	484

* Assumes $k = 2$.

resolution of two peaks ($R_s = 1.0$) for a series of α values, when $k = 2$. Obviously a value of $\alpha > 1.075$ is required to separate peaks by most packed column techniques, since plate counts > 7400 are not easily obtained. A good review on the choice of liquid phases was written by Supina and Rose [21]. Their table of the Rohrschneider Constants for 80 common liquid phases enables the experimenter to decide, almost by inspection, whether it is worth trying a particular liquid phase. Equally important, it identifies very similar phases. For example, in terms of selectivity, the following liquid phases have identical chromatographic properties: SE-30, OV-1, and OV-101; Celanese Ester No. 9 and diisodecyl phthalate; QF-1 and OV-210; and OS-124 and OV-25.

However, relative retention is not the sole criterion for choosing a liquid phase. Also important are temperature limitations (both minimum and maximum), absolute solubility, cost, and availability. The minimum temperature limit is determined by the viscosity or melting point of the liquid phase. As the liquid phase viscosity increases, the mass transfer between the gas and liquid phases becomes so slow that excessive peak broadening occurs. The maximum column temperature, on the other hand, is determined by the vapor pressure of the liquid phase and by its thermal stability (column bleed). Most manufacturers' accessory catalogs list maximum stationary phase temperatures, but they are frequently optimistic.

6.3.5. Temperature

6.3.5.1. Injection-port temperature

The conventional injection port for packed columns should be hot enough to vaporize the sample so rapidly that no loss in efficiency results from the injection technique. On the other hand, the injection port temperature must be low enough so that thermal decomposition is avoided. Injection port temperatures for capillary columns are different, as has been discussed earlier.

6.3.5.2. Detector temperature

The influence of temperature on the detector depends upon the type of detector employed. As a general rule, the detector and the connections from the column exit to the detector must be hot enough so that condensation of the sample and/or "column bleed" do not occur. Peak broadening and loss of component peaks are characteristic of condensation. The stability and, therefore, the detection limits of a TCD depend upon the stability of the detector temperature control, which should be $\pm 0.1°C$ or better. For FID, the temperature must be maintained high enough to avoid not only condensation of the samples, but also of the water or by-products formed in the combustion process. A reasonable minimum temperature for a FID is 125°C (see Chap. 6.3.6).

6.3.5.3. Column temperature

The column is temperature-controlled so that the separation will occur at a reproducible temperature. In addition, it is necessary for the column to be operable over a wide range of temperatures, from $-180°C$ up to 400°C. The control of column temperature is one of the easiest and most effective ways to influence the separation. Separations are determined by the ratio of distribution coefficients, and thus, α is temperature-dependent.

The column temperature should be high enough for the analysis to be completed in a reasonable length of time. On the other hand, higher column temperatures usually decrease the relative retention and the capacity ratio of sample components and therefore generally result in poorer resolution. According to a simple approximation made by Giddings [22], the retention time doubles for every 30°C decrease in column temperature. For most samples, the lower the temperature the better the separation. Fig. 6.7 shows the elution pattern of a hydrocarbon sample, chromatographed on the same column at 75°C, 110°C, and 130°C. At 75°C, the vapor pressures of the sample components are low and they move slowly through the column. Two isomers of octane are well resolved before the C_8 peak. The analysis time is 24 min. As the temperature increases, the retention times decrease. At 110°C the C_{12} peak is recorded in 8 min, and at 130°C the analysis is completed in 4 min. However, at the higher temperatures the resolution decreases and the octane isomers are no longer resolved.

6.3.5.4. Isothermal vs. programed temperature

Isothermal analysis means a chromatographic analysis that is performed at constant column temperature while in programed temperature the column temperature is increased with time, usually at a linear rate. Temperature programing is essential for the analysis of mixtures having a wide boiling range.

As shown in Fig. 6.8, isothermal operation limits GC analysis to samples of a narrow boiling range. At constant temperature, the early peaks, representing low-boiling components, emerge so rapidly that the peaks are sharp but overlap, while higher-boiling materials emerge later as short, broad peaks. In some cases, high-boiling components are not eluted at all, and may appear in a later analysis as baseline noise or "ghost" peaks. In temperature programing, the initial temperature is low and the early peaks are well resolved (larger k values). As the temperature

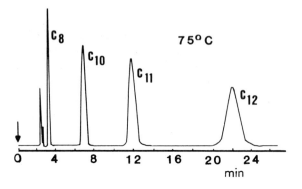

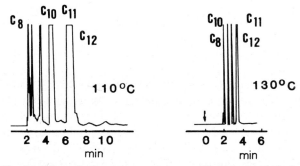

Fig. 6.7. Effect of column temperature on analysis time and resolution of a hydrocarbon sample.

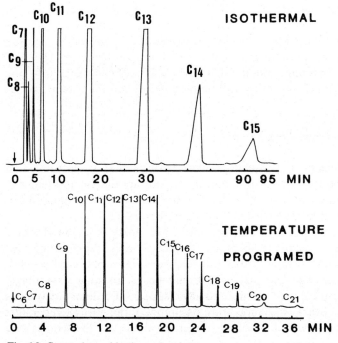

Fig. 6.8. Comparison of isothermal and temperature programed chromatograms.

increases, higher-boiling compounds appear as sharp peaks, similar in shape to the early peaks. A particular advantage is that trace components emerge as sharp peaks, which can be more easily distinguished from the baseline. For complex samples, total analysis time is shortened by temperature programing, although the column must be cooled and equilibrated before it can be reused. Generally, if the range of boiling points in a sample is 100°C or more, temperature programing is advisable.

6.3.6. Detectors

6.3.6.1. Detector characteristics

The chromatographic detector generates an electrical signal proportional to the amount of sample leaving the column. Detectors may be classified into two groups, concentration-dependent and mass rate-dependent detectors. In concentration-dependent detectors (e.g., TCD and ECD) the detector signal is proportional to the concentration of the sample in the carrier gas. In mass rate-dependent detectors (e.g., FID) the detector signal is dependent on the mass of sample passing through the detector per unit time (g/sec). We shall first define the primary detector characteristics.

6.3.6.1.1. Sensitivity
This means the amount of signal generated for a given sample concentration, or mass rate. A sensitive detector will generate a large electrical signal for a given sample size. Sensitivity can be measured as the slope of the plot of detector response vs. sample concentration or mass rate.

6.3.6.1.2. Noise
This refers to random, short-term detector response, depending on electrical properties, temperature sensitivity, or flow sensitivity. Long-term noise (minutes to hours) is commonly called drift. Noise is one factor which determines the minimum quantity of sample that can be detected. The amount of sample which generates a signal two times the noise level is defined as the minimum detectable quantity (m.d.q.). Sensitivity, peak width, and noise determine the m.d.q.

6.3.6.1.3. Universal response
This means that the detector generates a response for all sample components. This is a desirable characteristic. Among the commonly available detectors, only the TCD shows universal response.

6.3.6.1.4. Selective response
This means that the detector responds to only certain types of compounds; e.g., the flame photometric detector mainly responds to compounds containing S or P atoms. This is useful in certain specific applications, e.g., the determination of sulfur-containing pollutants in air.

References on p. A223

6.3.6.1.5. Linear range

This means the region over which the detector signal is directly proportional to sample concentration or mass flowrate. Stated in another way, it means the range over which the plot of log detector response vs. log concentration is linear with a slope of 1.0. A wide linear range is obviously useful for quantitative analysis of samples containing major, minor as well as trace components.

The two most commonly used detectors are the TCD and the FID.

6.3.6.2. Thermal conductivity detector

6.3.6.2.1. Theory of operation

The TCD works on the principle that a hot body will lose heat at a rate which depends upon the composition of the surrounding gas. Thus, the rate of heat loss can be used as a measure of the gas composition.

Fig. 6.9 shows a typical TCD, consisting of a tungsten filament supported inside a cavity. The cavity is in a stainless steel block to provide a constant reference temperature. The heated filament can lose heat to the cooler block by the following processes:

  (a) thermal conduction to the gas stream,
  (b) convection (free and forced),
  (c) radiation,
  (d) conduction through the metal contacts.

The major processes are heat loss through gaseous thermal conduction and forced convection. These two processes account for 75% or more of the total filament heat loss. Use of a light carrier gas, such as helium or hydrogen, will cause the loss by thermal conductivity to predominate. In the following discussion it is assumed that thermal conduction by the carrier gas is the only mode of heat transfer.

Heat is transferred instantaneously by conduction when carrier gas molecules strike the heated filament. The larger the flowrates, the greater the rate of heat loss.

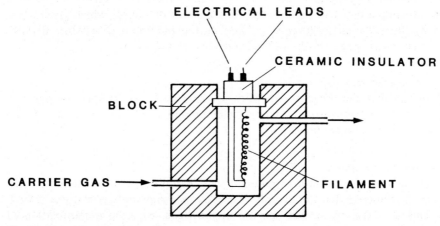

Fig. 6.9. Thermal-conductivity cell.

Thus, the TCD is flow-sensitive. Differences in thermal conductivity of gases are based on the mobility or speed with which the gas molecules diffuse: the smaller the molecule, the higher its mobility and the higher its thermal conductivity. Thus, hydrogen and helium, which are the smallest molecules, have the highest thermal conductivity. Table 6.4 gives the thermal conductivities (in c.g.s. units and at 0°C) of several compounds and shows how thermal conductivity decreases with increasing molecular weight.

6.3.6.2.2. Detector cell construction

The electrical resistance of the spiral metal filament in the TCD (see Fig. 6.9) varies greatly with temperature (i.e., it has a high temperature coefficient of resistance). In the most common mode, a constant current is passed through the filament, causing its temperature to rise. In a typical TCD, with helium carrier gas and a filament current of 175 mA, the filament may reach an equilibrium temperature of 100°C above the detector block temperature. When pure carrier gas is flowing through, the heat loss is constant and the filament temperature is constant. When a sample is eluted from the column, its molecules are larger, they will move more slowly and conduct less heat. The filament temperature will increase, causing a corresponding increase in its electrical resistance. It is this filament resistance change which is measured by a Wheatstone bridge circuit.

Filaments are chosen on the basis of a high temperature coefficient of resistance and resistance to chemical corrosion. Common filament metals are platinum, tungsten, and tungsten alloys. The popular WX filaments from GowMac are made of tungsten containing 4% rhenium. Thermistor beads are also used in TCD. They are made of rare-earth oxides and possess a negative temperature coefficient of resistance. They are generally used in the range of 0 to 100°C, but are not as popular as metallic filaments. Thermistor beads are more sensitive only at the lower temperatures, but they lack the stability and wide temperature range of metallic filaments. They are also useful in portable gas chromatographs, since their power requirements are small. The sensitivity of a TCD may be increased by increasing the filament current, decreasing the block temperature, and choosing a carrier gas with high thermal conductivity. In some cases, special filaments of higher resistance or

TABLE 6.4

THERMAL CONDUCTIVITIES OF SELECTED GASES

Compound	Thermal conductivity $(\lambda \times 10^5)$	Molecular weight
Hydrogen	41.6	2
Helium	34.8	4
Methane	7.2	16
Nitrogen	5.8	28
Pentane	3.1	72
Hexane	3.0	86

References on p. A223

TABLE 6.5

SUMMARY OF TCD CHARACTERISTICS

Minimum detectable quantity	10^{-8} g/sec; ca. 50 ppm
Response	universal
Linearity	10^4
Stability	good
Carrier gas	He or H_2
Temperature limit	400°C

specially designed cell blocks may increase sensitivity. Table 6.5 summarizes the characteristics of this detector.

6.3.6.3. Flame-ionization detector

6.3.6.3.1. Theory of operation

Ionization detectors operate on the principle that the electrical conductivity of a gas is directly proportional to the concentration of charged particles within the gas. In the FID a hydrogen flame serves as the ionizing source. Carrier gas from the column flows into the flame, which ionizes some of the organic molecules in the gas stream. The presence of charged particles (positive ions, negative ions, and electrons) within the electrode gap causes a current to flow through a measuring resistor. The resulting voltage drop is amplified by an electrometer and fed to a recorder.

It is helpful to think of the electrode gap as a variable resistor the resistance value of which is determined by the number of charged particles within the gap. When an organic component passes into the flame, it is combusted anc charged particles are formed, decreasing the resistance of the gap and increasing the current. This current is amplified and fed to the recorder. The recorder response is proportional to the quantity of organic compound eluted from the column.

6.3.6.3.2. Detector cell construction

Fig. 6.10 shows a diagram of a FID. Hydrogen and column effluent are mixed and burned in the flame. Air passes through the detector base to support the flame. Oxygen may also be used. In one common arrangement the flame jet is isolated and serves as one electrode. The cylindrical collection electrode is at 300 V positive. Charged particles generated in the flame migrate to the polarized electrodes and cause a current to flow.

6.3.6.3.3. FID response

The FID responds only to organic compounds. Some of the gases which give no response are: air, H_2O, noble gases, CO, CO_2, CS_2, NO, SO_2, and H_2S. Although the FID gives no response to the compounds listed, they may affect the response of other compounds if they are eluted together with them, and this effect may be difficult to recognize. The lack of response to air and water makes the FID

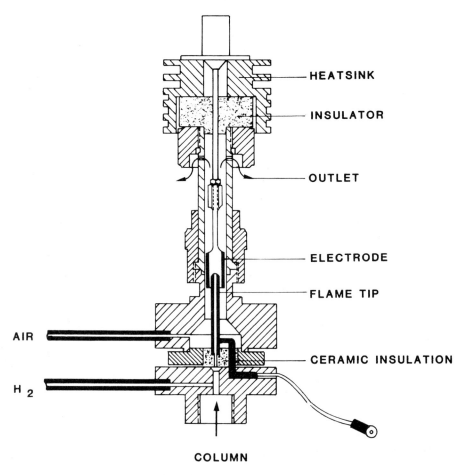

HEATSINK

INSULATOR

OUTLET

ELECTRODE

FLAME TIP

AIR

CERAMIC INSULATION

H$_2$

COLUMN

Fig. 6.10. Flame-ionization detector.

particularly suitable for the analysis of trace organic matter in air or water or aqueous samples, such as alcoholic beverages and biological materials.

6.3.6.3.4. Effect of hydrogen and air flowrates

The FID performance depends on the proper choice of gas flowrates. A general rule is to use a $1:1:10$ relative flow ratio of H$_2$/carrier gas/air. Thus, a carrier gas flow of 30 ml/min would require H$_2$ and air flowrates of 30 and 300 ml/min, respectively, for optimum performance of the FID. These ratios are only guidelines; it is best to determine optimum H$_2$ and air flowrates experimentally.

Fig. 6.11 (left) shows the relationship between FID response and H$_2$ flowrate (ml/min). The carrier gas flowrate was 30 ml/min for the curves shown. The FID response is a sensitive function of H$_2$ flowrate, and individual detectors should be calibrated to determine the H$_2$ flowrate that gives maximum response. The optimum

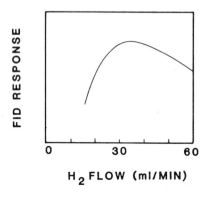
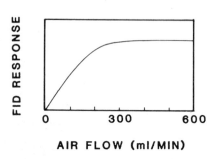

Fig. 6.11. Response of FID to hydrogen (left) and air (right) flow.

flowrate for this detector was 30 ml/min. Fig. 6.11 (right) shows the effect of air flow on FID response. A minimum of 300 ml/min is required for a good detector response. Additional air does not increase the detector response, but it may produce more noise.

Table 6.6 summarizes the FID characteristics. It is a very sensitive device with the widest linear range of any detector in common use. The combination of high sensitivity and wide linear range makes the FID an excellent detector for quantitative trace analysis.

6.3.6.4. Electron-capture detector

6.3.6.4.1. Operating principles

The ECD (Fig. 6.12) measures the loss of signal rather than an increase in electrical current. As the carrier gas flows through the detector, a radioactive ^{63}Ni or tritiated foil (β-emitters) ionizes the gas and slow electrons are formed. These electrons migrate to the anode, which normally has a potential of ca. 90 V. When collected, these slow electrons produce a standing current of ca. 10^{-8} A, which is amplified by an electrometer. If a sample containing electron-capturing molecules enters the detector, this standing current will be reduced. This loss in current is

TABLE 6.6

SUMMARY OF FID CHARACTERISTICS

Minimum detectable quantity	5×10^{-12} g/sec
Response	sensitive only to organic compounds
Linearity	10^6
Stability	excellent (relatively insensitive to temperature and flow changes)
Temperature limit	400°C
Carrier gas	N_2, He, or H_2

RADIOACTIVE FOIL

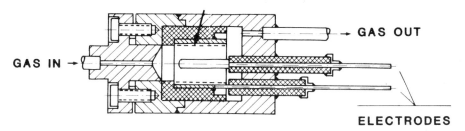

GAS IN →

→ **GAS OUT**

ELECTRODES

Fig. 6.12. Electron-capture detector.

displayed as a positive peak. Most modern ECD have pulsed-voltage variable-frequency power supplies which maintain a constant current. Without sample, the pulse frequency is very low. As the sample enters the detector, the frequency increases to offset the current loss due to the electron-capturing species. The pulse frequency is proportional to the sample concentration and can be used for quantitative analysis.

6.3.6.4.2. Detector selectivity and sensitivity

The ECD is extremely sensitive to certain molecules, such as polyhaloalkanes, conjugated carbonyls, nitriles, nitrates, aromatic polynitro compounds, and organometallics. It is virtually insensitive to hydrocarbons, alcohols, and ketones. Stated in another way, the detector selectively responds to molecules containing electronegative atoms or groups; these species easily capture an electron and thus produce a loss in standing current. Selective sensitivity to halides makes this detector especially valuable for the analysis of pesticides, some of which can be detected below picogram levels.

6.3.6.4.3. Radioactive source

A radioactive source is an essential part of the ECD. It effects the primary ionization of the carrier gas. Both ^3H and ^{63}Ni have been employed. The ^3H design was used first. Tritium on Ti foil is limited to 220°C and easily becomes contaminated with high-boiling samples. When the radioactive surface becomes coated, the primary emission decreases and the detector loses sensitivity. Tritium on Sc can be used up to 300°C, but the ^{63}Ni source can be heated to 350°C. Since it can be maintained at a higher temperature and therefore can be used for months without the need for cleaning, it is the most common source today.

6.3.6.4.4. Linearity

All ECD suffer from a limited linear range. Because the detectors are easily saturated, very dilute samples should be injected. Samples must be dry, since traces of water destroy the normal detector response. Table 6.7 summarizes the characteristics of this detector.

References on p. A223

TABLE 6.7

SUMMARY OF ECD CHARACTERISTICS

Minimum detectable quantity	10^{-12} g/sec
Response	very selective
Linearity	500–10,000
Stability	fair
Temperature limit	220°C (^{3}H); 350°C (^{63}Ni)
Carrier gas	N_2 or $Ar + 5\%$ CH_4

6.3.6.5. Nitrogen–phosphorus detector

Page and Wooley [23] have proposed a mechanism for the response of the NPD, which has also been named thermionic, sodium-thermionic, phosphorus, and phosphorus-sensitized FID. They wrote:

"Karmen and Guiffrida [24,25] have shown that a conventional flame-ionization detector shows a specific enhancement of response to nitrogen-, phosphorus- or halogen-containing compounds in the presence of the vapor of a sodium salt. Originally this was provided by introducing a gauze covered with sodium hydroxide into the flame, but later developments showed that an equal response resulted if a sodium salt was fused onto the electrode system [25] or if the burner tip was embedded in a ceramic tube [26] containing the sodium salt. It has been claimed that the conductivity of the flame produced by the sodium salt as it volatilizes is increased when a phosphorus-containing compound is eluted from a gas chromatograph column, and that this increase is a function of the amount of phosphorus (or nitrogen or halogen) in the eluate [26]. It is also claimed that quantities of the order of 10^{-10} gram of phosphorus (corresponding to a partial pressure of 10^{-8} atm in the flame gases) may be detected by this technique, and commercial detectors are now on the market, using cesium bromide instead of the sodium hydroxide or sulfate".

The NPD shows excellent selectivity towards phosphorus- and nitrogen-containing compounds and fair selectivity for halogens. It has been used extensively in pesticide residue analyses and in the analysis of biological samples, which contain nitrogen. Table 6.8 summarizes the characteristics of the NPD.

TABLE 6.8

SUMMARY OF NPD CHARACTERISTICS

Minimum detectable quant	10^{-11} g (parathion)/sec
Response	very selective, sensitive to N and P compounds, some halogens
Linearity	10^4
Stability	fair
Temperature limit	300°C
Carrier gas	N_2 or He

6.4. QUALITATIVE AND QUANTITATIVE ANALYSIS

6.4.1. Qualitative analysis

The chromatogram itself provides information useful for qualitative analyses. Both absolute and relative retention data are used. The simplest and most frequently used technique is the comparison of retention times of standards with components of the sample. Unfortunately, retention times are dependent on a large number of operating parameters, in particular, on column temperature and flowrate and even on the weight percent of liquid phase and sample size. For these reasons, relative retention times are more reliable than absolute retention times.

6.4.1.1. Relative retention

In this technique the retention of the analyte is measured relative to a standard. The use of relative retention values minimizes problems arising from small changes in column temperature or flowrate. The most widely used system for qualitative analysis is the "Retention Index" (R.I.) proposed by Wehrli and Kováts [27]. This system is based on the retention of any compound relative to n-alkanes. Experimentally, the system is simple: the analyte is chromatographed with a series of n-alkanes chosen so that the n-alkanes are eluted both before and after the analyte; a semi-log plot of adjusted retention time vs. carbon number of the n-alkanes is prepared; each n-alkane is assigned a R.I. of 100 times the number of carbon atoms (e.g., butane has a R.I. of 400); the analyte is entered on the linear plot for the n-alkanes, and its R.I. is either read from the graph or calculated by the equation:

$$\text{R.I.} = 100 \times \frac{\log r_{x,z}}{\log r_{z+1,z}} + 100z \tag{6.24}$$

where $r_{x,z}$ is the retention of analyte relative to a n-alkane with carbon number z, and $r_{z+1,z}$ is the retention of the n-alkane with $z + 1$ carbon atoms relative to the n-alkane with z carbon atoms.

The Kováts retention indices are probably the most widely used chromatographic data for qualitative analyses. Calculations can be made automatically by several commercially available data systems; the n-alkane standards are readily available; and many lists of R.I. values for different liquid phases and different temperatures are in the literature.

6.4.1.2. Auxiliary techniques

Unfortunately, comparisons of chromatographic retention data cannot confirm peak identity absolutely. Several compounds may have identical or very close retention times. Even the use of two columns with different liquid phases is not considered a confirmatory technique. Auxiliary techniques, such as MS, NMR, or IR are necessary. MS is the most widely used technique for GC peak confirmation. Directly coupled GC–MS systems are routinely used in many laboratories. NMR is

References on p. A223

less frequently used, since fairly large (mg) quantities of sample are required. IR is also useful and, with the more recent introduction of FTIR–GC, it is gaining in popularity.

6.4.2. Quantitative analysis

Most gas chromatographs are used for quantitative analysis. GC systems are well suited for quantitative analysis over a wide range of sample sizes ($10^{-12}-10^{-6}$ g). Either peak heights or peak areas can be measured and related to the quantity of the analyte. A variety of quantitative techniques are available.

6.4.2.1. Area normalization

This is the simplest procedure, based on the assumption that area percent for a compound, A, is equal to weight percent.

$$\text{wt\% } A = \frac{\text{Area}_A}{\Sigma \text{ Area}} \times 100 \tag{6.25}$$

where Σ Area is the total area. This is rarely the case. When a FID is used for high-boiling members of a homologous series, reasonable quantitative results are possible, but in all other cases, one of the techniques given below is recommended.

6.4.2.2. Detector correction factors

In this procedure individual correction factors are determined for each compound. They are used to correct the measured areas, and then a simple normalization of corrected areas will produce the proper weight percent of each component.

$$\text{wt\% } A = \frac{\text{Area}_A \cdot \text{Factor}_A}{\Sigma \text{ Areas} \cdot \text{Factors}} \times 100 \tag{6.26}$$

Detectors respond differently to different compounds, and for this reason a detector correction (or calibration) factor must be used for each compound. Fortunately, there are published lists of correction factors for many compounds for use with either TCD or FID [28].

Correction factors can also be determined experimentally. A plot of detector response (either peak height or peak area) vs. analyte quantity is made. This curve is often called a calibration curve. The slope of this curve (area/g) will give the corrected area when divided into the measured area of a peak. However, because some calibration curves have a limited linear range, samples must be diluted to produce an area which falls into this range.

6.4.2.3. Internal standard

Internal standardization is a popular technique in GC, particularly when only one component (or at most a few components) must be quantitated. An internal

TABLE 6.9

ACCURACIES OBTAINABLE IN GC

Concentration	Standard deviation (%)
>1.0%	1– 10
0.01–1%	10– 20
1–100 ppm	20–100

standard is chosen which is not normally present in the sample. It should be well resolved from all other peaks and be present at a concentration close to that of the analyte. A calibration curve is plotted by chromatographing at least three synthetic mixtures of internal standard and analyte. These mixtures must cover the range of concentrations expected in the sample. Ratios of peak areas are plotted against ratios of weights. Finally, a known amount of internal standard is added to a known amount of sample. The area ratios of this sample are determined and, when plotted on the calibration curve, the ratio of weights is obtained. Since the weight of internal standard added earlier is known, the weight of the sample component is easily calculated. This technique is recommended for manual syringe injections, since extremely accurate injections are not required. The critical steps are: (a) finding an appropriate internal standard and (b) blending accurately the mixtures for the calibration curve.

6.4.2.4. External standard (absolute calibration)

This method is simpler than the internal standard procedure, but it does require a very reproducible injection technique. It is the recommended procedure when sample valves can be used. Synthetic blends containing a range of accurately known concentrations of the analyte are made and used to prepare a calibration curve (peak area vs. concentration). This requires a pure sample of the analyte. The same volume of unknown sample is now injected; the analyte area is measured and the concentration is read from the calibration curve.

The accuracies obtainable by GC depend on many factors, including: accuracy of available standards, reproducibility of technique, reproducibility of chromatographic system, reproducibility of the data systems, and the particular algorithms used by the data system. Accuracy largely depends on sample concentrations, and Table 6.9 shows the range of accuracies expected under carefully controlled conditions and under the assumptions that the peaks are eluted with essentially no loss in the column and that a digital electronic integrator is used to measure peak areas.

REFERENCES

1 C.A. Cramers and J.A. Rijks, *Adv. Chromatogr.*, 17 (1979) 101.
2 G. Schomburg, in R.E. Kaiser (Editor), *Proc. 4th Intern. Symp. Hindelang 1981*, Hüthig, Heidelberg, 1981, p. 371.

3 K. Grob and G. Grob, *J. Chromatogr. Sci.*, 7 (1969) 584.

4 G. Schomburg, H. Behlau, R. Dielmann, H. Husmann and F. Weeke, *J. Chromatogr.*, 122 (1976) 55.

5 K. Grob and K. Grob, Jr., *J. Chromatogr.*, 151 (1978) 311.

6 K. Grob and K. Grob, Jr., *J. High Resolut. Chromatogr. Chromatogr. Commun.*, 1 (1978) 263.

7 M. Galli, S. Trestianu and K. Grob, Jr., *J. High Resolut. Chromatogr. Chromatogr. Commun.*, 2 (1979) 366.

8 M. Galli and S. Trestianu, *J. Chromatogr.*, 203 (1981) 193.

9 W. Jennings, *Gas Chromatography with Glass Capillary Columns*, Academic Press, New York, 2nd Edn., 1980.

10 L.S. Ettre and J.E. Purcell, *Adv. Chromatogr.*, 10 (1974) 1.

11 I. Halász and E. Heine, *Adv. Chromatogr.*, 4 (1967) 207.

12 M.N. Myers and J.C. Giddings, *Anal. Chem.*, 38 (1966) 294.

13 J.F.K. Huber, H.H. Lauer and H. Poppe, *J. Chromatogr.*, 112 (1975) 377.

14 C.A. Cramers, J.A. Rijks and P. Boček, *Clin. Chim. Acta*, 34 (1971) 159.

15 M.N. Myers and J.C. Giddings, *Anal. Chem.*, 37 (1965) 1453.

16 M. Golay in D.H. Desty (Editor), *Gas Chromatography 1958*, Butterworths, London, 1959, p. 36.

17 J.C. Giddings, *Anal. Chem.*, 36 (1964) 741.

18 D.E. Martire and D.C. Locke, *Anal. Chem.*, 37 (1965) 144.

19 C.A. Cramers, F.A. Wijnheijmer and J.A. Rijks, *J. High Resolut. Chromatogr. Chromatogr. Commun.*, 2 (1979) 329.

20 C.P.M. Schutjes, E.A. Vermeer, J.A. Rijks and C.A. Cramers, in R.E. Kaiser (Editor), *Proc. 4th Intern. Symp. Hindelang 1981*, Hüthig, Heidelberg, 1981, p. 687.

21 W.R. Supina and L.P. Rose, *J. Chromatogr.*, 8 (1970) 214.

22 J.C. Giddings, *J. Chem. Educ.*, 39 (1962) 569.

23 F.M. Page and D.E. Wooley, *Anal. Chem.*, 40 (1968) 210.

24 A. Karmen, *Anal. Chem.*, 36 (1964) 1416.

25 A. Karmen and L. Guiffrida, *Nature (London)*, 201 (1964) 1204.

26 L. Guiffrida, *J. Ass. Offic. Anal. Chem.*, 47 (1964) 293.

27 A. Wehrli and E. Kováts, *Helv. Chim. Acta*, 42 (1959) 2709.

28 W.A. Dietz, *J. Gas Chromatogr.*, 5 (1967) 68.

Chapter 7

Ion-exchange chromatography

H.F. WALTON

CONTENTS

7.1. HISTORICAL INTRODUCTION

Although synthetic ion exchangers were known since 1935, the separation of the lanthanide fission products during the second world war gave a powerful impetus to

References on p. A253

ion-exchange chromatography. It came to the attention of the scientific world at a memorable symposium held in New York in 1947 [1]. At that time the cation-exchange resins used in columns were mainly condensation products of phenol and formaldehyde, for the modern ion-exchange resins based on crosslinked polystyrene had only just appeared. At the symposium the importance of small and uniform particles of resin was noted, and column performance was shown to be improved by raising the temperature. The theoretical-plate model was elaborated to interpret the spreading of chromatographic bands. For the separation of lanthanides, buffered citrate eluents were employed to take advantage of differences in complex-ion stabilities, for it was recognized that ion exchange itself was not sufficiently selective to separate the lanthanide ions. The elements emerging from the columns were monitored continuously by measurement of their radioactivity.

These early researches laid the groundwork for the high-performance ion-exchange chromatography that we know today. The method was not restricted to inorganic ions: very soon, in 1951, the separation of amino acids by cation exchange was announced [2]. They were eluted from resin columns one meter long by citrate buffers flowing at 4 ml/h for about a week. The pH of the eluent was raised at intervals during this time, and the amino acids emerged, roughly, in the order of decreasing acid strength. They were detected and monitored by post-column reaction with ninhydrin. Another big task of biochemical analysis, stimulated by the need to know more about biological effects of radiation, was to separate the hydrolysis products of nucleic acids. This was accomplished by chromatography on columns of cation- and anion-exchange resins, the eluted products being detected by their UV absorbance [3]. It was seen that organic compounds did not have to be ionic to be retained on ion-exchange resins; sugars could be held as their negatively charged borate complexes [4] and could be absorbed as uncharged species from aqueous alcohol by both cation- and anion-exchange resins [5]. The second process was one of partition, not ion exchange.

Fast HPLC by ion exchange became possible with the development of pellicular ion exchangers in 1967 [6]. These were applied to the separation of nucleotides, with continuous monitoring of the effluent by a sensitive differential UV absorbance detector, the detector that is used in most of the liquid chromatography performed today. The HPLC of inorganic ions lagged behind that of organic compounds because of the difficulty of monitoring their appearance in the effluent. Long, laborious separations, in which many fractions were collected and individually analyzed, were necessary, but it was obvious that very large separation factors could be obtained. Cationic species were readily separated from neutral or anionic species because one charge type was retained by the resin while the other was not. The selective formation of complex anions or cations allowed the analysis of very complicated mixtures without the need for high-performance columns, and a vast literature that has appeared over the past 35 years describes many such separations. Anion exchange in aqueous hydrochloric acid solutions is a particularly powerful method of separating metals, because anionic metal-chloride complexes differ enormously in stability and in strength of binding to resins, and the differences can be enhanced by using mixed aqueous–nonaqueous solvents [7,8].

Today we are seeing the development of new detection methods and the fast, sensitive chromatographic analysis of inorganic ions. The exchangers themselves have undergone surprisingly little change. Basically, one type—exchangers based on crosslinked polystyrene—does most of the work.

7.2. ION-EXCHANGING MATERIALS

7.2.1. General considerations

Ion exchange is the reversible interchange of ions of like sign between a solution and a solid, insoluble body (Fig. 7.1). The solid must carry ions of its own, fixed ions that are attached by covalent bonds to the molecular framework, and exchangeable or mobile ions, held by electrostatic forces, that can move in and out of the solid and change places with ions from the solution, conserving electro-neutrality. Most of the mobile ions have charges opposite to those of the fixed ions and are called counterions. However, ions having the same charge sign as the fixed ions may also be present. They are called co-ions, and their concentration in the exchanger is regulated by the Donnan equilibrium, which will be discussed below.

The solid exchanger must have an open molecular framework that allows the mobile ions to move freely in and out. Some solid exchangers have an extensive surface that carries fixed ions and an electrical double layer; clay minerals are of this type. Conventional ion exchangers, however, have a three-dimensional structure that is porous on the molecular scale. The structure may be crystalline, as in many inorganic exchangers, or amorphous, as in organic polymers.

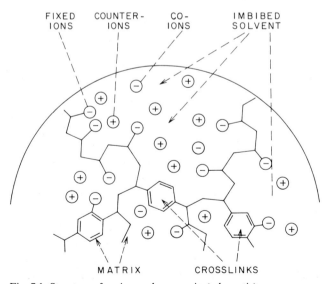

Fig. 7.1. Structure of an ion-exchange resin (schematic).

References on p. A253

7.2.2. Ion-exchange resins

Ion-exchange resins are crosslinked polymers that carry ionic functional groups. Typical resins are those made from styrene ($C_6H_5CH=CH_2$) and divinylbenzene ($H_2C=CH \cdot C_6H_4 \cdot CH=CH_2$). In the preparation of such resins, these two liquid compounds are mixed in the desired proportion, a chain-initiating catalyst is added, and the mixture is stirred in hot water containing a surfactant. Liquid droplets form, their size being influenced by rate of stirring, and polymerization thus gives perfectly spherical, transparent beads. The ionic functional groups are introduced into the crosslinked polystyrene matrix by appropriate chemical reactions. Sulfonic acid groups, $-SO_3H$, are added by treatment with sulfuric acid; the product is a cation exchanger. In the production of anion exchangers, quaternary ammonium groups are introduced by two consecutive reactions as follows, where X represents the aromatic polymer unit:

$$X-H + ClCH_2OCH_3 \rightleftharpoons X-CH_2Cl$$

$$X-CH_2Cl + N(CH_3)_3 \rightleftharpoons X-CH_2N(CH_3)_3^+ \, Cl^-$$

The crosslinked polymer structure looks like this:

Each aromatic ring, including the crosslinks derived from divinylbenzene, carries one functional group, as a rule. Chloromethylated polystyrene is the starting point for a variety of resins with special functional groups, such as the iminodiacetate group, $-CH_2N(CH_2COOH)_2$, which is incorporated into a chelating resin that has special affinity for heavy-metal ions and is used to collect traces of such metals from large volumes of natural waters. Other functional groups, like phosphonate ($-PO_3H_2$), can be introduced into the polymer directly.

A very important characteristic of these resins is the degree of crosslinking, which is determined by the proportion of divinylbenzene in the original monomer mix. "Eight percent crosslinked resin", the most common degree of crosslinking, means that the monomer mix contained 8 mole percent of divinylbenzene. The higher the degree of crosslinking, the tighter is the polymer structure and the more fixed ions per unit volume, but the harder it is for the mobile ions to diffuse in and out. Resins having low crosslinking allow fast diffusion and admit large counterions, but they swell inordinately in water and expand and contract with changes in concentration of the flowing solution; moreover, they are soft and collapse under high pressure. The 8% crosslinking commonly used offers a good compromise.

With anion-exchange resins the actual degree of crosslinking may be more than the mole per cent of divinylbenzene, the so-called "nominal" crosslinking, suggests. The $-CH_2Cl$ groups tend to link with benzene rings in neighboring polymer chains through the Friedel–Crafts reaction, eliminating hydrogen chloride. Another problem with quaternary-ammonium anion-exchange resins is that their hydroxyl forms, those in which the counterions are OH⁻, are somewhat unstable and slowly lose methanol, leaving tertiary-amine groups that are weakly basic. Decomposition is faster at higher temperatures and becomes serious above 60°C.

Cation-exchange resins of the sulfonated polystyrene type are well characterized, uniform, and very stable. The hydrogen-from resins decompose slowly above 100°C, but under normal operating conditions this breakdown is negligible.

Other than polystyrene resins, the only ion-exchanging polymers that are important in chromatography are the acrylate and methacrylate polymers, usually crosslinked with divinylbenzene, which contain carboxyl functional groups. These resins have a high affinity for heavy metals as long as the pH is high enough to ensure ionization of the carboxyl groups. The metal ions are easily stripped from the resin by elution with acid. Acrylic resins are soft and therefore unsuitable for high-pressure chromatography.

Resins of the condensation type are made from phenolic compounds and formaldehyde. Sulfonic groups can be introduced after condensation. Aliphatic polyamines can be condensed with formaldehyde to yield weakly basic anion exchangers. These resins have an important place in chemical processing, but very little importance in chromatography.

7.2.3. Macroporous resins

The polymers we have just described are internally homogeneous and are known as microporous, gel-type or conventional resins. A new type of polymer, called macroporous or macroreticular, has been developed to meet the needs of chemical processing, to combine fast ion exchange with low resistance to flow. These resins also have a place in chromatography.

Preparation of a macroporous resin requires a monomer mix containing a high proportion of crosslinking agent, say 50% of divinylbenzene, in a liquid that is a good solvent for the monomers but a poor one for the polymer. "Bead polymerization" is performed in the manner we have described. As the polymer forms, it precipitates in the form of very small particles, some hundreds of nanometers across, that stick to each other loosely and form roughly spherical aggregates, the size of the drops in the stirred liquid, that are internally very porous. In resins used for industrial purposes the aggregates are about 1 mm in diameter; special porous polymers made for chromatography have diameters of about 10 μm.

The best-known porous polymers in the U.S. are the "XAD resins" (Rohm and Haas, Philadelphia, PA, USA). The XAD-1, -2, and -4 resins are styrene polymers; the XAD-7 and -8 are acrylate polymers. They are hydrocarbons without added functional groups (though XAD-7 has carboxyl groups). Ionic groups can be introduced by treatment with sulfuric acid or by chloromethylation [9]. Macroporous resins have the advantage that they do not swell and shrink significantly when the solvent is changed, and they are particularly useful in nonaqueous solvents, where the conventional gel-type ion-exchange resins would shrink and become almost impermeable.

The nonionic macroporous polymers find important use in chemical analysis as collectors for traces of organic compounds in water [10,11], and are beginning to be used in HPLC [12,13]. Macroporous ion-exchange resins, on the other hand, have so far found little use in chromatography. Most of the available resins have particles that are too large for this purpose, and grinding only results in pulverizing the material. Attempts to obviate this problem by choosing macroporous resins that have been prepared in small particles sizes prove unsuccessful, because they produce chromatographic bands that are broad and show tailing. The reason may be that the tiny primary particles are inhomogenous, at least after sulfonation [14]. We may expect that the technology of producing macroporous ion-exchanging polymers will improve [15]. The field of "solvent-modified polymers" is wide and offers great possibilities [16].

7.2.4. Pellicular, bonded, and surface-modified exchangers

Conventional gel-type ion-exchange resins have the drawback that the exchanging ions must diffuse through the entire depth of the bead, and diffusion is slow. Exchange is faster with smaller beads, but then more pressure is needed; resistance to flow varies inversely as the square of the particle diameter. A novel solution is to coat beads of glass or silica, ca. 30 μm in diameter, with liquid monomer mix, and let the liquid film polymerize in situ, forming a film of polymer, ca. 1–2 μm thick, around the glass bead core. The film is then treated to introduce the ionic groups. The coated beads are called pellicular resins. Their introduction in 1967 [6] marked a major advance in the technique of HPLC. Whereas earlier it had taken many hours to separate nucleosides and bases from nucleic acids, they were now separated in a few minutes.

Pellicular resins are easy to pack into columns, and they combine fast mass transfer with low resistance to flow. However, the large particle diameter means that the "eddy diffusion" term in the band broadening is large, and with particles 30 μm in diameter one cannot obtain bands as sharp as with 5- to 10-μm particles. Pellicular resins have low exchange capacities, around 20 μeq/g, and are thus useless for preparative chromatography.

Bonded ion exchangers have ionic groups attached to a short carbon chain that is chemically, rather than physically, bound to a glass or silica core. Beads that are superficially porous give materials resembling the pellicular resins, with the same disadvantages, though they may have better physical and chemical stability. Internally porous silica microparticles, 5–10 μm in diameter, give bonded exchangers with much higher capacities and better resolving power. They are, however, more difficult to pack than the superficially porous materials and are not as robust. A typical reaction sequence producing bonded ion exchangers is this [17,18]:

$$-\underset{|}{\overset{|}{Si}}-OH + CH_3O \cdot \underset{|}{\overset{|}{Si}} \cdot CH=CH_2 \rightarrow -\underset{|}{\overset{|}{Si}}-O-\underset{|}{\overset{|}{Si}}-CH=CH_2$$

$$+ C_6H_5CH=CH_2 \rightarrow -\underset{|}{\overset{|}{Si}}-O-\underset{|}{\overset{|}{Si}}-(CH_2)_4-C_6H_5$$

The benzene ring is then sulfonated or chloromethylated; the chloromethylated product reacts with tertiary amines to give strong-base anion exchangers. These bonded ion exchangers have capacities which, on a volume basis, are comparable with those of gel-type resins.

Reaction of porous silica with $(CH_3O)_3SiCH_2CH_2CH_2NH_2$ gives a weakly basic anion exchanger, an "amino bonded phase" that is used to separate sugars [19,20]. "Glycophases" are an important class of bonded ion exchangers, used in HPLC of proteins. They are made by the reaction of controlled-porosity glass with an epoxide, $(CH_3O)_3Si(CH_2)_3OCH_2CH(O)CH_2$. The epoxy ring then serves as the point of attachment for a variety of nucleophilic reagents, like lactic acid, sulfuric acid or diethylamine, to give such functional groups as $-O-CH_2CH(OH)CH_2N(C_2H_5)_2$ or $-O-CH_2CH(OH)CH_2OCH_2COOH$ [21]. The ionic functional groups are attached to silica through a long, hydrophilic carbon chain that can be made even longer by reaction with additional epoxide molecules. The advantage for the chromatography of large molecules is clear. In addition to ion exchange, size exclusion has an important effect on retention, and proteins can be separated by size exclusion alone, if the chains attached to the glass or silica are hydrophilic but not ionic [22].

Surface-modified ion exchangers are homogeneous or microporous polymer beads (generally polystyrene) that have been chemically treated for a brief period so that they carry a thin surface layer of ion exchanger. Thus, e.g., a thin shell of sulfonated polystyrene may be supported on a core of unreacted polystyrene. The kinetics of formation of surface shells have been discussed [23].

The technique of "Ion Chromatography" (Chap. 7.5.4) depends on the use of such surface-active exchangers. The most suitable cation exchanger is made by sulfonating 50-μm spheres of 2% crosslinked styrene–divinylbenzene copolymer to a depth of 0.2 μm; the exchanger has a capacity of 20 μeq/g [24]. An anion exchanger can be prepared by coating the beads of this cation exchanger with very fine particles of strong-base anion-exchange resin; the attraction between the positive surface charge of the latter and the negative surface charge of the former holds the anion-exchange resin in place.

7.2.5. Inorganic ion exchangers

The first artificial ion exchangers were aluminosilicate gels. They had poor chemical stability, being easily attacked by acids and alkalis. With the growth of the nuclear power industry and the need for selective ionic absorbents that would be resistant to radiation, a new type of inorganic ion exchanger was developed. The most successful of these has been precipitated zirconium phosphate, a cation exchanger with high selectivity for cesium over rubidium, rubidium over potassium, and strontium over calcium. The fixed anions are phosphonate ions, which bind protons tightly; the exchange capacity and the selectivity therefore depend on pH. Selectivity is highest at low pH, where the capacity is lowest.

Zirconium phosphate is representative of a large class of cation exchangers that can be formally considered as combinations of hydrous oxides of elements of the fourth, fifth, and sixth groups of the periodic table [25]. Other examples include zirconium molybdate and tungstate and tin(IV) phosphate. Some hydrous oxides of single elements in these groups have useful ion-exchange properties: e.g., zirconium oxide acts as a cation exchanger at high pH and as an anion exchanger at low pH; antimony pentoxide, having a high affinity for sodium ions, is used to remove unwanted excesses of sodium after irradiation for activation analysis [26,27]; stannic oxide absorbs fluoride ions selectively [28]. Heteropoly acids form another large class of inorganic ion exchangers. Yet another is formed by the mixed ferrocyanides [25]. Silver hydrogen ferrocyanide retains cesium more than twice as strongly as rubidium.

Inorganic ion exchangers have not been used in HPLC, because their physical form is unsuitable. The amorphous materials pulverize easily, while the crystalline forms react too slowly. However, some very impressive separations of alkali and alkaline-earth metal ions have been made with short columns and gravity flow [29], and the very high selectivities for certain ions make batch separations feasible in some cases. The main uses of these exchangers have been in radiochemical separations.

7.2.6. Exchangers based on cellulose and dextran

Exchangers in which functional groups are attached to matrices consisting of modified celluloses or dextrans crosslinked with epichlorohydrin (Sephadex exchangers; Pharmacia) are widely used in biochemical analysis for absorbing and exchanging large ions. They may carry sulfonate, carboxylate, phosphonate, weak or strong base functionalities. Because of their physical form, they must be used with gravity flow or under only moderate pressure [30]. Ion-exchanging hydrophilic, macroporous glycol–methacrayte polymers ("Spherons") absorb and exchange proteins and carbohydrates, and are rigid enough to offer the possibility of forced-flow, high-speed chromatography [31].

7.3. PHYSICAL PROPERTIES OF ION-EXCHANGE RESINS

7.3.1. Swelling and osmotic pressure

Conventional gel-type, microporous resins are internally homogeneous and behave like drops of concentrated electrolyte solution. Indeed, concentrated solutions of p-toluenesulfonic acid and its salts are good thermodynamic models for sulfonated polystyrene cation exchangers. The more highly crosslinked the resins, the more concentrated is the internal solution, because the crosslinks act like springs to restrain the swelling that is a consequence of the osmotic pressure. The magnitude of the internal pressure can be estimated as mRT, where m is the molality of the mobile ions within the resin; the fixed ions do not contribute to the pressure. In an 8% crosslinked polystyrene-type resin, the internal molality is about 5 or more. The internal pressure is then $5RT = 125$ atmospheres.

A more convincing way of calculating the internal pressure is to consider the effect of pressure on the partial molal free energy of water: $(\partial \overline{G}/\partial P)_{T,n} = \overline{V}$, where

$\overline{V}$ is the partial molal volume of liquid water, P is the pressure, T is the temperature, and n the mole fraction of water. $\overline{G}$, the partial molal free energy, is also called the chemical potential.

Consider two ion-exchange resins, one having normal crosslinking, the other having very low crosslinking. Let each contain the same amount of water in relation to the fixed ionic groups. The mole fractions of water in each resin may be considered the same, and the water is in the same chemical environment. The vapor pressure of water above the normally crosslinked resin is designated p, the vapor pressure above the weakly crosslinked resin p', the internal pressures within the two resins P and P', respectively. Now, the chemical potential, $\overline{G}$, of water must be the same inside and outside the resin, if equilibrium exists. The vapor pressure outside the normal resin, p, is greater than that outside the weakly crosslinked resin, p', because the water inside the normal resin is under a greater pressure. The free energy gain when a mole of water is transferred from the weakly crosslinked to the normal resin equals:

$$RT \ln \frac{P}{P'} = \overline{V}(P-P')$$

If the crosslinking of the first resin is very low, P' is close to zero, and P is the osmotic pressure of the solution inside the normal resin.

In a classic series of experiments [32,33] it was found that an 8% crosslinked polystyrene sulfonic acid resin, saturated with water at 100% humidity, contained 11.5 moles of water per mole of ionic groups. A 0.5% crosslinked resin of the same type contained 11.5 moles of water per mole of ionic groups when the humidity was only 90%. The internal osmotic pressure of the 8% crosslinked resin was therefore $RT/V \ln(100/90) = 143$ atmospheres, taking $\overline{V} = 18$ cc/mole and $T = 298°$K.

The amount of water absorbed by a resin depends on the hydration of the counterion: e.g., a lithium-loaded cation-exchange resin absorbs more water than a potassium-loaded resin. The water uptake also depends on the concentration of the external solution, for it is the difference in osmotic pressure between the internal and external solutions that determines the swelling. Changes in the swelling affect the performance of a resin in a chromatographic column. Such changes are serious in resins of low crosslinking, but not with the common 8% crosslinked resins. Volume changes do occur in the latter, but they are small and, in a packed column under pressure, they can usually be accommodated within the interstitial volume. When the ambient solution is diluted, the resin beads swell, but they do not burst the column; they merely increase the back pressure. The change in the interstitial volume should be noted if capacity factors are being measured.

7.3.2. The Donnan equilibrium; co-ion uptake

When an ion-exchange resin is in equilibrium with a salt solution, the chemical potential of the salt, a "component" in the sense of the phase rule, must be the same inside and outside the resin. Therefore, there are co-ions as well as counterions inside the resin. Writing concentrations in place of activities, and considering a sodium-form cation-exchange resin in equilibrium with a solution of NaCl,

$$\left[\overline{Na^+}\right]\left[\overline{Cl^-}\right] = [Na^+][Cl^-] = c^2$$

where c is the external molal concentration of the salt and bars over the symbols denote the resin phase. For a uni–divalent salt like $CaCl_2$,

$$\left[\overline{Ca^{2+}}\right]\left[\overline{Cl^-}\right]^2 = [Ca^{2+}][Cl^-]^2 = 4c^3$$

The internal concentration of Cl^- ions is less than the external concentration, because the internal concentration of Na^+ or Ca^{2+} ions is much larger. The "electrolyte invasion", or entrance of co-ions and associated counterions, increases rapidly as the external concentration increases, and is considerable where anion- or cation-exchange resins are used, e.g., in high concentrations of HCl (see below).

7.3.3. Nonaqueous and mixed solvents

Ion-exchange resins swell less in nonaqueous solvents than in water, and in nonpolar solvents they do not swell at all (unless the hydrocarbon matrix is solvated). In mixtures of water with other solvents, they tend to take up water preferentially. However, this depends on the nature of the counterion: e.g., cation-exchange resins carrying quaternary-ammonium counterions may sorb alcohol in preference to water, but if the counterions are strongly hydrated, like sodium or calcium, water is sorbed in preference to alcohol. The interior of the resin in mixed solvents is primarily aqueous. Much information is available on the distribution of binary solvent mixtures in anion- and cation-exchange resins carrying various counterions [34,35]. A typical set of curves for the distribution of ethanol and water in a cation-exchange resin with different counterions is shown in Fig. 7.2 [34].

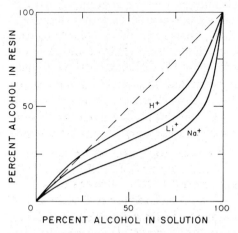

Fig. 7.2. Distribution of water and alcohol between liquid and a sulfonated polystyrene cation exchanger, 8% crosslinked, with different counterions. (Reproduced from *J. Chromatogr.*, 127 (1976) 44, with permission [34].)

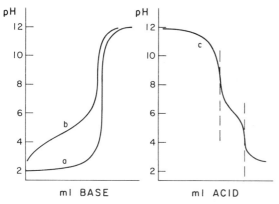

Fig. 7.3. Titration of hydrogen and hydroxyl forms of ion-exchange resins. a=Sulfonic acid cation exchanger; b=carboxylic acid cation exchanger; c=quaternary ammonium anion exchanger containing weakly basic groups.

7.3.4. Effect of pH

In strong-acid and strong-base resins the hydrogen and hydroxyl ions are held and exchanged just like other ions. In weak-acid and weak-base resins, however, these ions have a special status, being bound covalently. The degree of ionization depends on the pH. For example, at low pH, exchangers having carboxyl or phosphonate groups are weakly ionized and have a low capacity for cations other than H^+. Moreover, they are weakly hydrated, at the low degree of swelling makes diffusion very slow. If the pH is increased to allow full ionization, the resins expand considerably. The very great effect of pH on swelling restricts the use of these resins in columns.

The effect of pH on ionization is demonstrated by a potentiometric titration of a suspension of the resin in a neutral salt solution, like KCl, with a strong acid or a strong base. Typical curves are obtained like those in Fig. 7.3. It should be noted that the "strong-base" anion exchanger used in this case actually contained a considerable proportion of weakly basic groups, which affected the absorptive behavior of this resin at low pH.

7.3.5. Ion-exchanging capacity

The "capacity" of an ion exchanger is expressed as the number of equivalents of exchangeable ions per kg (or meq/g) of exchanger, referred to a particular ionic form of the exchanger in the dry state. It may be measured by titrating the hydrogen or hydroxyl form of the exchanger in the manner just described. Two portions of the air-dried resin are taken. One of them is used to determine the moisture content from the weight loss after drying it in an oven at 110°C. The oven-dried sample should not be used for the titration, nor should the resin be stored in the oven-dried form, because drying may cause chemical decomposition and is very likely to fracture the beads.

References on p. A253

Theoretically, linear uncrosslinked polystyrene with one sulfonic acid per aromatic ring should have an exchange capacity of 5.4 eq/kg (or meq/g). Crosslinking reduces the capacity somewhat and capacities close to 5.0 meq/g are found in practice. Polyacrylate carboxylic cation-exchange resins have capacities around 10 meq/g, but in this case the effective, or usable capacity depends on the pH. For chromatography, it is helpful to express the capacity in relation to the volume of a packed column. For the common sulfonated polystyrene resins with 8% crosslinking this capacity is about 2 meq/ml, for strong-base anion-exchange resins about 1 meq/ml.

7.4. EQUILIBRIUM AND SELECTIVITY

7.4.1. Ion-exchange equilibrium

The exchange of two singly charged ions, A^+ and B^+, on a resin, Res, may be represented by

$$A^+ + BRes \rightleftharpoons B^+ + ARes$$

This reversible reaction has an equilibrium quotient, Q.

$$Q = \frac{[ARes][B^+]}{[BRes][A^+]} \quad \text{or} \quad \frac{[\overline{A}^+][B^+]}{[\overline{B}^+][A^+]}$$

where the barred symbols show the resin phase. The true equilibrium constant, K, is obtained from Q by introducing the activity coefficients. The activity coefficient ratio in the solution can in principle be measured experimentally, or it can be calculated with fair certainty. Activities in the resin phase are referred to the pure homoionic resins as standard states, and may be found by measuring Q over the complete range of resin composition, from pure A-resin to pure B-resin. The equilibrium constant, K, is calculated from the equation [36]

$$\ln K = (z_B - z_A) + (n_2 - n_1)z_A z_B \ln\frac{P}{P_0} + \int_0^1 \ln K_a \, dN_B$$

where z_B and z_A are the charges on ions B and A; n_1 and n_2 are the number of moles of water per gram-equivalent of pure A- and B-resins; P and P_0 are the vapor pressures of the pure salt solutions and of pure water; and N_B is the equivalent fraction of cation B in the resin. K_a is the quotient Q times the ratio of activity coefficients in solution.

In chromatography, fortunately, the equivalent fraction of one of the ions in the resin is nearly always small, and activity coefficients in the resin may be considered constant. Usually it is sufficient to know the distribution ratio, D.

$$D = \frac{[ARes]}{[A^+]} \quad \text{or} \quad \frac{[\overline{A}^+]}{[A^+]}$$

The value of D depends on the competing ion, B, and its concentration, and it is strongly affected by complexing agents in the solution. Temperature has little effect, since the enthalpy change accompanying ion exchange is generally small. If the ions A and B have the same charge, D is inversely proportional to $[B^+]$; if A is doubly charged and B singly charged, so that two ions of B displace one of A, D is inversely proportional to the square of $[B^+]$. Many tables of distribution ratios are found in the literature. The common units are ml/g. If a column is packed with w grams of resin (dry weight) and has void volume V_0, the retention volume of a small injection of ions A, having the distribution ratio D in the flowing solution, equals $Dw + V_0$.

The distribution ratio D can be calculated from the equilibrium quotient, Q, the capacity of the resin, C meq/g, and the concentration of the eluting ions, $[B^+]$. For the simple case of singly charged ions, $D = QC/[B^+]$. For exchanges between ions of equal charge, Q has no units, but with ions of unequal charge, the concentration units used in Q must be specified. Generally they are meq/ml in the solution, and equivalent fractions, or meq ion/meq resin, in the exchanger.

7.4.2. Selectivity orders of cations

For alkali and alkaline-earth metal ions in the common sulfonic acid cation-exchange resins, the binding to the resin becomes stronger with increasing atomic weight:

$$Li^+ < Na^+ < K^+ < Rb^+ < Cs^+ \text{ and } Mg^{2+} < Ca^{2+} < Sr^{2+} < Ba^{2+}$$

Transition and post-transition metal ions are held more strongly than cations of comparable size in the above series; e.g., under similar conditions, Ag^+ and Tl^+ are bound more strongly than Cs^+, and divalent "heavy metals" more than Ca^{2+}. At the salt concentrations commonly used in chromatography, $0.1\ M$ and less, divalent ions are held more strongly than univalent ions, but it should be noted that the exchange between univalent and divalent ions shifts with dilution, the divalent ions moving into the resin as the solution is diluted.

In an 8% crosslinked polystyrene sulfonate resin, K^+ is held about three time as strongly as Li^+, but the rise in selectivity from K^+ to Cs^+ is much smaller. Hydrogen ions are held more strongly than Li^+ but more weakly than Na^+. Crosslinking affects selectivity; the differences in binding are almost twice as large in a 16% crosslinked as in an 8% crosslinked resin.

Much greater selectivity differences are found in exchangers where covalent binding plays a part. In iminodiacetate chelating resins there is a factor of 10^3 or 10^4 between the affinity of the resin for the most strongly bound (UO_2^{2+}, Hg^{2+}) and the most weakly bound (Ba^{2+}, Mg^{2+}) divalent metal ions. Here, selectivity follows the order of complex-ion stabilities in solution [37,38].

It seems clear that ionic hydration plays a part in cation-exchange selectivity. The ions that are most strongly hydrated (Li^+, Mg^{2+}) are the ones most weakly held by sulfonic acid resins. It may be supposed that the more hydrated ion, exchanging with a less hydrated ion, tends to move out of the resin, where the water content is limited and some of the water is bound to the fixed ions, into the outer solution, where these constraints are absent. A more quantitative argument considers the work, $P\,\Delta V$, required to swell the resin when a less hydrated ion, like K^+, is replaced by a more hydrated ion, like Na^+. The internal pressure, P, is considerable (see Chap. 7.3.1). If factors other than the swelling energy are neglected, it is possible to formulate

$$RT \ln K = P(V_A - V_B)$$

where K is the equilibrium constant (Chap. 7.4.1) and V_A and V_B are the volumes of swollen A- and B-resins, respectively, per mole of counterions [39,40]. This theory explains why some resins are more selective, but it does not explain why Na^+ is preferred over K^+ by carboxylic cation-exchange resins.

A theory proposed by Eisenman [41] to account for ion selectivities of glass electrodes has been applied to explain affinity reversals in ion exchange. Part of the glass-electrode selectivity is due to the ion-exchange equilibrium at the surface of the glass. It was found that aluminosilicate glasses that are high in Al show the same selectivity order for alkali-metals as that found in sulfonated polystyrene resins, but glasses that are almost free from Al show the reverse order: Li^+ is the most strongly bound, Cs^+ the least. The difference has been attributed to the size and electrostatic field strength of the fixed ions. In a pure silicate, the fixed charges are concentrated on exposed O atoms ($-Si-O^-$) and the field strength is very high. In an aluminosilicate, the fixed charge is located around an Al atom in the solid lattice, and distributed around the four O atoms to this Al atom; the field strength is thus low. If the field strength is low, counterions attached to the fixed ions retain their water of hydration, and the smallest hydrated ions, namely Rb^+ and Cs^+, are held most strongly. If the field strength is high, however, the force between the fixed ion and the counterions is sufficient to displace some of the water of hydration. Now the smallest unhydrated ion, Li^+, is the most strongly held.

This theory can be extended to organic polymers and their fixed ions. Sulfonate ions are large and have low field strength, whereas carboxylate ions are smaller and have higher field strength, which may explain the preference of such resins for Na^+ over K^+. Non-coulombic interactions between counterions and the resin polymer play a part. Fluorocarbon polymers with functional sulfonate ions show the same selectivity orders as polystyrene sulfonates, but the discrimination between K^+, Rb^+ and Cs^+ is much greater, and Cs^+ is held 15 times stronger than Li^+ [42]. The high selectivities of inorganic ion exchangers, mentioned above, are due to the well-defined lattice spacings in the microcrystals of these materials.

7.4.3. Selectivity orders of anions

Halide ions in strong-base quaternary ammonium anion-exchange resins follow a sequence like that of the alkali metal ions: F^- is the most weakly held, followed by Cl^-, Br^-, I^-. However, in contrast to cation exchange, where the selectivity is rather small, I^- is held 100 times stronger than F^- in an 8% crosslinked polystyrene-type resin. The OH^- ion is held as weakly as F^- on $-N(CH_3)_3^+$ fixed ions in the so-called "Type I" anion-exchange resins, but in "Type II" resins — those with fixed $-N(CH_3)_2CH_2CH_2OH^+$ — OH^- is held more strongly, almost as strongly as Cl^-.

The affinity for nitrate is intermediate between Br^- and I^-, but SCN^- and ClO_4^- are held more strongly than I^-.

For the oxy-anions of a given charge, it seems to be a universal rule that the larger the anion, the more strongly it is held: nitrate is held more strongly than nitrite, sulfate more strongly than sulfite, and perchlorate more strongly than chlorate. Binding is stronger for methacrylate than for acrylate, and the fumarate ion (*trans-*) is held much more strongly than the isomeric but less extended maleate ion (*cis-*) [43]. Condensed phosphate ions are more strongly held the greater their molecular weight, provided, of course, that their charges are the same [44] and that the ions are not so large that they cannot enter the resin.

Anions are larger and less hydrated than simple inorganic cations, so that the electrostatic attraction between fixed ions and counterions is less important in anion exchange than in cation exchange. The major influence on anion-exchange selectivity seems to be the hydrogen-bonded structure of water [45]. Large anions of low ionic charge exert a "structure-breaking" effect on the water outside the resin [46]. The larger they are, the more energy it takes to insert them in the water, so that they tend to be driven out of the water and into the resin. The effect of increasing the ionic charge is to increase the ion-dipole forces and to displace the ion into the aqueous phase: thus, e.g., MnO_4^{2-} is more weakly bound than MnO_4^-, but the effect of concentration on the distribution ratio must also be considered. Thus, all generalizations regarding affinity sequences must be applied with caution.

7.5. EXPERIMENTAL METHODS

7.5.1. General; simple column operations

Ion exchangers are mainly used in columns. Occasionally, analytical operations do not involve chromatography but batchwise shaking. The commercial ion-exchange papers, i.e. papers loaded with finely ground ion-exchange resins, are used for collecting traces of metals as well as for PC, and TLC is also performed with ion-exchanging materials. In this chapter we shall consider only column operations. The advantage of working with columns rather than with batches is that a solution flowing down the column will continually encounter fresh sorbent, so that the exchange is forced to proceed in the desired direction, even though the equilibrium quotient may be unfavorable.

Sometimes, the objective merely is to exchange one kind of ion for another, without separating species of like charge. For example, the total electrolyte content of a solution can be measured by first converting all dissolved salts to their corresponding acids and then titrating the acids with standard base: an aliquot of the solution to be analyzed is passed through a column of strong-acid cation exchanger in its hydrogen form and the effluent plus rinse water is collected and titrated. (Carbon dioxide from bicarbonates and carbonates is first removed by boiling the solution. These ions are determined by titrating a separate sample with standard acid.)

A similar operation is performed to remove cations that interfere with the titration of anions in a sample: sulfate ions, e.g., may be titrated with barium perchlorate by using an adsorption indicator, but almost all metal ions interfere. They are replaced by hydrogen ions by passing the sample solutions through a column of strong-acid cation exchanger.

For these operations the column must contain enough resin to absorb all the cations in the sample, plus an excess sufficient to avoid breakthrough, but the column must not be too large. A common mistake is to use a column that is far too large. Then the analysis will take too long and unnecessarily large volumes of water needed for rinsing will unduly dilute the sample before it is titrated. Knowing the capacity of the resin on a volume basis, the appropriate column size can be estimated. A column 1 cm in diameter and 15–20 cm long, containing ca. 30 meq of resin should be adequate for most purposes. Before the unwanted cations start to break through and appear in the effluent, the column is regenerated by washing with dilute acid and then rinsed with water. Regeneration and rinse may be repeated many times; a column that is kept clean can be reused almost indefinitely.

To maintain a sharp front of metal ions in the column and avoid premature breakthrough, the resin particles must be small enough for fast mass transfer and the flowrate must not be too great. A suitable bead size for short gravity-flow columns is 100–200 mesh (0.075–0.15 mm particle diameter); a suitable flowrate is 1–2 ml/min. Smaller particles give flowrates that are too slow for gravity flow.

7.5.2. Columns for gravity flow

Chromatographic tubes for gravity flow are usually made of glass and have a fritted disc at the lower end to support the resin and a stopcock to regulate the flow. At the upper end a funnel is attached, which serves for filling the tube and holding the resin when the bed is backwashed to remove dirt or air bubbles. In operating a column, it is essential to avoid entrapped air bubbles. The fluid must never be allowed to drain from the column or, if this happens, the air must be expelled by backwashing the column before using it again. Short columns of fine resin (100 mesh and smaller) are less likely to run dry, because the surface tension of water is high enough to keep the water level from falling more than a millimeter or so below the top of the resin. Long columns and columns of coarser resin should be fitted with an outlet reaching above the resin to ensure that they do not run dry.

Before the tube is filled with resin, the resin is stirred with water in a beaker to allow the particles to swell. Any small particles ("fines") are decanted, and then the slurry is stirred while pouring it into the tube, letting the beads settle as evenly as possible. If dry beads of a gel-type resin were put into a glass tube and then wetted, the beads would swell and break the tube. Pellicular resins may be dry-packed, but these resins are not used for gravity flow.

7.5.3. High-resolution columns

For high-resolution chromatography one must use small particles, but the resistance to flow is so great that pressure must be applied. Therefore, stainless-steel

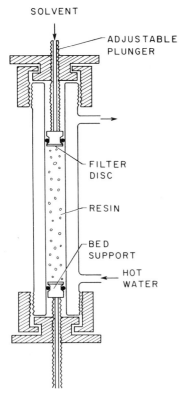

SOLVENT

ADJUSTABLE
PLUNGER

FILTER
DISC

RESIN

BED
SUPPORT

HOT
WATER

Fig. 7.4. Jacketed glass column of HPLC Courtesy of Glenco Scientific, Houston, TX, USA.

columns and HPLC equipment (Chap. 4) are required. Ion-exchange resins, being hydrophilic, are much easier to pack than fine-particle reversed-phase packings. Slurry packing is usually employed, with pressures not much higher than those ultimately used in operating the column.

Gel-type resins with less than 8% crosslinking are soft, and must be packed and used with care; too much pressure will cause the beads to collapse. Even with 8% crosslinked resins appreciable volume changes may be anticipated if the solvent composition is altered during operation. In such cases it is advantageous to use glass columns with adjustable bed supports. A useful design, shown in Fig. 7.4, includes as a very desirable feature a water jacket for temperature control. Jacketed glass columns are used in amino acid analyzers. Glass columns resist corrosion and may be operated at pressures up to 1000 psi (70 atm).

7.5.4. Ion Chromatography

A major advance in the high-resolution chromatography of inorganic ions was made in 1975 [47]. Until then, the column chromatography of inorganic ions had

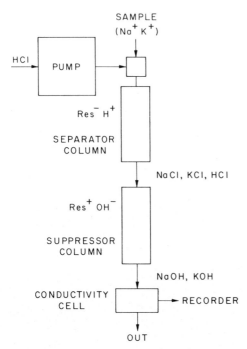

Fig. 7.5. System for Ion Chromatography.

lagged behind that of organic compounds due to difficulties with continuous detectors. Electrical conductivity was applicable to the detection of inorganic ions, but the trouble was that the eluents themselves were highly conducting. In the new method, excess eluent is removed before the effluent enters the conductivity cell. In addition, rapidly acting surface-active exchangers (described in Chap. 7.2.4) are used to perform the separations, giving sharp bands and adequate resolution.

Instrumentation for "Ion Chromatography" is shown schematically in Fig. 7.5. Two columns are coupled in series, the "separator column" that resolves the mixture into its individual ions, and the "suppressor column" that removes the excess eluent ions. The first column is packed with low-capacity surface-active resin, the second with a standard high-capacity gel-type exchanger.

Suppose a mixture of alkali-metal cations is to be analyzed. The separator column contains a cation-exchange resin, and the eluent is $0.01\,M$ HCl. (The low acid concentration is required by the low capacity of the exchanger.) The suppressor column is packed with a strong-base anion-exchange resin in the hydroxyl form. If a sample of NaCl solution is injected, Na^+ ions are retarded in the separator column but in due course emerge as NaCl, accompanied by excess HCl. In the suppressor column the HCl is absorbed, but NaCl is converted to NaOH, which is analyzed by conductivity measurement.

To analyze mixtures of anions, the separator column is packed with a low-capacity surface-active anion-exchange resin, and the eluent is most usually a mixture of

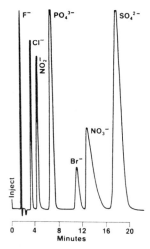

Fig. 7.6. Ion chromatogram of an anion mixture. Concentration column, 50×3 mm; separator column, 500×3 mm; suppressor column, 250×6 mm; eluent, $0.003\ M$ $NaHCO_3$–$0.0024\ M$ Na_2CO_3; flowrate, 128 ml/h; injection volume, 10 μl; concentrations, 5 ppb of each anion. (Courtesy of Dionex Corp., Sunnyvale, CA, USA.)

Na_2CO_3 $(0.0024\ M)$ and $NaHCO_3$ $(0.003\ M)$. Again, the eluent concentration must be low enough to match the low capacity of the column and allow sufficient retention of the ions to be analyzed, as well as to avoid overloading the suppressor column, which is in this case packed with a strong-acid cation exchanger in the hydrogen form. This resin converts the excess eluent into a solution of carbonic acid, which has a very low conductivity, while the anions of the sample emerge as their acids, which have a high conductivity. Fig. 7.6 shows a typical recorder trace obtained in Ion Chromatography of a mixture of anions. Retention times are in the order of a few minutes, and ion concentrations below 1 mg/l can be measured in 250-μl samples.

Ion Chromatography is especially useful for anions. Metallic cations can be analyzed in other ways, such as plasma emission and atomic absorption spectrometry, but anions cannot. The order of appearance of anion peaks generally follows the selectivity order described in Chap. 7.4.3. The position of the phosphate peaks can be varied by changing the pH of the eluent; the more highly charged species, HPO_4^{2-} and PO_4^{3-}, predominate at higher pH and the retention time is increased. Weakly ionized, weakly conducting acids, like boric acid, give no peaks or very small ones.

The weak part of Ion Chromatography is the suppressor column, which causes additional peak broadening and must be regenerated from time to time. Moreover, the surface-active separator resins themselves have particles some 50 μm in diameter, large enough to cause significant band broadening by eddy diffusion, even though mass transfer is fast. However, samples to be analyzed seldom contain more than 5 or 6 components, and the resolution obtainable is adequate for this purpose. Ion Chromatography is proving very successful in water analysis, including that of boiler

References on p. A253

feed water and environmental samples, and in many other fields [48–51]. The different variables involved, and their optimization, have been discussed [50,51].

7.5.5. Ion Chromatography without suppression

It is possible to obviate the suppressor column and still use electrical conductivity detection by eluting with very dilute solutions having low conductivity and strong displacing power. For example, potassium benzoate and phthalate solutions (10^{-3} to $5 \cdot 10^{-5} M$) were selected as eluents for the separation of anions on a low-capacity resin, made by treating macroporous polystyrene with chloromethyl ether and a tertiary amine [52]. Most inorganic anions caused the conductivity to increase when they were displaced from the column. Cations, separated by chromatography on surface-sulfonated macroporous polystyrene, have been detected by the decrease in conductivity of the $0.0015 M$ nitric acid eluent [9]. Dispensing with the suppressor column results in bands sharper than those obtained in conventional Ion Chromatography, and this should lead to higher sensitivity. However, the greater background conductivity cancels out this advantage and, moreover, the detector is reading, not the conductance of the eluted ions alone, but the difference between their conductance and that of the equivalent quantity of displacing ions [51].

If a detector is selective for the ions of the analyte and does not respond to the ions of the eluent, there is no need for a suppressor column. Thus, electrochemical or colorimetric detection may be used. For example, the lanthanide ions have been detected through their suppression of the anodic current at a mercury drop in a solution containing EDTA [53] or by post-column reaction with a chromogenic reagent, Arsenazo I or 4-(2-pyridylazo)resorcinol (PAR) [54]. Thus, there is no need

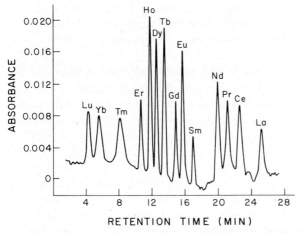

Fig. 7.7. Separation of lanthanide ions on the cation-exchange resin Aminex A-5, 8% crosslinked, 13 μm. Column, 100 × 4 mm; injected, 10 μl of a solution, ca. 10 ppm of each lanthanide; eluent, α-hydroxyisobutyric acid, pH 4.6; 20-min gradient from 0.17 m to 1.0 M; flowrate, 0.8 ml/min. (Reproduced from *Anal. Chem.*, 51 (1979) 1434, with permission [54].)

to use dilute eluents and low-capacity ion-exchange resins, and the great separating potential of conventional gel-type resins in small particle sizes can be exploited. By use of 13-μm, 8% crosslinked sulfonated polystyrene in a column 10 cm long and 4 mm wide, the 14 lanthanides have been cleanly separated in 30 min (Fig. 7.7).

7.6. METAL SEPARATIONS THROUGH COMPLEX IONS

7.6.1. General considerations

We return now to ion exchange performed in simple, open columns without elaborate equipment, for the purpose of separation rather than quantitative analysis. Fractions are collected, containing single components of a complex mixture, and the amount of each component is determined by whatever method the analyst chooses, without concern about interference from the sample matrix or eluent. There is much need for such separation procedures: metallic constituents must be determined in rocks or minerals, e.g., for industrial purposes or in geochemical research; minor or trace constituents must be accurately measured in special alloys or "pure" materials; metals must be recovered from water or contaminated soils in environmental protection; and in activation analysis it is often necessary to separate minor constituents after irradiation.

Ion exchange, in itself, is not particularly selective for metal ions, but combined with complex-ion formation it can be very selective indeed. Separation factors of 100, 1000 and higher are not uncommon, allowing useful separations to be achieved, often in a short time, with gravity-fed columns.

Formation of anionic complexes by metal ions may be exploited in two ways: either complex formation is used to remove the metals from a cation exchanger, as in the chromatography of lanthanides and actinides, or the metals may be attached as negatively charged complexes to an anion exchanger. The latter is the more useful procedure.

7.6.2. Anion exchange of metal complexes in hydrochloric acid

Most metals associate with Cl^- ions in aqueous HCl. Where association proceeds far enough to result in the formation of negatively charged complex ions, these ions may be sorbed on an anion-exchange resin. The higher the concentration of HCl, the more the anionic complexes are stabilized. The distribution of the metal between the resin and the aqueous solution depends on two factors: the stability of the negatively charged complex in aqueous HCl, and the affinity of the anion-exchange resin for this complex.

Fig. 7.8 shows the variation with HCl concentration of the distribution ratio of some typical metal ions between the solution phase and a quaternary-ammonium anion-exchange resin. The range of distribution ratios is enormous, keeping in mind the logarithmic scale. Iron(III) is held almost 100 times stronger than Zn(II), even though the formation constant of $FeCl_4^-$ in water is extremely small. The most

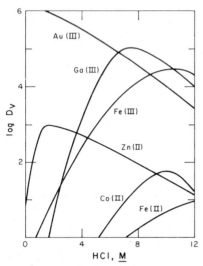

Fig. 7.8. Distribution ratios of various cations between a strong-base anion exchanger and aqueous hydrochloric acid. (Adapted from ref. 7.)

strongly sorbed metals, with D values over 10^4, are mainly trivalent species that form 4-coordinated, singly-charged complexes: e.g., Fe(III), Ga(III), Au(III), Tl(III). That these ions are more strongly held by the exchanger than doubly charged complexes like $ZnCl_4^{2-}$ is in accordance with the theory of anion-exchange selectivity of Chu et al. [45]. The doubly charged ions interact more strongly with water dipoles and are therefore displaced out of the resin and into the solution. However, theoretical speculations must be tempered by great caution, for the HCl solutions are very concentrated and much of the acid enters the resin phase. For many metals, the D values pass through a maximum and then fall as the acid concentration is increased. The most likely explanation is that, after the fully coordinated anions are formed, raising the chloride-ion concentration merely displaces the complexes from the resin by anion exchange.

The paper by Kraus and Nelson [7], which is quoted very widely, shows a periodic table in which a highly characteristic graph of log D against HCl concentration appears for each element. The alkali and alkaline-earth metals, Sc, Y, Al, the lanthanides, Ni, Ac, and Th are not sorbed from aqueous HCl at any concentration. With the aid of these graphs it is possible to devise a vast number of separation schemes. A typical example is afforded by a separation of iron, cobalt, nickel and zinc, which is oftern performed as a lecture demonstration. The procedure is as follows: A column of strong-base anion-exchange resin, 100–200 mesh, about 15 cm by 1 cm, is washed with 9 M HCl, and 1 ml of a solution containing the four metal chlorides in 9 M HCl is applied to the column. On elution with 9 M HCl, a green solution of nickel chloride passes out of the column and is collected. The band at the top of the column has the deep blue color of the $CoCl_4^{2-}$ complex. If 3 M HCl is now passed through, the blue cobalt zone is displaced down the column and changes to pink Co^{2+} (aq.); the solution flowing out of the column is first blue, then pink. Cobalt is collected, and then 1 M HCl is passed through. The brown iron band moves down, and yellow iron(III) is collected. Finally, the colorless zinc chloride is eluted with water.

Numerous separations of this type are reported in the literature, many of them in conjunction with neutron activation analysis. The eluted metals can be recovered for further qualitative and quantitative analysis, simply by evaporating the HCl.

Clearly, complexing eluents other than HCl could also be used. H_2SO_4, HNO_3 and HBr have been employed, and HF is useful for the metals of the fourth, fifth and sixth groups of the periodic table, particularly Zr, Hf, Nb, and Ta ions, which are strongly hydrolyzed in water. Fluoride is virtually the only ligand capable of successfully competing with the water and giving stable anionic complexes that can be completely resolved and accurately determined.

7.6.3. Effect of nonaqueous solvents

Mixing water with solvents of lower dielectric constants, such as acetone or alcohol, profoundly affects the distribution ratios of the chloro complexes [8]. Attractions between unlike electric charges are increased, so that the complexes are stabilized: e.g., in acetone–water (9:1), Ni^{2+} is complexed and retained by the anion-exchange resin when the HCl concentration is 0.5 M. Co^{2+} is sorbed by the resin from a 1:1 mixture of 1 M HCl–acetone. Fe^{3+}, on the other hand, is not sorbed from acetone–6 M aqueous HCl (9:1). In this solvent, the Fe^{3+} complex is almost colorless, instead of the bright yellow that is observed in water, apparently because the iron exists as a solvated ion pair, $H^+FeCl_4^-$, which is not held by the anion-exchange resin.

The use of nonaqueous solvents gives an added dimension to ion-exchange separations of metal ions. Elution orders can be changed, which is often desirable: e.g., for the isolation of a small amount of one metal from a large excess of another by retaining the first on a small column while letting the excess of the second metal pass through. Nonaqueous solvents, like acetone, are less viscous than water, so that they flow more rapidly, and more volatile, so that they are more easily evaporated. Moreover, less HCl has to be removed, because the separations do not require the high acid concentrations that are needed in aqueous media.

A vast amount of work on anion- and cation-exchange separations of metals in mixed solvents by Korkisch was summarized in 1969 in an important book [55]. Ion exchange was combined with solvent extraction to separate uranium, iron, and other elements from nuclear raw materials [56]. More details on such separations are given in Chap. 22.2.

7.6.4. Cation-exchange separations

Complex ions have been used to enhance cation-exchange selectivity since the first separations of the lanthanides, described in the introduction to this chapter. Citrate, 2-methyllactate (α-hydroxyisobutyrate), EDTA, and related complexing agents have been used in cation-exchange separations of the lanthanides, actinides, alkaline earths, and many other elements. So have oxalic, malonic, hydrochloric, nitric, and sulfuric acids, and just as in anion exchange, nonaqueous solvents have been used to great advantage. The effect of ethanol on the cation-exchange distribution of many elements in HCl solutions has been thoroughly investigated by Strelow et al. [57] and effective schemes have been worked out for separating many elements [58]. A practical objective of these studies was to make accurate and definitive analyses of silicate rocks.

The effect of complexation of cation exchange is not simply the mirror image of the effect on anion exchange, particularly in concentrated solutions: e.g., iron(III) is strongly sorbed by anion-exchange resins from $9\,M$ HCl and it is assumed that negatively charged $FeCl_4^-$ complexes enter the resin. However, iron(III) is also sorbed from $9\,M$ HCl by polystyrene-type cation-exchange resins with $D = 10^3$. The same is true of Ga(III). The polystyrene resin matrix seems to act as a nonaqueous solvent, like the ethers, ketones, and esters that extract Fe(III) so well from $6-9\,M$ aqueous HCl. What is even more surprising is that $HClO_4$ in concentrations above $6\,M$ causes most metal ions to be absorbed with $D = 10$ or more by sulfonated polystyrene cation exchangers [59].

As to the effect of mixing the water with a nonaqueous solvent, ethanol is found to increase the equilibrium quotients for the exchange of noncomplexing ions, those of the alkali and alkaline-earth metals, with resin in the H^+ form [57,60]. In the alkaline earth series, the effect is small with Mg^{2+}, but much larger with Ba^{2+}, so that selectivity between these ions is increased by adding the alcohol. These effects can be interpreted in terms of hydration energies [58], on the basis that the water:alcohol ratio is less inside the resin than outside, and that the internal water is less hydrogen-bonded.

7.7. CHROMATOGRAPHY OF ORGANIC COMPOUNDS

7.7.1. General considerations: matrix interactions

The applications of ion-exchange chromatography to organic compounds are many and varied, and specific applications are described in other chapters of this book. We shall limit our discussion to some generalities and a few particular methodologies.

It is very important to realize that ion-exchanging polymers have carbon–hydrogen skeletons that act like nonaqueous solvents and interact with uncharged, as well as charged, organic compounds. Ion-exchange resins of the polystyrene type may be used for the chromatography of such nonionic and nonpolar compounds as polycyclic aromatic hydrocarbons and chlorinated biphenyls [61]. Mixed aqueous–nonaqueous solvent mixtures, such as water–acetonitrile, are used. Because of the reduced swelling of the resin in these solvents, it is advantageous to use weakly (say, 4%) crosslinked resins.

Cation-exchange resins of the polystyrene type are excellent stationary phases for

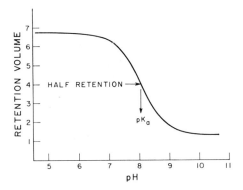

Fig. 7.9. Distribution of a weak acid between a buffered solution and a cation-exchange resin (schematic).

chromatography of polar compounds having aromatic character [62]. Many analgesic drugs fall into this category: phenols, phenol ethers, aromatic amides, and purines. There is an affinity between the π-electron systems of these compounds and those of the polystyrene matrix of the resin. Polyacrylate resins show much less affinity. The retentions can be changed by changing the solvent composition: increasing the nonaqueous component decreases the retention, and the decrease is greater, the more hydrophobic the solutes. If the solute is a weak acid, changing the pH has a predictable effect (see Fig. 7.9). The uncharged, undissociated form, present at low pH, is sorbed by the resin, while the charged anionic form, present at high pH, is not sorbed. The pH of half retention is equal to the pK_a of the acid in the solvent used. Anions are excluded from the interior of a cation-exchange resin by the Donnan equilibrium and are not sorbed even to the slight extent that is found in nonionic styrene polymers [63].

In this application ion-exchange resins are like reversed-phase packings. The ionic groups modify the hydrophobic character of the resin polymer, and because they are hydrated, they cause the polymer to swell in solvents that contain water, making the entire polymer accessible to solute molecules. The nature of the inorganic counterions affects the retention of nonionized solutes: e.g., resin loaded with Ca^{2+} or Li^+ are better sorbents for such compounds than Na^+-loaded resins [62].

In a sense, ion-exchange resins can also act in the "normal-phase" mode, sorbing highly polar solutes from mixed solvents that contain water. The interior of the resin is more aqueous than the external liquid (Fig. 7.2) and is therefore a better solvent for highly polar compounds, such as sugars. Sugars and other carbohydrates may, therefore, be separated chromatographically on columns of cation- and anion-exchange resins with 70–90% ethanol as the mobile phase [5,64]. Some retention of sugars is observed on cation exchangers with water as the mobile phase. This retention depends on the nature of the counterions and may be related to complex formation between the counterion and the sugar [65].

It is evident that many factors affect the interaction of organic molecules with ion-exchange resins, and that neutral molecules are bound as well as ions. While these interactions may not be well understood, they can certainly be exploited. Very complex mixtures have been analyzed by chromatography on ion-exchange resins, like urine [66] and wastewater [67]. With a strong-base macroporous anion exchanger of $7 \mu m$ particle size, up to 100 peaks could be observed in a 100-min chromatogram of urine, and it was possible to identify some of these peaks by noting how their positions change with pH [15].

7.7.2. Ion-exclusion chromatography

The Donnan equilibrium and the exclusion of negative ions from cation exchange resins can be applied in the chromatography of organic and inorganic acids. On elution simply with water, strong inorganic acids appear at the column void volume, while weaker acids are retained to an extent depending on the ionization constants [68,69]. Aromatic acids were also separated by elution with water [70]. The carboxylic acids of the Krebs cycle were eluted nearly, but not quite, in the order of their acid strengths by $0.001-0.1 M$ HCl [71]. Using buffered eluents and taking advantage of the relation shown in Fig. 7.9, nucleic acid derivatives were separated [72]. Weakly crosslinked resins (4% or even 2%) are preferred in this kind of chromatography, as less porous resins are likely to exclude the large anions so strongly that they all appear near the void volume. Ion-exclusion chromatography gives short retention times and sharp, narrow peaks, which result in good separation and high sensitivity. The acids of the Krebs cycle can be detected by use of a suppressor column packed with a silver-loaded cation-exchange resin, which absorbs the excess of HCl from the eluent, leaving the organic acids to be detected by conductivity [51].

7.7.3. Ligand-exchange chromatography

Ligand-exchange chromatography is used, e.g., to separate amines and amino acids. The stationary phase is a cation-exchange resin loaded with the cations of metals that form strong complexes with these compounds. Most commonly, the counterion is Cu^{2+}, but Ni^{2+}, Zn^{2+}, Cd^{2+}, and other ions have been used. The eluent is usually a solution of ammonia. The metal ions stay on the column, while the ligands attached to these ions, the amines or amino acids, are displaced by the ammonia molecules. The most weakly bound ligands are eluted first, the most strongly bound ligands last. Elution orders depend not only on the metal–ligand interactions but also on the interactions of the ligand molecules with the resin matrix and with the solvent. Metal–ligand formation constants in aqueous solution are a poor guide to ligand-exchange chromatography. Primary amines are much more strongly bound to metal ions in the resin than are secondary amines, which are, however, bound more strongly than tertiary. The more extended and hydrophobic the carbon chain of the amine, the more the compound is driven out of the water and into the resin. The stereochemistry of the ligand is very important, particularly if there are two groups capable of coordinating in a chelate ring [73,74].

Carboxylic polyacrylate resins are preferable to sulfonated polystyrene resins, because the latter may bind aromatic ligands too tightly and because the carboxyl group holds the metal ions much more strongly than does the sulfonate group. Ideally, the metal ions should remain attached to the resin, but this is never the case. The aqueous ammonia eluent contains some ammonium ions, and these exchange with the metal ions in the resin to some extent. The metal-ion loading of the resin may be held constant by adding metal salt to the eluting solution.

Because the nature of the metal ion and of the resin polymer and its functional groups affect the process, many different elution orders are possible [75]. As has been noted, the ligand binding is very dependent on the stereochemisty. This dependence is well illustrated by the chromatography of isomeric amino sugars, which incidentally are retained much more strongly than are other sugars, acidic, or neutral amino acids [76].

The ligand-exchange chromatography of amino acids has been investigated in detail. The effects of resin type, metal ion, ammonia concentration, and concentration of dissolved metal ions have been carefully studied and correlated with theory [77,78]. Ligand-exchange chromatography has been applied to peptides, carboxylic acids, hydroxyl compounds, and sulfur compounds [73]. Among the disadvantages of the method are the rather slow kinetics, which lead to undue band broadening, and the use of alkaline eluents, which promotes the oxidation of some solutes and may cause difficulties in detection.

7.7.4. Separation of optical isomers by ligand exchange

Where a metal ion, like Cu(II), is attached simultaneously to two chelating ligands, the two ligand molecules are held in a specific orientation with respect to one another, and their shapes strongly affect their interactions. If the ligands are asymmetric, optically active amino acids, the DD- and LL-combinations have very different interaction energies.

One way to exploit this effect in the chromatographic separation of amino acid enantiomers is by use of an exchanger that carries optically active functional groups. Many such exchangers have been synthesized, most of them based on polystyrene. In extensive studies made by Davankov and Zolotarev [79], molecules of L-proline and L-hydroxyproline were attached to a crosslinked polystyrene matrix having a very open structure. The molecular structure at the active sites was this:

The resin was then loaded with Cu(II) from a copper–ammonia solution, and columns of this resin were used for the chromatography of mixtures of D- and L-amino acids; the eluent was aqueous ammonia. The amino acids were resolved into their D- and L-forms, the L-form emerging first in nearly every case. Thus, the

References on p. A253

DL-combination with the fixed ligand (L-proline) was more stable and more strongly retained than the LL-combination. The separation factors between enantiomers varied greatly from one amino acid to another, being largest with proline itself. D-proline was retained four times stronger than L-proline. Enantiomers of alanine and serine showed the smallest separation factors, ca. 1.1. Other workers have attached asymmetric amino acid molecules to the stationary phase in different ways, and L-proline has been grafted to a silica base, with improvement in the ligand-exchange kinetics [80].

Another way to exploit the different stabilities of the mixed complexes is to form these complexes in the mobile phase, with an optically active amino acid in the eluent. Hare and Gil-Av [81] eluted with an aqueous acetate buffer that contained Cu(II) and L-proline in 1:2 ratio. The stationary phase was a regular sulfonated polystyrene cation exchanger, 8% crosslinked, with small particle size. The column, which was only 12 cm long, was operated at 75°C. It was allowed to come to equilibrium with the eluent until it was fully loaded with copper. Then a sample of a DL-amino acid was introduced. The L-amino acids emerged from the column before their D-enantiomers. The amino acids were detected by a post-column reaction with o-phthalaldehyde, a reagent that forms fluorescent derivatives with primary amines and amino acids but not with secondary amines; thus it did not respond to the proline in the eluent. Separation factors between isomers did not exceed 1.28 and were thus smaller than those found with chiral stationary phases— but the bands were much sharper, and the separation took only 90 min. It may be inferred that the actual ligand exchange takes place in the mobile phase and that the ion-exchange resin accepts 1:1 metal–ligand complexes (positively charged) while the 1:2 complexes (uncharged) exist primarily in the mobile phase.

The stationary phase may be octadecyl silica, the standard bonded "reversed phase" without ionic groups [82]. In this case, an eluent containing Cu(II) acetate and L-proline in the ratio 1:2 brings D-amino acids out of the column before L-amino acids, the reverse of the order found by Hare and Gil-Av. It may be postulated that in both cases the LL-mixed complex is the more stable, but that this remains in the mobile phase where the ion-exchange resin is used [83], whereas it is partitioned into the stationary octadecyl phase [82]. Again, separation factors of up to 1.2 are obtained, and, again, the peaks are very sharp.

7.8. PAIRED-ION CHROMATOGRAPHY

In paired-ion chromatrography, ionic compounds are separated by chromatography on a nonpolar, hydrocarbon bonded phase, e.g. C_{18}, by adding to the eluent a hydrophobic ion of charge opposite to the ions to be separated. Thus, e.g., the anions of sulfa drugs can be separated on a reversed-phase column by using an eluent that contains tetrabutylammonium ions: the ion pair, $N(C_4H_9)_4^+ X^-$, is sorbed by the bonded phase. The question arises whether the ion pairs are formed in the solution and then distributed between the two phases, or whether they are formed within the stationary phase. It is possible that the tetrabutylammonium ions themselves are sorbed by the stationary phase, with small anions like chloride or nitrate balancing their charges in an electrical double layer. If this is the case, the stationary phase has been converted into an anion exchanger, and the sulfa drug anions are retained by ion exchange with the small counterions of the double layer.

The phenomenon has been much studied and widely applied, particularly in the pharmaceutical field [83]. With regard to its mechanism, it appears fairly certain that smaller pairing ions, like tetrabutylammonium, generally remain in the mobile phase until they form their pairs and become absorbed, while larger pairing ions like dioctylammonium or cetylpyridinium saturate the bonded phase and convert it into a dynamically coated ion exchanger [84]. Thus, paired-ion chromatography may be regarded as a special kind of ion-exchange chromatography.

REFERENCES

1 Symposium, *J. Amer. Chem. Soc.*, 69 (1947) 2769.
2 S. Moore and W.H. Stein, *J. Biol. Chem.*, 192 (1951) 663.
3 W.E. Cohn, *J. Amer. Chem. Soc.*, 72 (1950) 1471.
4 J.X. Khym and L.P. Zill, *J. Amer. Chem. Soc.*, 73 (1951) 2399.
5 L.I. Larsson and O. Samuelson, *Acta Chem. Scand.*, 19 (1965) 1357.
6 C.G. Horváth, B.A. Preiss and S.R. Lipsky, *Anal. Chem.*, 39 (1967) 1422.
7 K.A. Kraus and F. Nelson, *Proc. 1st U.N. Conf. Peaceful Uses Atomic Energy, Geneva* 7 (1955) 113.
8 J.S. Fritz and D.J. Pietrzyk, *Talanta*, 8 (1961) 143.
9 J.S. Fritz, D.T. Gjerde and R.M. Becker, *Anal. Chem.*, 52 (1980) 1519.
10 G.A. Junk, J.J. Richard, M.D. Grieser, D. Witiak, J.L. Witiak, M.D. Arguello, R. Vick, H.J. Svec, J.S. Fritz and G.V. Calder, *J. Chromatogr.*, 99 (1974) 745.
11 G.R. Aiken, E.M. Thurman, R.L. Malcolm and H.F. Walton, *Anal. Chem.*, 51 (1979) 1799.
12 R.G. Baum, E.P. Saetre and F.F. Cantwell, *Anal. Chem.*, 52 (1980) 15.
13 K. Aramaki, T. Hanai and H.F. Walton, *Anal. Chem.*, 52 (1980) 1963.
14 S. Patell and J.C.R. Turner, *J. Sep. Process Technol.*, 1 (1979) 42; *C.A.*, 92 (1980) 147674f.
15 K. Seta, M. Washitake, T. Anmo, N. Takai and T. Okuyama, *J. Chromatogr.*, 181 (1980) 311.
16 V.A. Davankov, S.V. Rogozhin and M.P. Tsyurupa, *Ion Exchange and Solvent Extraction*, Vol. 7, Dekker, New York, 1978, p. 29.
17 J.P. Lefèvre, A. Divry, M. Caude and R. Rosset, *Analusis*, 3 (1975) 533.
18 M. Caude and R. Rosset, *J. Chromatogr. Sci.*, 15 (1977) 405.
19 R. Schwarzenbach, *J. Chromatogr.*, 117 (1976) 206.
20 A.D. Jones, I.W. Burns, S.G. Sellings and J.A. Cox, *J. Chromatogr.*, 144 (1977) 169.
21 S.H. Chang, R. Noel and F.E. Regnier, *Anal. Chem.*, 48 (1976) 1839.
22 Y. Kato, K. Komiya, H. Sasaki and T. Hashimoto, *J. Chromatogr.*, 193 (1980) 29, 311.
23 G. Schmuckler and S. Goldstein, *Ion Exchange and Solvent Extraction*, Vol. 7, Dekker, New York, 1978, p. 1.
24 T.S. Stevens and H. Small, *J. Liquid Chromatogr.*, 1 (1978) 123.
25 A. Clearfield, G.H. Nancollas and R.H. Blessing, *Ion Exchange and Solvent Extraction*, Vol. 5, Dekker, New York, 1973, p. 1.
26 T.E. Gills, W.F. Marlow and B.A. Thompson, *Anal. Chem.*, 42 (1970) 1831.
27 M. Abe and K. Uno, *Sep. Sci. Technol.*, 14 (1979) 355.
28 N. Jaffrezic-Renault, *J. Inorg. Nucl. Chem.*, 40 (1978) 539.
29 K.A. Kraus, H.O. Phillips, T.A. Carlson and J.S. Johnson, *Proc. 2nd U.N. Conf. Peaceful Uses Atomic Energy, Geneva*, 28 (1958) 3.
30 J.X. Khym, *Analytical Ion Exchange Procedures in Chemistry and Biology*, Prentice-Hall, New York, 1974, Chap. 3.

31 O. Mikeš, P. Štrop, M. Smrž and J. Čoupek, *J. Chromatogr.*, 192 (1980) 159.
32 G.E. Boyd and B. Soldano, *Z. Elektrochem.*, 57 (1953) 162.
33 F. Helfferich, *Ion Exchange*, McGraw-Hill, New York, 1962, Chap. 5.
34 A.R. Rodriguez and C. Poitrenaud, *J. Chromatogr.*, 127 (1976) 29.
35 H. Ruckert and O. Samuelson, *Acta Chem. Scand.*, 11 (1957) 303, 310.
36 G.L. Gaines and H.C. Thomas, *J. Chem. Phys.*, 21 (1953) 714.
37 R. Rosset, *Bull. Soc. Chim. Fr.*, (1964) 1485.
38 R. Rosset, *Bull. Soc. Chim. Fr.*, (1966) 59.
39 H.P. Gregor, *J. Amer. Chem. Soc.*, 70 (1948) 1293.
40 H.P. Gregor, *J. Amer. Chem. Soc.*, 73 (1951) 642.
41 G. Eisenman, *Biophys. J., Suppl.* 2 (1962) 259.
42 H.L. Yeager and A. Steck, *Anal. Chem.*, 51 (1979) 862.
43 M. Caude, J.P. Lefèvre and R. Rosset, *Chromatographia*, 8 (1975) 217.
44 F.H. Pollard, D.E. Rogers, M.T. Rothwell and G. Nickless, *J. Chromatogr.*, 9 (1962) 227.
45 B. Chu, D.C. Whitney and R.M. Diamond, *J. Inorg. Nucl. Chem.*, 24 (1962) 1405.
46 H.S. Frank and W.Y. Wen, *Disc. Faraday Soc.*, 24 (1957) 133.
47 H. Small, T.S. Stevens and W.C. Bauman, *Anal. Chem.*, 47 (1975) 1801.
48 E. Sawicki, J.D. Mulik and E. Wittgenstein (Editors), *Ion Chromatographic Analysis of Industrial Pollutants*, Vol. 1, Ann Arbor Sci. Publ. Ann. Arbor, MI, 1978.
49 J.D. Mulik and E. Sawicki (Editors), *Ion Chromatographic Analysis of Environmental Pollutants*, Vol. 2, Ann Arbor Sci. Publ., Ann Arbor, MI, 1979.
50 A. Jardy and R. Rosset, *Analusis*, 7 (1979) 259.
51 C.A. Pohl and E.L. Johnson, *J. Chromatogr. Sci.*, 18 (1980) 442.
52 D.T. Gjerde, G. Schmuckler and J.S. Fritz, *J. Chromatogr.*, 187 (1980) 35.
53 J.F. Boissoneau, M.J. Repellin and A. Eglem, *Analusis*, 8 (1980) 230.
54 S. Elchuk and R.M. Cassidy, *Anal. Chem.*, 51 (1979) 1434.
55 J. Korkisch, *Modern Methods for the Separation of Rarer Metal Ions* Pergamon, New York, 1969.
56 W. Koch and J. Korkisch, *Microhim. Acta*, 5 (1972) 1434.
57 F.W.E. Strelow, C.R. Van Zyl and C.J.C. Bothma, *Anal. Chim. Acta*, 45 (1969) 81.
58 F.W.E. Strelow, *Ion Exchange and Solvent Extraction*, Vol. 5, Dekker, New York, 1973, Chap. 2.
59 F. Nelson, T. Murase and K.A. Kraus, *J. Chromatogr.*, 13 (1964) 503.
60 F.W.E. Strelow and C.R. Van Zyl, *Anal. Chim. Acta*, 41 (1968) 529.
61 T. Hanai and H.F. Walton, *Anal. Chem.*, 49 (1977) 1954.
62 H.F. Walton, G.A. Eiceman and J.L. Otto, *J. Chromatogr.*, 180 (1979) 145.
63 F.F. Cantwell and Su Puon, *Anal. Chem.*, 51 (1979) 623.
64 O. Samuelson, *Ion Exchange and Solvent Extraction*, Vol. 2, Dekker, New York, 1969, p. 167.
65 R.W. Goulding, *J. Chromatogr.*, 103 (1975) 229.
66 C.D. Scott and N.E. Lee, *J. Chromatogr.*, 83 (1973) 383.
67 W.W. Pitt, R.L. Jolley and C.D. Scott, *Environ. Sci. Technol.*, 9 (1975) 1068.
68 K. Tanaka, T. Ishizuka and H. Sunahara, *J. Chromatogr.*, 174 (1979) 153.
69 K. Tanaka, T. Ishizuka and H. Sunahara, *J. Chromatogr.*, 177 (1979) 21.
70 J. Lehotay and M. Traiter, *J. Chromatogr.*, 91 (1974) 261.
71 V.T. Turkelson and M. Richards, *Anal. Chem.*, 40 (1978) 1420.
72 R.P. Singhal, *Separ. Purif. Methods*, 3 (1974) 339.
73 V.A. Davankov and A.V. Semechkin, *J. Chromatogr.*, 141 (1977) 313.
74 C.M. de Hernandez and H.F. Walton, *Anal. Chem.*, 44 (1972) 890.
75 H.F. Walton and J.D. Navratil, *Anal. Chem.*, 47 (1975) 2443.
76 J.D. Navratil, E. Murgia and H.F. Walton, *Anal. Chem.*, 47 (1975) 122.
77 M. Doury-Berthod, C. Poitrenaud and B. Tremillon, *J. Chromatogr.*, 131 (1977) 73.
78 M. Doury-Berthod, C. Poitrenaud and B. Tremillon, *J. Chromatogr.*, 179 (1979) 37.
79 V.A. Davankov and Yu. A. Zolotarev, *J. Chromatogr.*, 155 (1978) 285, 295, 303.
80 A. Foucault, M. Caude and L. Oliveros, *J. Chromatogr.*, 185 (1979) 345.
81 P.E. Hare and E. Gil-Av, *Science*, 204 (1979) 1226.

82 E. Oelrich, H. Preusch and E. Wilhelm, *J. High Resolut. Chromatogr. Chromatogr. Commun.*, 3 (1980) 269.
83 G. Schill, *Ion Exchange and Solvent Extraction*, Vol. 6, Dekker, New York, 1978, p. 1.
84 J.H. Knox and J. Jurand, *J. Chromatogr.*, 149 (1978) 297.

Chapter 8

Gel chromatography

ROBERT P. BYWATER and N.V.B. MARSDEN

CONTENTS

8.1. INTRODUCTION

Gel chromatography is a simple technique which has had an immeasurable impact on the progress of research in the life sciences. The term gel chromatography was introduced by Determann [1] to describe separations, predominantly of macromolecules, in gels where the selectivity was determined mainly by molecular size. Although molecular sieving has retained a leading role in gel chromatography, other partitioning phenomena are also now recognized as important. Gel chromatography has been extensively reviewed in the past [2], and there are a number of monographs [3–6] dealing with this subject. In view of this extensive coverage, we shall emphasize the mechanistic aspects of gel chromatography with the aim of giving the experimenter some insight into the potentialities and pitfalls inherent in the technique.

The modern era of gel chromatography was apparently ushered in by attempts to solve the problem of separating chemically similar substances, i.e. substances differing only in their degree of polymerization [7]. Historically, Ingelman, who crosslinked dextran in 1946, paved the way for the later development of dextran gels [8]. However, the idea of molecular-sieve chromatography in its present form emerged slowly. The basic principle did not suddenly become clear, revealed as it were by a flash of comprehension. Indeed, at first, other concepts obscured the true path of progress. It now seems almost paradoxical that molecular-sieve properties were once considered deleterious in adsorption chromatography with porous support material [7,9,10].

Deuel and Neukom [11], who were the first to publish a report on the use of an epichlorohydrin crosslinked gel, formed from the galactomannan of locust bean gum, suggested that the elution volume of a given solute might be a measure of its molecular size. A little later, Lindqvist and Storgårds [12] and, almost simultaneously, Lathe and Ruthven [13,14] reported molecular sieving in columns of starch. The latter authors also reported convincing data on the separation of amino acids, proteins, and nonelectrolytes. Meanwhile, after preliminary experiments with starch, Ingelman's crosslinked dextran gels were tested by Porath and Flodin [15], and the remarkable properties of these gels and the development of gel filtration are now a matter of history [16,17]. The term "gel filtration" was suggested by Tiselius for the molecular sieving method, which was intensively investigated by Flodin, Porath, Hjertén, Gelotte, and their colleagues. A major technical break-through was the preparation of the gels in bead form by Flodin *.

The epichlorohydrin crosslinked dextran gels (Sephadex), originally introduced for use as molecular sieves with water as the sole solvent [18], were followed shortly afterwards by gels of polyacrylamide, covalently crosslinked with N,N'-methylene-bis(acrylamide), which were reported to have similar sieving properties [19]. At that time, dextran appeared to be much superior as a starting material when compared with other polysaccharides, such as cellulose, starch, or locust bean gum [18]. Fractionation of very large molecules requires gels having a low matrix concentration and a high water content. Under these conditions, the dextran gels have the disadvantage of being soft and mechanically weak. The size of solute that can be fractionated can be extended by using agar [20,21] or agarose gels [22], and the properties of the latter can further be improved by crosslinking [23]. The degree of crosslinking necessary has only a small effect on the permeability of these gels, but it confers a great advantage in that it enables separations to be made in media which dissolve the noncovalently crosslinked gels, as well as in apolar solvents [18]. A yet more recent development is the use of polysaccharide and polyacrylamide composite gels of improved rigidity and high porosity (cf. Chaps. 8.2.6 and 8.2.7).

8.2. PACKING MATERIALS FOR GEL CHROMATOGRAPHY

Recent reviews [1–6] have covered the subject of available packing materials for gel chromatography with such commendable thoroughness that it seems superfluous to catalog these materials again. Suffice it to say that a variety of commercial gels are available that are based on different polymers, some natural, some synthetic, and some composite. What is of greater interest is the question of how the gel structure is related to chromatographic performance, in particular, to selectivity (see Chap. 8.4). Although the basic chemistry of the polymers comprising the gels is known (Figs. 8.1–8.7), the detailed microarchitecture of the gels is not yet sufficiently well understood for any precise explanation or prediction of chromatographic behavior. While the technique of gel chromatography has entered its third decade without any sign of abatement in utilization or, indeed, in further development, the investigation of the ultrastructure of these gels is still in its infancy.

---

* Swedish Patent 358,894 (1961).

References on p. A321

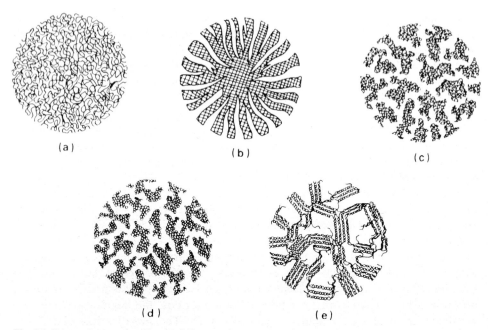

Fig. 8.1. Schematic representation of different gel types: (a) xerogel; (b) porous glass (aerogel); (c) porous silica (aerogel); (d) organic macro-reticular polymer (xerogel–aerogel hybrid); (e) agarose (xerogel–aerogel hybrid). (Reproduced from *Chromatography of Synthetic and Biological Polymers, Vol. 1, Column Packings, G.P.C., G.F. and Gradient Elution,* Ellis Horwood, Chichester, 1978, p. 1, with permission [30].)

8.2.1. Dextran gels

Dextran is a polymeric glucan, obtained microbiologically by the action of *Leuconostoc mesenteroides* on sucrose. Dextrans used for the purpose of crosslinking consist of α-D-(1 → 6)-linked units, to an extent of 90–95%, the rest being mainly α-D-(1 → 3)-linked. Crosslinking by epichlorohydrin yields a gel with the structure represented schematically in Fig. 8.2. Crosslinked dextran gels are available commercially under the trade names Sephadex (Pharmacia Fine Chemicals AB, Uppsala, Sweden) and Molselect (Reanal, Budapest, Hungary). The porosity of dextran gels is determined by the following factors:

(a) concentration of crosslinking reagent,
(b) concentration of dextran during polymerization,
(c) molecular weight of dextran.

The first two factors are readily comprehensible: increase in concentration of dextran, or crosslinks, or both, will naturally decrease the average pore size. The effect of polymer length is rather more difficult to predict; in general, as far as is known, an increase in chain length may be expected to cause an increase in porosity [24].

It is possible to calculate approximately the concentration of crosslinks from

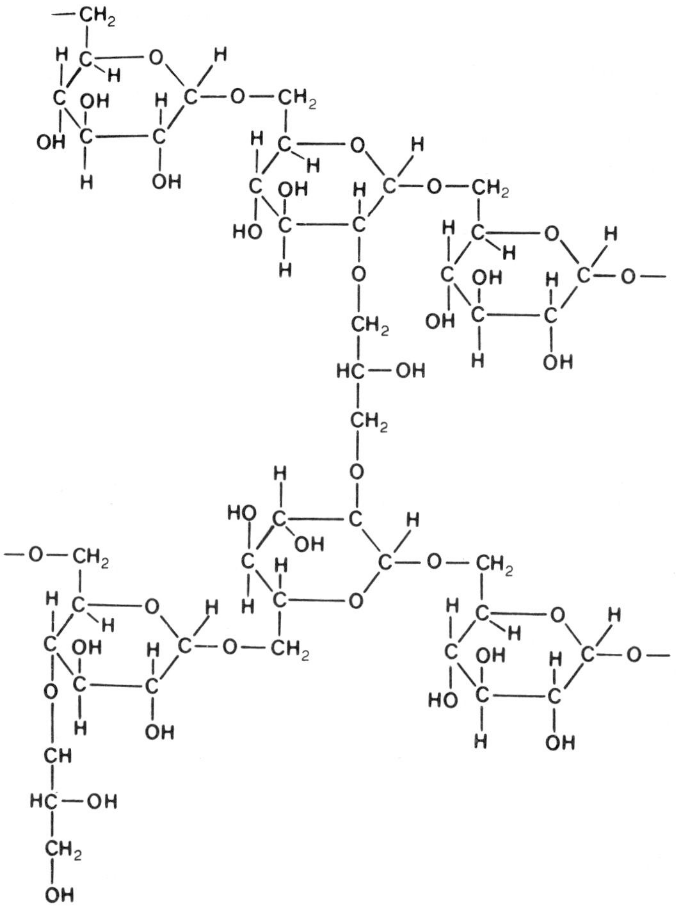

Fig. 8.2. Schematic representation of Sephadex. (Reproduced from *Dextran Gels and Their Application in Gel Filtration*, Pharmacia, Uppsala, 1962, with permission [16].)

either tritium exchange or labeled crosslink data and to establish some correlation between the degree of crosslinking and the selectivity. In the Sephadex G series, this affinity behavior accords well from G-100 down to the most highly crosslinked gel, G-10. Certain types of solute show a tendency to retardation, due to adsorption or affinity phenomena. Many solutes are adsorbed in some way by the very tightly crosslinked gels, G-10, G-15, and G-25. Solutes of aromatic (e.g., polynuclear aromatics) or heterocyclic (e.g., nucleosides and nucleotides) character show particularly marked tendencies to accumulate in these gels [25]. It would be reasonable to ascribe this behavior to adsorption due to $n-\pi$ interactions, as discussed in Chap. 8.3. The affinity of other compounds, such as cyclohexane, cannot be explained in this way; evidently, some hydrophobic tendencies are to be found in polysaccharide gels which are predominantly hydrophilic in character (see Chap. 8.3).

References on p. A321

If we consider how the microarchitecture is derived from the basic polymer structure, it is possible to calculate the average pore size of the gel, but the pore size distribution is not so easily determined. From purely intuitive considerations, it would seem reasonable to suppose that the narrower the pore size distribution, the steeper the selectivity curve will be. The extreme case is that of a matrix with uniform pore size, for which the selectivity curve is almost vertical, i.e. with a sharp cut-off. This is shown by certain porous glasses [26,27] and, e.g., ultrafiltration membranes. Not only is the size of the pores important but, as Giddings [28] has pointed out, so also is the shape [29]. Thus, for spherical molecules, highest resolution is obtained with uniform parallel planes in the pore structure, while a random arrangement is more favorable for rod-like molecules.

8.2.2. Polyacrylamide gels

Even less is known about the microarchitecture of polyacrylamide gels. Porosity is controlled by the concentration of N,N'-methylenebis(acrylamide), which copolymerizes to form the crosslinks of the future matrix, unlike the case of dextran gels, where the crosslinks are built onto the existing polymer. N,N'-Methylenebis(acrylamide) is likely to form long chains, which may or may not ultimately form a crosslink. The selectivity of polyacrylamide media can, in general, be said to be that of a neutral matrix, modified somewhat by tendencies to hydrophobic interaction. After prolonged storage or use, the amide groups on the matrix tend to hydrolyze, leaving carboxyl groups, which will form centers for ion-exchange interactions. Polyacrylamide gels of the Bio-Gel P series are commercially available (Bio-Rad, Richmond, CA, USA).

8.2.3. Poly(acryloyl morpholine) gels

These gels are copolymers of acryloyl morpholine and methylenebis(acrylamide) [30], supplied commercially under the name Enzacryl (Koch-Light Ltd., Colnbrook, Great Britain). They have the advantage of being equally compatible with aqueous and organic solvent systems, and show virtually no hydrogen isotope exchange.

8.2.4. Hydroxyethyl methacrylate gels

These gels, marketed under the trade name of Spheron (Lachema, Prague, Czechoslovakia), are available in a wide range of porosities and give a family of selectivity curves that span the regions of molecular weight that are important in protein fractionation [31]. Fig. 8.3 is a schematic representation of the structure of Spheron, but very little is known about the microarchitecture. Compared with polysaccharide gels, these gels have a considerably greater matrix volume. This does not appear to be detrimental to the selectivity, but reduces the column capacity for proteins.

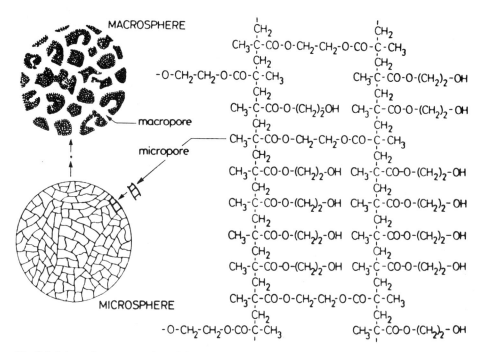

Fig. 8.3. Schematic representation of the structure of Spheron gels. (Reproduced from *Chromatography of Synthetic and Biological Polymers, Vol. 2, Hydrophobic, Ion Exchange and Affinity Methods G.P.C., G.F. and Gradient Elution*, Ellis Horwood, Chichester, 1978, p. 91, with permission [31].)

8.2.5. Agarose gels

These represent a class of gelling material that is altogether different from any of the aforementioned types in that agarose forms gels spontaneously. They do not derive their pore structure from the uptake of water under the constraint of chemical crosslinks, but rather from a special arrangement of the polysaccharide chains (Fig. 8.4), in which stretches of polysaccharide are involved in intimate hydrogen bonding with another or several other stretches of polysaccharide from another chain. The repetitive hydrogen-bonding arrays are interrupted at intervals to give rise to stretches of random coils after which a new hydrogen-bonded segment is encountered. This gives rise to bundles of rigid polymer aggregates, which are oriented in any direction within the gel, and it is these that give rise to the extraordinary rigidity

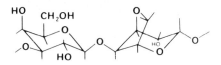

Fig. 8.4. Repeating disaccharide unit in agarose: D-galactose, β-(1,4)-L-anhydro-3,6-galactose.

References on p. A321

of agarose gels. Different porosities are attained by allowing gels to form from solutions of different concentration. Commercial gels, such as Sepharose (Pharmacia) and Bio-Gel A series (Bio-Rad) are available, having agarose concentrations of as low as 0.5%. These gels are thus extremely porous, having exclusion limits of up to 10^7 daltons. Gels based on dextran, polyacrylamide, or hydroxyethyl methacrylate cannot be obtained in such porosities; they would be too soft. Agarose gels have some of the characteristics of classical xerogels [1] (Fig. 8.1); i.e. they derive their stability as much from water, or more correctly from the interaction between water and the matrix, as from the matrix itself. They are, on the whole, rather soft gels, but are surprisingly rigid despite the low solid matrix content. It is possible to increase the rigidity quite considerably through covalent crosslinking by using, e.g., epichlorohydrin. Here, the crosslinks do not affect the porosity, as in the case of most other polysaccharide gels. Rather, they stiffen an already formed structure by complementing the hydrogen bonds with glyceryl bridges. Such crosslinked agarose gels are commercially available under the trade name Sepharose CL (Fig. 8.5).

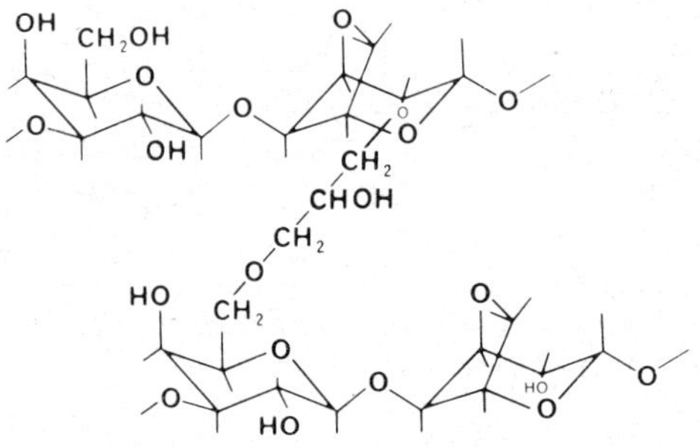

Fig. 8.5. Hypothetical crosslinking unit in Sepharose gels.

The structure shown in Fig. 8.6 is, of course, only hypothetical, though good evidence for helical stretches of the polymer, stabilized by hydrogen bonding, has been presented by Rees [32]. However, his suggestion as to how these helices become entwined in the gelling process is difficult to reconcile on topological grounds. The

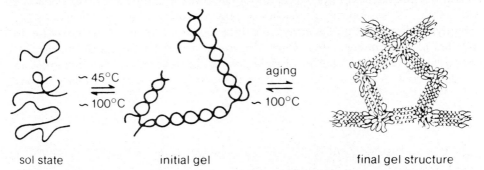

sol state   initial gel   final gel structure

Fig. 8.6. Stages in the formation and aging of agarose gels. (Reproduced from T. Låås, *Acta Univ. Upsaliens. (Dissertation)*, 1975, with permission [34].)

detailed microarchitecture is not known, but the model proposed in Fig. 8.6 is supported by the electron microscope data obtained by Amsterdam et al. [33]. Fig. 8.6 shows the formation and maturation, i.e. formation of stable bundle structures, of agarose [34].

8.2.6. Composite mixtures of agarose and polyacrylamide

The great porosity of agarose gels leaves room for the formation of polymer structures within the pores. This supposedly increases rigidity while maintaining adequate porosity for protein fractionation. Such materials are available in different grades under the trade name of Ultrogel (LKB Produkter, Bromma, Sweden) with varying concentrations of polyacrylamide/agarose. They form a family of gels with selectivity curves that cover the most important ranges for protein separation [35]. Little has been published about the details of the chemistry of these gels, and their detailed microarchitecture remains unknown.

8.2.7. Covalent composites of dextran and polyacrylamide

This kind of material, known commercially as Sephacryl (Pharmacia) possesses certain advantages over dextran gels, due to the formation of the polyacrylamide regions of the gel by radical polymerization directly into allyl groups in a matrix of allyl dextran. The conventional way of showing the chemical structure (Fig. 8.7) does not convey the essential features of the gel and its microarchitecture. The polyacrylamide is believed to form a granular structure, strung out along a matrix or web of dextran, with large pores between the granular regions. The structure is probably more akin to that of the aerogels, e.g., as in Fig. 8.1c and d, and the relatively high rigidity of the gels is a consequence of this granular structure. Sephacryl thus represents a significant step towards the production of gel-chromatography media rigid enough to be used under conditions of very high flowrate. As distinct from all

TABLE 8.1

COMPOSITION AND SOME CHROMATOGRAPHIC PROPERTIES OF SEPHACRYL GELS

Sephacryl grade	Dextran content	Polyacrylamide content	Exclusion limit, daltons		Flowrate at $\Delta P/\Delta L = 3$ [*], in cm/h
			proteins	dextrans	
S-200	10%	9.5%	$3 \cdot 10^5$	$8 \cdot 10^4$	30
S-300	7%	9.5%	$1.5 \cdot 10^6$	$4 \cdot 10^5$	30
S-400	2%	9.5%	$1.5 \cdot 10^7$	$2 \cdot 10^6$	30
S-500	1%	9.5%		$2 \cdot 10^7$	35
S-1000	0.3%	9.5%		10^8	35

[*] $\Delta P/\Delta L$ is the drop in hydrostatic pressure per unit length of chromatographic column (a dimensionless number).

References on p. A321

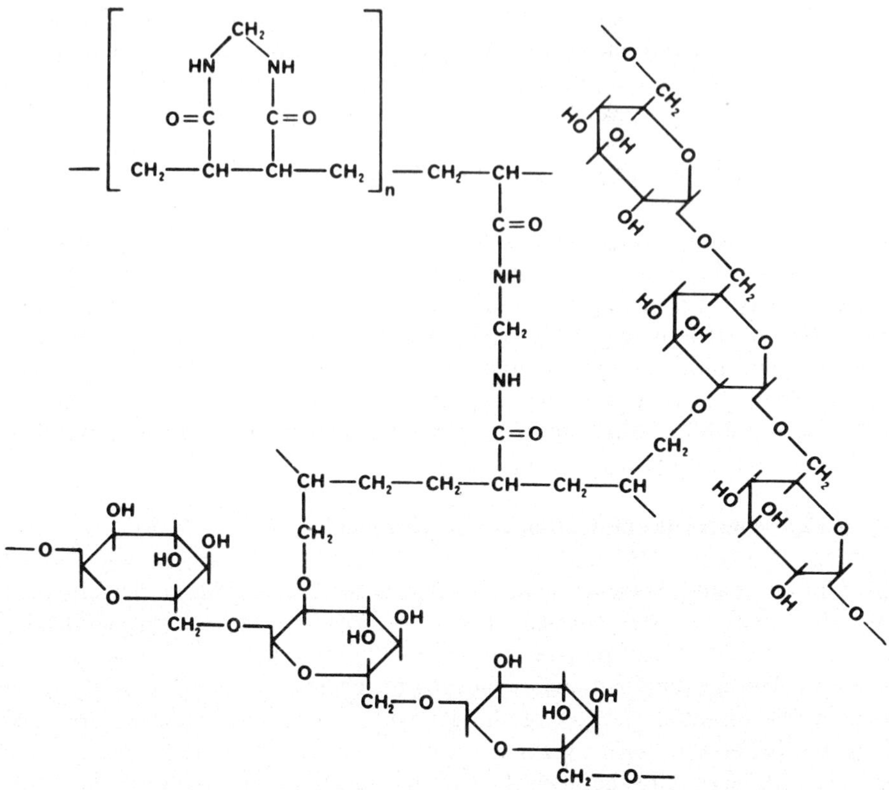

Fig. 8.7. Schematic representation of the structure of Sephacryl gels. (Reproduced from T. Låås, *Acta Univ. Upsaliens. (Dissertation)*, 1975, with permission [34].)

the aforementioned gels, usually classified as "soft gels", Sephacryl may be regarded as a semi-rigid gel. As previous reviews have not dealt with these gels, some of their properties are summarized in Table 8.1.

8.2.8. Rigid gels

It is, of course, desirable to carry out gel-filtration separations as rapidly as possible. To a considerable extent, this has been achieved in separations of compounds with low molecular weight and of certain synthetic polymers by HPLC. However, in separations of macromolecules there are several factors that limit the applicability of existing HPLC media and thus call for the development of new media. High speed is in itself of no benefit unless the resolution (effectivity and selectivity) of the column packing is sufficiently good. The relation between resolution and flowrate is given by

$$\text{HETP} = \left(\frac{1}{2d\lambda} + \frac{D_{\mathrm{m}}}{Vd^2} \right)^{-1} \tag{8.1}$$

where HETP is the height equivalent to a theoretical plate, d is the bead diameter, D_m is the solute diffusion coefficient in the mobile phase, V is the flowrate, and λ is a correction factor. Thus, it is apparent that resolution diminishes with flowrate.

Gel filtration media should have as little background (nonspecific) adsorption as possible. Although this is a general requirement, it should always be considered in relation to what is being separated. Proteins are well known to possess tendencies to aggregate or bind to surfaces. Their own surfaces abound with charged groups, aromatic groups, hydrophobic regions and the like, so that the condition of low, nonspecific binding is particularly hard to fulfill in the case of proteins. The most important HPLC packings available today are based on divinylbenzene/polystyrene or silica, and both kinds of material bind and denature proteins irreversibly. Furthermore, until recently they have not been available in the desired range of porosity. This situation has dramatically changed by the introduction of gels in which the divinylbenzene/polystyrene or silica surface is coated with a hydrophilic layer. In this way, the advantages of a rigid backbone matrix and of a hydrophilic polymer with low background adsorptive properties have been combined. Gels possessing these features that have recently been introduced are SW- and PW-type gels from Toyo Soda Co., Tokyo, Japan, and the Mono Q, S, and P and Polyanion SI gels from Pharmacia Fine Chemicals.

8.3. RELATION BETWEEN SOLUTE STRUCTURE AND PARTITIONING IN CHROMATOGRAPHY

The molecular size range covered by gel chromatography is vast, the steric exclusion limits covering several orders of magnitude from about 10^3 daltons in the most highly crosslinked Sephadex to more than 10^8 in the most porous Sephacryl gel. At the upper end of the scale, molecular size appears to be the determinant property, but as the gel matrix concentration increases and the porosity diminishes, interactions with the smaller penetrant species may be expected to increase in importance. As the starting point for a discussion on the properties of the dextran gels we have therefore selected a highly crosslinked type, Sephadex G-15, because it exhibits both steric exclusion and interactive phenomena.

8.3.1. Selectivity of Sephadex G-15 when water is the sole solvent

In an attempt to describe the behavior of solutes in a systematic way, saturated hydrocarbons and their hydroxylated derivatives, i.e. alcohols, diols, and polyols, were selected as the model compounds [36]. There emerged two essentially contrasting patterns of behavior, depending on the polarity of the compound.

8.3.1.1. Weakly polar and nonpolar saturated nonelectrolytes

The distribution coefficient is defined as $K = C_g/C_0$, where C_g and C_o are the concentrations within the gel and in the external solvent. C_g is usually defined as the concentration either in the whole gel or in the solvent imbibed by the gel. The corresponding chromatographic distribution coefficients, K_{av} [37] and K_d [38] are then calculated as follows:

$$K_{av} = \frac{V_e - V_o}{V_t - V_o} \quad \text{and} \quad K_d = \frac{V_e - V_o}{V_s - V_o}$$

where V_e is the elution volume, V_o is the void volume, V_t is the volume of the gel column, and V_s is the total volume of solvent in the column.

Fig. 8.8 shows the relation between the logarithm of K_d and the number of carbon

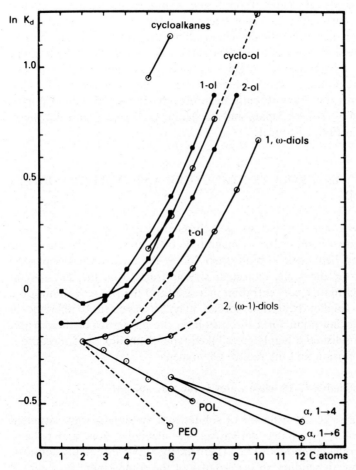

Fig. 8.8. Logarithm of distribution coefficients of Sephadex G-15 at 25°C in relation to the number of C atoms in different aliphatic series. The alcohols are denoted by 1-ol etc. and the amides by filled squares. POL are polyhydric alcohols and PEO is the slope connecting ethylene glycol and triethylene glycol; α, $(1\rightarrow4)$ and α, $(1\rightarrow6)$ are the slopes of lines connecting glucose to maltose and isomaltose, respectively. They represent the slopes of the malto- and isomaltodextrins. (Redrawn from *J. Polym. Sci. Polym. Lett. Ed.*, 18 (1980) 271, and reproduced with permission [36].)

atoms for several series of hydrocarbon derivatives, namely 1-, 2-, and tertiary alkanols, diols, amides, polyhydric alcohols, and sugars [36]. It is clear that the polar polyols, poly(ethylene oxide)s, and oligosaccharides towards which the gel apparently behaves as a molecular sieve, act in a way that is quite different from the other series. The latter, the monohydroxyalcohols, diols, and amides, become increasingly less polar as a series is ascended, and it is evident that they have an affinity for the gel which is a steric relation in the sense that it is related to the length of the hydrocarbon moiety. The plots for the higher alcohols, amides, and $1,\omega$-diols tend to have similar slopes, and this would probably also be the case with the $2,(\omega-1)$-diols, if sufficiently long homologs were available. Since the standard free energy of transfer into the gel (ΔG^0) is related to the distribution coefficient as follows

$$\Delta G^0 = -RT \ln K \tag{8.2}$$

these series probably approach approximately linear free energy relations (LFER) [39]. Each decrement $\Delta(\Delta G^0)$ must correspond to the addition of one methylene group. In the case of the 1-alcohols and amides, i.e. series which begin with a single carbon atom, the initial slope is either zero (alcohols) or reversed (amides). This presumably depends on the influence of the polar groups. Thus, the first two amides behave as though they belonged to a series exhibiting molecular sieving. However, as the hydrocarbon chain lengthens, the methylenes, sufficiently far from the polar amide group, are able to exert their effect. Similarly, the gel does not discriminate between methanol and ethanol. The fact that methanol, ethanol, and 1-propanol have K_d values below unity may not be due to steric factors, since it has been reported that the three lower alcohols were repelled from a hydrocarbon/water interface, presumably being preferentially retained in the bulk of the aqueous phase. A possible reason for this is that they can be accepted as components of a cooperative water structure [40].

This behavior demonstrates that the effect of a methylene group can be nullified by a polar group; the approximate negative LFER among the higher members suggests that the polar group has a short-range influence, limited essentially to one or two neighboring carbons [41]. These data further suggest that long-chain alcohols are effectively hydrophobic [42], and thus serve as valid models for the hydrocarbons, which are much less soluble in water. In addition, the actual nature of the polar group is probably unimportant [41,43], as is reflected by the similar behavior of the aliphatic amides and alcohols (Fig. 8.8).

The affinity-reducing effect of the aliphatic hydroxyl group is illustrated in Fig. 8.9; perhydroxylation results in a polyol having partitioning properties that are quite different.

8.3.1.2. Polar saturated nonelectrolytes

A polar series, such as the polyhydric alcohols [36,44], behaves on Sephadex G-15 in a way that is characteristically different from their less polar analogs, as illustrated in Fig. 8.8. In this case, there is an approximate positive LFER character-

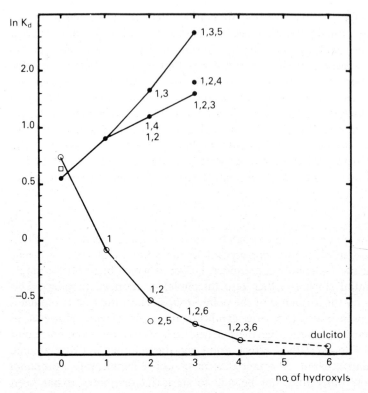

Fig. 8.9. Logarithm of distribution coefficients of hexane (○) and benzene (●) and some of their hydroxyl derivatives in Sephadex G-15 at 25°C. The numerals beside the experimental points refer to the particular derivative. Although 1,2- and 1,4-benzenediols are shown as having the same values, the latter is slightly higher. The point for hexane was calculated assuming that $\Delta G^0(n\text{-hexane}) - \Delta G^0(\text{cyclohexane}) = \Delta G^0(1\text{-hexanol}) - \Delta G^0(\text{cyclohexanol})$. The point indicated by (□) refers to cyclohexanol. (Redrawn from *J. Polymer. Sci. Polym. Lett. Ed.*, 18 (1980) 271, and reproduced with permission [36].)

istic of gel-filtration or gel-permeation chromatography (GPC). Whereas the region of negative LFER is confined to the region where ΔG^0 is negative ($K_d > 1$), a positive LFER is associated with positive ΔG^0 values ($K_d < 1$), as is evident in Fig. 8.8.

The positive LFER (steric exclusion) is the basis of gel filtration and GPC. In the case of a LFER the standard transfer free energy of a polymer may be written as the sum of the contributions from its constituent units [45,46]. Thus, for a homogeneous polymer, such as a homopolysaccharide with a degree of polymerisation (DP) equal to n

$$-\ln K_d = \frac{1}{RT}\left[\Delta G_1^0 + \Delta G_n^0 + \sum_2^{n-1} \Delta G_i^0\right] \tag{8.3}$$

where ΔG_1^0 and ΔG_n^0 refer to the two terminal units and ΔG_i^0 to the intermediate ones. As far as oligosaccharides are concerned, all the component free energy terms are for practical purposes equal, at least above the first, since the relationships are linear, beginning with glucose [47].

Eqn. 8.3 is, in fact, an expanded form of the Brønsted equation [48].

$$K = \exp(\lambda M / RT) \tag{8.4}$$

where λ is an interaction parameter and M is the molecular weight [49] or, more properly, the molecular size, defined in a way relevant to the gel (see below). The sign of λ can be positive (sorption-dominated interaction) or negative (steric exclusion-dominated); the value of this parameter varies in a complex manner, depending on the type of gel, the solvent, and the polymeric solute.

8.3.1.3. Cyclic unsaturated nonelectrolytes

As shown in Table 8.2, there are only small, irregular differences between the ΔG^0 values for cyclohexane, cyclohexene, the two cyclohexadienes, and benzene in Sephadex G-15 [36]. The lack of a particular influence of conjugation or aromaticity is also reflected in the enthalpies, which decrease by about 2 kJ/mole for each double bond. The standard enthalpy (ΔH^0) was calculated from the Van't Hoff equation

$$d \ln K / dt = \Delta H^0 / RT^2 \tag{8.5}$$

and the entropy (ΔS^0) from the equation

$$\Delta G^0 = \Delta H^0 - T\Delta S^0 \tag{8.6}$$

As discussed below, the dynamic, column-chromatographic K_d values [38] are quasi-equilibrial; ΔH^0 values calculated from the Van't Hoff equation are probably reliable, since the enthalpies of solution of hydrocarbons calculated from this equation agreed well with those obtained calorimetrically [50].

If the aromatic hydrocarbons provide no clue to the well-documented aromatic affinity of the dextran gels [3,51–62], hydroxylation unmasks a clear divergence from the behavior of saturated compounds. As shown in Fig. 8.9, addition of a hydroxyl to the aromatic ring markedly increases the affinity. If the hydroxyl is not on the ring, however, the affinity decreases as with saturated compounds. Thus, 4-cresol has a higher K_d value than toluene, whereas the K_d of benzyl alcohol is lower. Methoxybenzene has a lower K_d value than phenol, indicating that the affinity-increasing effect of the methyl group is less than the loss of affinity due to removal of the hydroxyl hydrogen [36].

8.3.1.4. Acyclic nonelectrolytes containing double bonds

Although it is evident that the affinity-increasing effect of the hydroxyl in an aromatic compound depends on its being on the ring, this effect is not limited to aromatic compounds but occurs also in compounds containing a single double bond. Amino groups have an effect similar to hydroxyls, as shown by increasing affinity in the acetone–acetamide–urea series (Table 8.3). Further, successive N-methylation of

TABLE 8.2

DISTRIBUTION COEFFICIENTS (K_d), FREE ENERGIES (ΔG^0), AND ENTHALPIES (ΔH^0), IN kJ mole^{-1}, AT 25°C FOR SOME ALIPHATIC AND AROMATIC COMPOUNDS ON SEPHADEX G-15 [36]

Compounds	K_d	ΔG^0	ΔH^0
Cyclopentane	2.60	−2.37	–
Cyclohexane	3.12	−2.82	10.6
Cyclohexene	2.64	−2.41	8.59
1,3-Cyclohexadiene	2.55	−2.32	6.17
1,4-Cyclohexadiene	2.69	−2.45	–
Benzene	2.82	−2.57	4.88
Toluene	3.72	−3.26	5.32
Ethylbenzene	4.59	−3.78	–
Benzaldehyde	2.81	−2.56	3.13
Cyclopentanol	1.21	−0.472	–
Cyclohexanol	1.40	−0.834	7.34
1,2-*trans*-Cyclohexanediol	1.01	−0.025	3.75
myo-Inositol	0.611	1.22	0.84
Phenol	4.06	−3.47	−0.56
Methoxybenzene	3.66	−3.21	2.99
4-Methylphenol	5.12	−4.05	–
4-Ethylphenol	5.91	−4.40	–
Benzyl alcohol	2.28	−2.04	3.99
1-Phenylethanol	2.30	−2.06	–
3-Phenyl-1-propanol	2.94	−2.67	–
1,2-Benzenediol	4.94	−3.96	−4.13
1,3-Benzenediol	6.27	−4.55	−6.85
1,4-Benzenediol	5.08	−4.03	−6.14
1,2,3-Benzenetriol	6.07	−4.47	−8.31
1,2,4-Benzenetriol	6.58	−4.67	–
1,3,5-Benzenetriol	10.35	−5.79	−14.3

urea reduces the affinity so that the ΔG^0 values of acetone and tetramethylurea are nearly the same. N-Methyl derivatives of thiourea also show this trend. The behavior of the unsaturated compounds is not peculiar to Sephadex. Bio-Gel P-2 shows essentially the same affinity sequences, both with regard to aromatic hydroxylation and N-methylation [62].

8.3.1.5. Electrolytes

The gel chromatography of inorganic electrolytes has received a good deal of attention and has been extensively reviewed by Yoza [63]. Not only dextran [64,65]

TABLE 8.3

DISTRIBUTION COEFFICIENTS (K_d) AND MEAN STANDARD FREE ENERGIES (ΔG^0), AT 25°C, OF UREAS AND THIOUREAS AND SOME RELATED COMPOUNDS ON SEPHADEX G-15 [36]

Compounds	K_d	ΔG^0
Acetone	0.859	0.378
Acetamide	0.945	0.140
N-Dimethylacetamide	0.788	0.589
Urea	1.187	−0.424
N-Methylurea	1.075	−0.179
N,N′-Dimethylurea	1.015	−0.036
N-Dimethylurea	1.010	−0.022
Tetramethylurea	0.857	0.382
Thiourea	2.232	−1.990
N-Methylthiourea	1.846	−1.519
N,N′-Dimethylthiourea	1.740	−1.373
N,N′-Diethylthiourea	1.801	−1.459

but also polyacrylamide [66–68], poly(acryloyl morpholine) [69], and hydroxyethyl methacrylate [70] gels exhibit selectivity to both anions and cations, and the following applies to both Sephadex and polyacrylamide gels, unless noted otherwise.

The measurement of ion distribution coefficients is discussed by Roth [65]. Elution with an electrolyte is mandatory in chromatography on the Sephadex gels in order to eliminate Donnan exclusion effects due to the low concentration of fixed carboxylate groups. The presence of a background of eluting electrolyte also allows an ion to move essentially independently of the counterions, otherwise a salt-distribution coefficient is obtained. The presence of the eluting electrolyte does not, of course, imply that the partitioning of an ion within the gel is independent of the counterions; electroneutrality must be conserved and gel/ion interactions in a quasi-neutral gel must involve the pairing of the ions.

When water is the sole solvent, the selectivity is greater for simple anions than for alkali metal or alkaline-earth cations [71]. The order of elution for alkali metal cations in Sephadex gels, $Li^+ < Na^+ < Cs^+ < Rb^+ < K^+$, is not that of the crystal or so-called hydrated radii [72] but is one of the orders found by Eisenman in cation-selective glass electrodes [73]. This, together with the fact that ion partitioning in these gels is highly dependent on the nature of the eluting anion [65,70,74–76], indicates that steric exclusion is not an important factor. Although the individual anionic K_d values are very dependent on the nature of the eluent anion (Table 8.4), the latter does not affect the order of elution, which is that of the Hofmeister or lyotropic series [75–78], as shown in Table 8.5. The eluting anion affects the K_d values of the test anions and cations in opposite directions. Thus, with sulfate (low K_d) as eluent, cationic K_d values are low; with perchlorate (high K_d), they are high [71]. However, elution with sulfate results in a K_d value for a test anion which is

TABLE 8.4

K_d VALUES OF TRIS(2-AMINO-2-HYDROXYMETHYLPROPANE-1,3-DIOL) HALIDES ELUTED WITH DIFFERENT ANIONS FROM SEPHADEX G-10, AT 25°C [75]

Eluent anions	F^-	Cl^-	Br^-	I^-
Acetate	0.385	0.702	1.050	2.482
Cl^-	0.329	0.609	0.924	2.081
Br^-	0.247	0.545	0.822	1.772
ClO_4^-	0.192	0.380	0.535	–

higher than that obtained on elution with perchlorate. It appears, therefore, that the cations accompany the eluting anions whereas the latter compete with test anions for the gel. In contrast to the eluent anion, the nature of the eluent cation, among the alkali metal series, has little effect on the anionic distribution coefficient [67].

The anionic (and cationic) K_d values are essentially independent of the concentration of the eluent electrolyte, provided the latter is high enough (for Sephadex G-10 > ca. $10^{-2} M$) to suppress Donnan exclusion effects [64,65,67,74]. These properties of the anion can be understood in terms of the model shown in Fig. 8.10. Consider a univalent test anion Z^- eluted with an univalent anion X^- in the presence of a common cation M^+. Assuming that electroneutrality is conserved, and thus, neglecting electrical potentials in the quasi-neutral gel, we may write:

$$C_x + C_z = C_m \tag{8.7}$$

TABLE 8.5

K_{av} VALUES AND LYOTROPIC NUMBERS OF SOME ANIONS IN SEPHADEX G-15

Anions	K_{av} *	N **
Citrate	0.15	–
Sulfate	0.20	2.0
Carbonate	0.31	–
Fluoride	0.35	4.8
Acetate	0.39	–
Bicarbonate	0.46	–
Chloride	0.54	10.0
Nitrite	0.60	10.1
Bromide	0.71	11.5
Nitrate	0.74	11.6
Iodide	1.27	12.5
Perchlorate	1.45	11.8
Thiocyanate	1.54	13.3

* From ref. 78.
** From J.W. McBain, *Colloid Science*, Reinhold, New York, 1950, p. 131.

EXTERNAL   SOLUTION   GEL   COMPARTMENT

Species   Concentration   Species   Concentration

X^- C_x XG^- N_{xg}

Z^- C_z ZG^- N_{zg}

M^+ C_m MG^+ N_{mg}

Fig. 8.10. Model of ionic distribution in aqueous gel systems. C_x, C_z and C_m are the molar concentrations of two anions and a cation in the external solution. N_{xg}, N_{zg} and N_{mg} are the concentrations of neutral sorption sites occupied by the different ion pairs.

and

$$N_{xg} + N_{zg} = N_{mg} \tag{8.8}$$

Now, by definition

$$K_{xm} \cdot C_m \cdot C_x = N_{mg} \cdot N_{xg} \tag{8.9}$$

and

$$K_{zm} \cdot C_m \cdot C_z = N_{mg} \cdot N_{zg} \tag{8.10}$$

where K_{xm} and K_{zm} are the salt distribution coefficients. The distribution coefficient of the anion Z^- when eluted with X^- is defined as:

$$(K_z)_x = \frac{N_{zg}}{C_z} \tag{8.11}$$

whence it can be derived that

$$(K_z)_x = \frac{K_{zm}}{K_{xm}^{1/2}} \left(\frac{1 + C_z/C_x}{1 + K_{zm} \cdot C_z/K_{xm} \cdot C_x} \right)^{1/2} \tag{8.12}$$

Eqn. 8.12 shows that the value of $(K_z)_x$ depends on the nature of X^- but that it becomes essentially independent of the concentration of X^- at low values of the ratio C_z/C_x when

$$(K_z)_x \approx K_{zm}/K_{xm}^{1/2} \tag{8.13}$$

In practice, eqn. 8.13 should hold over the whole useful concentration range in Sephadex, since at low values of C_x, where deviations would occur, the selectivity is drastically reduced, because of Donnan effects [79]. A relation for three anions can be derived from eqn. 8.13

$$\left[\frac{(K_z)_x}{(K_y)_x}\right]^{1/2} \approx \frac{(K_x)_y}{(K_x)_z} \tag{8.14}$$

8.3.2. Electrolytes in mixed solvents

The selectivity of Sephadex for ions may be changed and even greatly enhanced in mixed solvents. Thus, in methanol–water (7:3, w/w) complete separation of all five lower alkali metal cations can be achieved on Sephadex G-25 in a column of moderate length [80–82]. In this case, the aqueous elution order $Li^+ < Na^+ < Cs^+ < Rb^+ < K^+$ is maintained. As this is also the order of the water–methanol solubility ratios, it has been suggested that the latter may be responsible for the enhanced selectivity. However, this cannot be correct, since the compositions of the solvent inside and outside the gel are not sufficiently different [83].

Anion selectivity can also be greatly modified by change of solvent. Thus, in methanol–water (7:3, w/w) the selectivity of Sephadex G-25 for the halides is almost completely abolished. However, with acetonitrile–water (3:2, w/w) the selectivity is enhanced, while the aqueous order, $Cl^- < Br^- < I^-$, is reversed [84].

8.3.3. Gel-permeation chromatography

The term gel filtration [15] is usually limited to chromatography in polar gels with water or other polar solvents. Gel-permeation chromatography (GPC), a term introduced by Moore [85,86], has apparently become firmly attached to the use of less polar resins in the determination of molecular-size distributions. Vaughan [87] seems to have been first to explore this method with nonpolar resins and nonaqueous solvents. He reported some fractionation of a polystyrene with a broad molecular-weight distribution by means of crosslinked polystyrene beads. Later, Brewer [88] separated polymers from low-molecular-weight compounds, and Curtis-Jones [89] obtained good separations of low-molecular-weight organic compounds. The determination of the molecular-weight distributions by using columns calibrated with carefully characterized polymers was also reported about the same time [85,90,91].

Since, partitioning—not unexpectedly—appears to be a simpler process for the elution of a linear polymer by an ideal (θ) solvent [92] from a nonpolar or weakly polar gel, this case will be considered first. For an account of the kinematics of chromatography reference may be made to Ouano [93]. The theoretical basis of exclusion chromatography has been dealt with in considerable detail [94–97]. It seems to be generally accepted that with sufficiently low flowrates this type of partitioning can be treated as quasi-equilibrial [94,97–100], although chromatography, being a flow-through system, is liable to perturbations that hinder establishment of equilibrium [101]. In general, however, transport properties apparently become relevant only when rates of flow through the column are too fast for the establishment of local equilibrium between the stationary and mobile phases. Under these conditions, lateral diffusion becomes a limiting factor [102–104]. In addition, irregularities in hydrodynamic flow, deformation of the eluted polymer under shear strain, deformation of the gel due to the operating pressure, and osmotically induced variations in the degree of gel swelling may also affect partitioning [104].

8.3.3.1. Flow models

The flowrate can actually be utilized to achieve separations of colloidal particles. This appears to have been first reported by Pedersen [105], who separated monomeric and oligomeric albumin fractions on Sephadex gels. He also noted that steric selectivity was exhibited by a number of other materials, not necessarily gels. The larger the surface area of the packing material in the column, i.e. the smaller the particle size, the lower was the molecular-weight range in which separation occurred [105]. He furthermore showed that with small glass spheres (20–35 μm in diameter) macromolecular separation was possible. Pedersen suggested that this phenomenon be called exclusion chromatography and pointed out that it was analogous to the flow of blood in small vessels, where the erythrocytes moved at a faster rate than the average velocity of the plasma.

This method, later called hydrodynamic chromatography, was used to separate mixtures of polymerized latexes and colloidal dispersions of silica and carbon blacks [106]. That interactions between the packing material and the colloidal particles may have a significant influence on the particle separation was shown by varying the ionic strength of the eluent. DiMarzio and Guttman [107,108] showed theoretically that an isolated polymer molecule, flowing down a thin capillary, will move faster than the solvent, because the center of the particle cannot approach the wall closer than its radius. Since the velocity of flow increases with increasing distance from the wall, as predicted by Bernoulli's theorem [109], larger molecules will have larger velocities than small ones, so that separation by flow (SBF) occurs. A mathematical model based on this theory, which enabled particle number ratios to be predicted to within 10% of the values obtained by electron microscopy, has subsequently been described [110].

The general problem of separation in a flowing system was considered by Guttman and DiMarzio [111], who did not view the solvent space within the gel beads as a stationary region [112] but as composed of fine channels, allowing a through-flow. Since the equivalent hydrodynamic volume of the solute was an important variable in SBF as well as in GPC (see below), it was of interest to ascertain the interrelationship. In this model, Guttman and DiMarzio distinguished between two extreme cases: (a) a high flowrate and/or low solute diffusion constant where SBF is important, and (b) a low flowrate and/or high solute diffusion constant where SBF is unimportant. In the second case, SBF is equivalent to an equilibrium model.

Verhoff and Sylvester [113] described a similar model with a relatively fast flow in the interstitial channel and a slow flow in the narrower confines of the beads. Casassa [114] noted that, if certain approximations in the Verhoff–Sylvester theory are eliminated, it comes into agreement with the Guttman–DiMarzio theory when, as is usual in GPC, the flowrates are slow. With faster flowrates [100], however, the effects of flow within the gel beads may make significant contributions to separations. Further, gels differ greatly in their matrix concentration, water content, rigidity, porosity, and almost certainly in their internal hydrodynamic characteristics. Thus, it seems more likely that internal flow may occur in Sephadex G-200 ($\sim 5\%$ matrix) than in Sephadex G-10 ($\sim 60\%$ matrix).

8.3.3.2. Equilibrium models

For the case when the flowrate is slow enough to give quasi-equilibrium, empirical rules applied to model systems have often been used to describe the relation between the distribution coefficient and the molecular size of the solute or the pore dimensions of the gel. These theoretical models have usually been applied to relatively simple and rigid molecules and pore networks [115], and it is assumed that the solvent within the gel beads constitutes a stationary compartment. Thus, Porath [116] and Squire [117] considered spherical molecules in conical pores, recognizing that the conical volume available to the center of the penetrant sphere is somewhat less than the volume of the cone itself and dependent on the radius of the penetrant. Waldmann-Meyer [118] tested this model and found that it fits well with literature data on porous glasses [26,27]. Laurent and Killander [37] utilized an equation of Ogston [119] for the partitioning of spheres in a random network of rods.

Especially in the macromolecular domain, the partitioned species are usually not spherical. Giddings et al. [94], who considered the distribution of rigid penetrants in inert porous networks, concluded that a new parameter, called the mean external length $(\bar{L})$, uniquely determines partitioning. In the special case of spherical molecules in a network of fibers of finite diameter, they obtained the same equation (Ogston) as used by Laurent and Killander [37]. Their conclusions were essentially the same as those of Casassa [96] and Casassa and Tagami [97], who considered the important case of linear and branched flexible polymer chains, a class of solute much used in GPC (cf. Fig. 8.11). The cavities in the gel were treated as either spheres, infinite cylinders or infinite slabs, i.e. with a volume bounded by two parallel infinite planes. It was found that partitioning was rather insensitive to the geometry of the cavity, a conclusion not at all unexpected in view of the degree of success of so many simple pore models in accounting for observed partitioning behavior [120]. The distribution coefficient was actually the fraction of all allowed chain conformations that can exist inside the cavities within the gel, i.e. the value is simply a measure of the residual conformational entropy of the penetrant molecules within the gel. Thus, assuming no interaction with the gel, the transfer enthalpy is zero [94] and

$$\Delta G_{\text{tr}}^0 = - T \, \Delta S_{\text{tr}}^0 \tag{8.15}$$

where

$$\Delta S_{\text{tr}}^0 = R \ln(\Omega_i / \Omega_o) \tag{8.16}$$

where Ω_i and Ω_o are the numbers of attainable configurations (or, for flexible molecules, attainable conformations) within equal volumes of pore and external bulk fluids, respectively. It then follows from eqn. 8.2 that

$$K_d = \Omega_i / \Omega_o \qquad (8.17)$$

The ratio Ω_i / Ω_o should thus vary inversely with molecular size.

8.3.3.3. Molecular-size calibration

The characteristic molecular dimension for exclusion from the cavities, as calculated by Casassa and Tagami [97], is, as pointed out by Van Krefeld [121], the same as the parameter $\overline{L}$ of Giddings et al. [94], a quantity first calculated some years previously [122,123]. This molecular dimension is independent of the molecular geometry; it is determined by the extreme groups, the shielded regions in the interior of a molecule having no direct influence. In a θ solvent which does not interact with the polymer [92] $\overline{L}$ is the mean random-flight dimension, but in a good solvent the chain is expanded beyond this. However, the use of the mean-square size of the real chain should be acceptable [99]. For a linear polymer, the latter is related simply to the radius of gyration [94], which is, according to Giddings et al. [94], the next most successfully correlated parameter.

From a study of GPC in linear and nonlinear polystyrenes Benoit and coworkers [95,115] concluded that the effective hydrodynamic volume (EHV) was the factor which determined partitioning, and they suggested its usefulness for universal calibration [95]. Boni et al. [124] came to the same conclusion from a study of linear polyethylene, polystyrene, and polybutadiene fractions in trichlorobenzene and tetrahydrofuran. EHV is the product of the limiting viscosity number, $[\eta]$, and the molecular weight. From a comparison of the behavior of polystyrene and other polymers in poor and θ solvents Dawkins and Hemming [125–127] also concluded that the EHV was a universal calibration, provided corrections were made for gel/solute interactions.

However, the validity of universal calibration has been questioned on theoretical grounds [86,90]. If EHV is a universal calibration parameter there must be a unique relation between the hydrodynamic radius and $\overline{L}$, but this is unlikely. Theoretically, there seems to be a significant difference in the EHV calibration between compact and more extended molecules [98]. However, in the special case of species of similar type, e.g. for both linear flexible chains and those with limited branching, the correlation with EHV should be good. A universal calibration parameter should be independent of the nature of both solute and solvent (and the gel). However, as Dintzis and Tobin [128] reported, whereas dextran and amylose had the same calibration line in dimethylsulfoxide, the line was different for polystyrene fractions in tetrahydrofuran.

The best fit between theory and experiment seems to have been achieved by use of the column packing with perhaps the most rigid but certainly the best defined and most regular pores, i.e. the porous glasses, introduced by Haller [26,27]. Interactions always constitute a problem in exclusion chromatography, particularly in good solvents. Belenky et al. [129], in fact, concluded that there is a continuous transition between GPC and adsorption chromatography, but a linear calibration of K_d is possible as a function of molecular weight within the limits of a homologous series; this is exhibited very clearly by oligosaccharides (Chap. 8.3.5).

8.3.3.4. Available volume

The fundamental equation relating the elution volume, V_e, of a solute to its distribution coefficient, K_d, is [97]

$$V_e = V_o + K_d \cdot V_i \tag{8.18}$$

where V_o is the void or interstitial volume and V_i is the volume within the gel particles penetrated by the solvent. K_d (or K_{av}) may be interpreted as the fraction of solvent (or gel) accessible to the solute, the solute concentration in the accessible domain being equal to that outside the gel. If steric exclusion were the only partitioning mechanism, this would be true only for the simple case of rigid, spherical molecules.

Fig. 8.11 illustrates the exclusion effect for three differently shaped molecules in an internal space, visualized as a hollow cylinder. Fig. 8.11A shows the simplest case of a rigid sphere of radius r, which is the closest its center can approach the wall. The situation is the same for the thin rod (B) of length $2r$ only when it is perpendicular to the axis of the cylinder. At other angles, its mass center can approach the wall more closely than r. However, the nearer it is to the wall, the fewer are the number of permitted orientations (configurations). The latter type of problem was considered by Giddings et al. [94]. Fig. 8.11C represents a random-flight polymer chain. Any part of this molecule can be in any part of the internal space, but the wall decreases conformational freedom. If the reference end is set at 0, it is evident that some conformations are forbidden. The simple case of steric exclusion

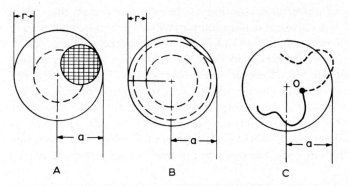

Fig. 8.11. Schematic diagram illustrating the exclusion effect in a cylindrical void of radius a: (A) hard sphere of radius r; (B) thin rod of length $2r$ in two orientations in the plane of the cross-section; (C) random-flight chain with one end at point O, showing allowed conformation (solid curve) and forbidden conformation (dotted curve). (Reproduced from *J. Phys. Chem.*, 75 (1971) 3929, with permission [114].)

in A is not essentially different from B and C. A sphere has a uniquely defined conformation. Its position is specified by a single point, and its exclusion is defined in terms of real space, i.e. the circle of closest approach of its center in Fig. 8.11A. The rod or flexible molecule, on the other hand, if in a sufficiently large volume, would be free to assume any configuration or possible conformation. However, only a fraction of these are permissible in the confined spaces of the gel, and in this sense these molecules are excluded from part of their configurational space. Thus, although no part of the actual volume of a pore would be inaccessible to the molecule if it were infinitely thin, the concentration inside the pore is lower than that outside, the ratio of the concentrations being the ratio of the conformational possibilities (eqn. 8.17). For each type of molecule the final result is the same, $K \leqslant 1$. In the case of a thin rod or a flexible polymer chain, it is clear that the minimal dimension has little relevance to its ability to enter a pore. Clear evidence of this was obtained by Haller [27] with porous glasses having a narrow distribution of pore sizes. Thus, the rod-shaped tobacco mosaic virus, 15 nm in diameter and 300 nm long [130], was excluded from pores 170 nm in diameter.

8.3.4. Exclusion chromatography of polar solutes in good solvents

In good solvents, such as water, permeation of polar solutes into the gel cavities may be diminished by two additional factors: (a) the entropy change on transfer of a flexible-chain polymer to a cavity is increased because the polymer is, on the average, expanded beyond random-flight dimensions before being hindered by the cavity; and (b) there will be an enthalpy change due to the greater density of intramolecular contacts in a chain in narrow confines. These problems can possibly be treated theoretically [131,132].

The introduction of the dextran and polyacrylamide gels was followed by much work on their steric exclusion properties. Their usefulness in the analysis of homologous series, such as the polyglycans, i.e. dextran, Ficoll, starch, inulin, etc., soon became evident [16,133–135] and is now well established. This technique has also proved useful both in analyses of oligosaccharide structure [47,136] and in gaining information about the interactions between the gel matrix, the solvent, and the solute [137]. However, it is not only with respect to linear, repeating polysaccharides that gel chromatography on Sephadex and other polar gels has had an important impact in biochemistry. Proteins were early substrates for gel chromatography [138] and, not surprisingly, in view of the considerable variation in their secondary and tertiary structure, anomalies in their behavior soon became evident. This difficulty can be overcome, to a large extent at least, by "randomizing" their structure with a surfactant, such as sodium dodecyl sulfate (SDS), or a so-called chaotropic electrolyte, such as guanidinium chloride [139–145] or guanidinium thiocyanate [146].

8.3.5. Oligosaccharides

As has already been mentioned, the exclusion ranges of Sephadex gels cover several orders of magnitude, and it is only to be expected that interactions involving

References on p. A321

the gel and penetrating solutes should become increasingly important as the concentration and degree of substitution of the matrix (by crosslinking) rises in the more highly crosslinked types. The studies of Brown and his co-workers, mainly on the elution of homologous oligosaccharides and poly(ethylene oxides) (PEO) from highly crosslinked dextran, cellulose, and polyacrylamide gels, have yielded a good deal of information on gel/solute/solvent interactions [48,137,147–152]. It was concluded [149] that in such systems simple steric exclusion was the exception rather than the rule, since partitioning was determined not only by steric factors but also by the relative polarities of the gel, solute, and solvent. That the gel surface is far from inert is demonstrated by the finding that, whereas PEO were more excluded than cellodextrins on the two polar gels Sephadex G-15 and Bio-Gel P-2, the situation was reversed on the nonpolar polystyrene (Poragel 60). The role of the solvent is also very important, as Fig. 8.12 shows for the cellodextrins on Sephadex G-15 in three polar solvents, namely water, formamide, and DMSO.

The existence of a positive LFER for a homologous series indicates steric exclusion but does not, of course, exclude the possibility of interactions. For want of a better index of molecular size, the degree of polymerisation (DP) is often used in correlating oligosaccharide data. Water is far from being an ideal solvent and saccharide/water interactions are complex [153], but the different glycosidic linkages, which lead to conformational differences [154], may reflect the behavior of different homologous oligosaccharide series in gels, although intramolecular hydrogen bonding also contributes to altering the surface of the cellodextrins. As Table 8.6

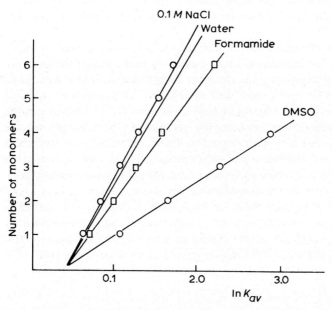

Fig. 8.12. Partitioning of cellodextrins on Sephadex G-15 in three polar solvents. (Reproduced from *J. Chromatogr.*, 59 (1971) 335, with permission [148].)

TABLE 8.6

CONFORMATIONAL CLASSIFICATION OF POLYSACCHARIDES WITH DIFFERENT GLYCO-
SIDIC LINKAGES [154]

Description	Polyglucan	Polygalactan	Polyxylan
Extended and ribbon-like	α-1,3	α-1,3	α-1,3
	β-1,4	α-1,4	β-1,4
Flexible and helical	β-1,3	β-1,3	β-1,3
	α-1,4	β-1,4	α-1,4
Rigid and crumpled	α-1,2	α-1,2	α-1,2
	β-1,2	β-1,2	β-1,2
Flexible and rather extended	1,6	1,6	

shows, the isomaltodextrins [α-D-$(1 \rightarrow 6)$ linkage] are more extended in aqueous solution than the maltodextrins [α-D-$(1 \rightarrow 4)$] [154], and this is consistent with the greater exclusion of the former from two Sephadex gels and Bio-Gel P-4 [47]. Further, in the Sephadex gels the rigid cellodextrins gave a calibration plot almost identical with that of the isomaltose series. This behavior is not confined to chromatography on Sephadex. There are essentially the same interrelationships on polyacrylamide gels [47,155] and also, interestingly, in PC with mixed solvents [156]. Conformational differences are also important in the chromatography of larger polysaccharides: thus, dextran was more excluded than the more compact poly-sucrose, Ficoll, on Sephadex G-200 [157].

8.3.6. Small, polar, saturated nonelectrolytes

Although, as stated in Chap. 8.3.1.2, positive LFER are found for homologous series, such as the PEO and polyhydric alcohols from ethanediol upwards [36,44] "steric anomalies" often occur when the lower-molecular-weight homologs are chromatographed on tightly crosslinked dextran and polyacrylamide gels. For exam-ple, from Bio-Gel P-4, 6-O-methyl-D-glucose emerged midway between a di- and a trisaccharide [158]. This is not unexpected, since considerable variation in K_d values may occur among isomers, such as the aldohexopyranoses. The differences among the latter appear to be correlated with conformational instability [44,159–162], although it has been claimed [163,164] that sorption also probably plays an im-portant role in the partition of this type of compound.

The LFER of the oligosaccharide series are thus probably a result of both steric exclusion and (weak) interactions with the gel [147]. In the series discussed in Chap. 8.3.5 the common monomer is the anhydroglucose residue (AGR), and it is implied that the interactions should be more or less independent of the monomer, the conformational differences arising from different modes of linkage being the dis-tinguishing features. However, this may be an oversimplification, since the chemi-sorption of cellodextrins on cellulose gel has been reported [149]. That interactions also occur with AGR is also evident from the behavior of the cycloamyloses: thus, the larger cycloheptaamylose emerged later than the smaller cyclohexaamylose from Sephadex G-15 [165], although it should be noted that the reverse order was observed in the pioneering experiments on starch gels [12].

8.4. SOLUTE PARTITIONING AND THE STRUCTURE OF A DEXTRAN GEL IN WATER

8.4.1. Gel structure

As discussed in Chap. 8.3.3.2, very slow flowrates yield quasi-equilibrium conditions. However, under practical operating conditions, faster flowrates may be desired. In this case, diffusion within the gel becomes important. It seems to be generally agreed [48,166] that there is a lack of diffusional specificity, i.e. the ratio of the diffusion coefficient of a solute in the gel, D_s, to that in the bulk mobile phase, D_0, is largely independent of chemical structure. The fact that $D_s/D_0 < 1$ is attributed to the obstruction due to the matrix, which lengthens the diffusion path. D_s/D_0 also decreases with increasing molecular weight, presumably because of an increased probability of matrix/solute collisions. Both the static and the dynamic structure of the gel must significantly affect diffusional processes. However, present-day knowledge of the detailed microscopic structure of gels and of their dynamic properties is not sufficiently comprehensive for a quantitative or predictive picture to be formed. This should be forthcoming as techniques, such as diffusional measurements [48,167,168], NMR [169], neutron scattering [170,171], and spin labeling [172,173] throw more light on gel structure and dynamic behavior.

It is quite evident that the crosslinking density is intimately related to the partitioning properties of a Sephadex gel. Crosslinking introduces new chemical structures into the gel and, apart from the influence on the sorptive properties, the presence of crosslinks has several effects:

(a) It restricts the water (or other solvent) content of the gel and increases the swelling pressure.

(b) It reduces the porosity of the matrix and the mobility of the dextran chains.

(c) By substitution, it alters the nature of the matrix and increases the number of ether oxygens.

(d) The reduced dimensions of the spaces between the chains may mean that there is a structural shift in the imbibed water due to the relatively greater contribution of surface-perturbed water in the water-swollen gel particles.

A lower water content and increased matrix concentration allows fractionation at lower molecular-weight ranges. Although the diether-linked glycerol crosslinks of the Sephadex gels reduce the "saccharide" nature of the parent dextran, they do not decrease the polarity of the surface but may, in fact, increase it slightly. Thus, each new crosslink introduces two glyceryl ether groups ($-OCH_2CH(OH)CH_2O-$), replacing two hydroxyl groups. The effect of this in terms of the fragment constants of Hansch and Leo [174] is a net change in the log P_0 parameter of -0.7, indicating, if anything, an increase in hydrophilicity. Of course, any local constraints in the sugar residues, or cyclization of the crosslinking groups, could modify this situation somewhat.

8.4.2. Crosslinking

The crosslink ratio, X^R, is defined as the ratio between the molar concentrations of crosslinks, C^X, and AGR, i.e. C^X/AGR [175]. This is half the value of the crosslinking density, which is defined as the fraction of AGR which is crosslinked [24]; there are two crosslinked AGR to each linkage. Since the introduction of crosslinks removes two hydroxyl hydrogens, determination of the latter by hydrogen isotope exchange (HIE) [176,177] will yield information about the crosslink ratio.

The crosslinked unit structure (CLU) in Sephadex is a diether-linked glyceryl moiety (Fig. 8.2) that resembles a saccharide. As mentioned above, a simple crosslinking structure with linear mono- or oligomeric crosslinks should not differ much in polarity from the parent dextran. During the reaction with the crosslinking agent, epichlorohydrin, some of the latter is incorporated into pendant side-arms, which thus do not contribute to crosslinking [16]. Furthermore, the crosslinks or side-arms may be oligomeric or branched, and new ring structures may also be formed, e.g., by the reaction of a hydroxyl group with a dihydroxypropyl group attached to an AGR. The resulting dioxolane structure will contribute considerably to the rigidity of the matrix, and, like a simple acyclic diether structure, is less polar than water.

Bonhoeffer [178] was the first to observe that deuterium exchanges with the hydroxyl groups of cellulose. Whereas in cellulose the accessibility of the hydroxyl groups to deuterium is limited on account of the crystalline regions [179–183], it is complete in amylose and starch [184] and the same may be expected of dextran [185,186]. Thus, deuterium exchange could be a measure of the hydroxyl concentration. If the details of the crosslinking structure were known, the concentrations of crosslinks and side-arms could then be calculated from HIE. This is illustrated in Fig. 8.13. The introduction of a glyceryl crosslink (Sephadex) removes two hydroxyl hydrogens and introduces one hydroxyl, i.e. a net loss of one OH group. Similarly, there is a net gain of one hydroxyl with a side-arm. For n-meric side-arms (I) and crosslinks (II) the changes in hydroxyls (ΔOH) are given by the formulae

$$\Delta OH(I) = K \cdot n \tag{8.19a}$$

and

$$\Delta OH(II) = K \cdot n - 2 \tag{8.19b}$$

where K is the number of nonterminal hydroxyls on the CLU; in the case of Sephadex, $K = 1$. An equation can then be derived [175] for the relation between the concentrations of crosslinks (C^X), CLU(C^L) and hydroxyls (C^{OH})

$$C^X = \frac{1}{2}\left[\frac{3(1000 - C^L M^L)}{M^R} + K \cdot C^L - C^{OH} \right] \tag{8.20}$$

References on p. A321

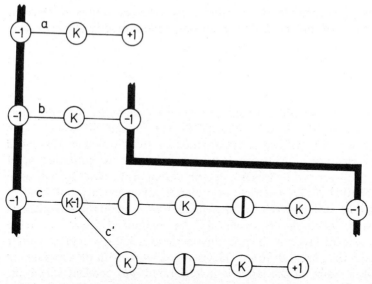

Fig. 8.13. Diagram of simplified crosslinking structure. The two thick black lines represent dextran chains. A monomeric pendent side-arm (a) removes one hydroxyl from an AGR but introduces one at its free end. If, as in Sephadex, there is also a nonterminal hydroxyl, there is a net gain of one OH. A monomeric crosslink (b) similarly results in a net loss of one hydroxyl. The trimeric crosslink (c) with a dimeric side-arm branch (c') results in a net increase of three hydroxyls which is simply the sum of the changes due to the trimeric crosslink ($n-2=3-2=1$) and the dimeric side-arm ($n=2$). See text for further details.

where M^L and M^R are the molecular weights of the CLU and AGR, respectively.

HIE is of greatest practical usefulness if the crosslinking structure is simple, and it is most easily tested if the number of CLU in the gel can be estimated directly, i.e. if they can be identified by a peculiar atom or group, or if they are labeled. HIE was therefore tested in two divinylsulfone crosslinked dextran gels (DVS) in which the molar concentrations of CLU and sulfur are equal. In each gel the number of crosslinks was close to that of the CLU, i.e.

$$C^X \approx C^L$$

(8.21)

thus indicating that the great majority of the latter were present as monomeric crosslinks [175]. It is, however, rather improbable that such a simple structure would be found with the shorter and more reactive CLU of Sephadex and, in fact, a more complicated structure has been reported (Chap. 8.4.2). Nevertheless, the structural properties given in Table 8.7 have been calculated on a basis of this simple model. Although the individual values may be in error, the relations between the different gels should be more reliable. In the table, the hydroxyl concentrations in the gels are calculated from the tritium distribution coefficients, $K_d^*(T)$, which are obtained by comparing the elution volumes of tritiated water and water labeled with an oxygen isotope [187], as the latter does not exchange with the gel [188]. The concentrations of hydroxyls, crosslinks, AGR, and ether oxygens (Table 8.7) can then be obtained, as described in ref. 175. In this context, the term "ether oxygens" refers to both ring and glycosidic oxygens. In calculating the properties listed in Table 8.7, it was assumed that some of the CLU were present as side-arms, the side-arm/crosslink ratio being taken as 0.1. This is within the range of values found in epichlorohydrin-crosslinked starch gels [189].

The term matrix in Table 8.7 refers to the dry substance of the gel. The decrease in water regain due to the increase in crosslink concentration means that the AGR and matrix concentrations rise, although relatively less than that of the crosslinks. This discrepancy is further exaggerated by the much higher crosslink ratios in the most highly crosslinked gels, G-15 and G-10. Thus, whereas the AGR concentration increases about seven-fold between G-100 and G-10, the increase in CLU concentration is some fifty-fold. The relation between the crosslink ratio and the matrix concentration is shown in Fig. 8.14. It is evident that the gels G-15 and G-10 are in a specially highly crosslinked class and, as is discussed in Chap. 8.4.4.2, this is correlated with some of their extreme properties.

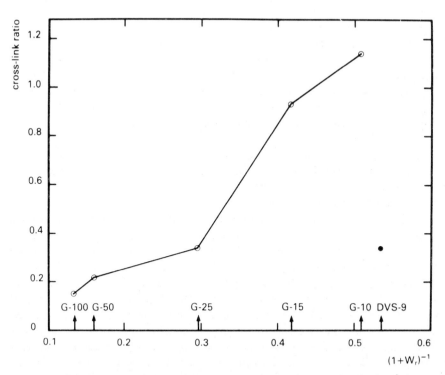

Fig. 8.14. Calculated crosslink ratio in relation to the matrix concentration $(kg \cdot kg^{-1})$ in water-swollen Sephadex gels. See text for further details.

TABLE 8.7

STRUCTURAL PROPERTIES OF SEPHADEX GELS, CALCULATED FROM HYDROGEN ISO-
TOPE EXCHANGE, ASSUMING A MONOMERIC CROSSLINKING MODEL

Properties	G-100	G-50	G-25	G-15	G-10
Water regain	13.8	7.47	2.38	1.26	0.91
Matrix concentration, $kg \cdot kg^{-1}$ (wet bead)	0.068	0.118	0.296	0.431	0.524
Tritium distribution coefficient $[K_d^*(T)]$	1.012	1.021	1.061	1.075	1.091
Wet gel, mole/l					
hydroxyls (C^{OH})	1.16	1.95	4.84	5.00	5.29
anhydroglucose residues (AGR)	0.40	0.70	1.80	2.33	2.68
crosslinks (C^X)	0.06	0.16	0.61	2.20	3.04
ether oxygens (C^E)	0.936	1.73	4.88	9.26	11.8
Crosslink ratio $(X^R = C^X/AGR)$	0.148	0.228	0.337	0.944	1.14
C^E/C^{OH}	0.807	0.887	1.01	1.85	2.22

8.4.3. Microscopic studies of gel structure and properties

Transmission electron microscopy, has been used to examine freeze-etched speci-
mens of specially-prepared polyacrylamide gels [190]. A random network was not
seen in any of the gels studied, which varied in water content and degree of
crosslinking. Instead, all had an open structure in the submicrometer range. It has
been suggested that aggregates having a high molecular weight are formed in a sol
state during crosslinking [24]. When gelation occurs, there is a rapid depletion of the
concentration of available sol domains, leading to local enhancements of the matrix
concentration. The thin walls of the "cells" are thought to be composed of high
concentrations of longitudinally arrayed polyacrylamide chains. In highly crosslinked gels the membrane walls are deformed, and clustering is observed [191].
Similar findings have been reported in the case of Sephadex [192] and Sepharose
[33]. These transmission electron micrographs of xerogels have much in common
with the microheterogeneous structure proposed several years ago by Flodin [16].

Scanning electron micrographs of Sephadex gel beads have revealed that each
type of neutral bead, at least, has a typical pattern of surface folding [193,194]. Since
Sephadex G-10 is almost featureless and the degree of folding increases from G-15
up to G-200, it was concluded that this folding reflects the degree of surface
shrinkage occurring on drying the beads [193]. Although surface folding was not
observed in starch gel beads (Pharmacia), polyacrylamide gel (Bio-Rad P-2), ion-retardation resin AG 11A8, or Dowex 1-X2 (an anion exchanger), it is not peculiar to
Sephadex, since it was clearly evident in highly permeable open-pore polyurethane
beads [195]. The occurrence of this phenomenon suggests that beads exhibiting it
have a shell with different swelling characteristics. Scanning electron microscopy has
also been used for a rough survey of the radial distribution of alkali halides in
Sephadex G-25. Beads which had been equilibrated with different electrolyte solu-

tions were frozen, cut into sections 10 μm thick, and dried, and the X-ray fluorescence was measured [196]. As Fig. 8.15 shows, there was no sign of any major ionic radial heterogeneity across the surface of the section.

8.4.4. Solute partitioning in relation to the structure of the dextran gel

The matrix concentrations in the water-swollen Sephadex beads range from about 5% in G-200 to some 60% in G-10. Increasing the matrix concentration has two obvious effects: (a) the average porosity will be decreased and (b) the concentration of sorption centers (if any) will be increased, provided that crosslinking does not

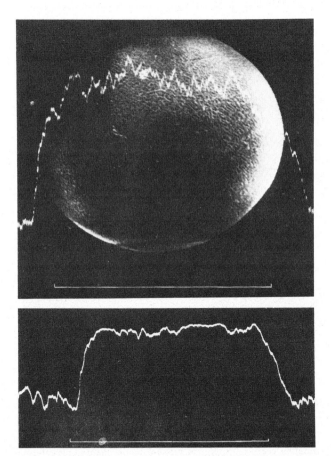

Fig. 8.15. Top: scanning electron microscope view of a dried frozen section, originally 10 μm thick, from a bead of Sephadex G-25. The surface fold pattern is evident. Superimposed on the scanning electron micrograph of the section is a line scan of the Cl, K_α peak. The gel bead had been immersed previously in 0.2 M KCl for about 24 h. The white scale line corresponds to 100 μm. Bottom: line scan of the Cl, K_α peak from another section of a G-25 bead, pretreated as above. The white scale lines correspond to 50 μm. (Reproduced from *Experientia*, 30 (1974) 572, with permission [196].)

have a sufficiently strong obliterating or weakening effect on these, as seems unlikely. Solutes which partition predominantly due to steric exclusion should therefore exhibit a decrease in K_d value with decreasing water regain. If sorption is the dominant mechanism, the converse should be true. The other most striking change, which parallels that of the crosslink ratio, is the change in the proportion of ether oxygens (Table 8.7). The ether oxygen/hydroxyl ratio changes very little between G-100 and G-25, but rises sharply thereafter.

8.4.4.1. Polar saturated nonelectrolytes

Steric exclusion seems to be the distinguishing feature in partitioning of solutes of this type. As shown on the left side on Fig. 8.16, the K_d values in Sephadex gels of

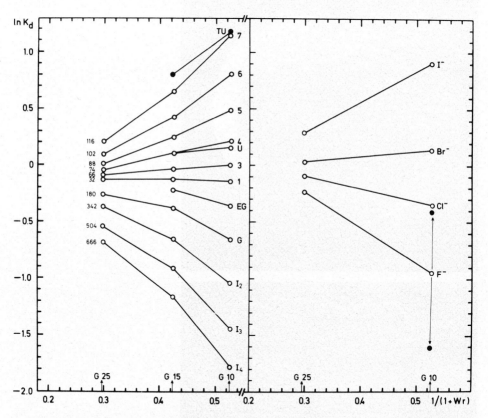

Fig. 8.16. The logarithm of the distribution coefficients, K_d, in relation to the matrix concentration $[1/(1 + W_r)]$ in water-swollen Sephadex gels at 25°C. The left part of the figure shows the $\ln K_d$ values of nonelectrolytes. The numerals on the right of the graphs refer to different 1-alkanols; I_2, I_3, and I_4 are isomaltodextrins, G=glucose, EG=ethylene glycol, U=urea, and TU=thiourea. The numerals on the left are the molecular weights, in daltons. The right part of the figure gives the halide values when eluted with chloride. The arrowed filled circles are the fluoride values when eluted with sulfate (high) and perchlorate (low). In all cases the eluent anion concentration was 0.2 M.

glucose and the first three isomaltodextrins (I_2, I_3, I_4) decrease with increasing matrix concentration. Higher oligomers are omitted from the figure because they are excluded from G-10.

8.4.4.2. Unsaturated and less-polar saturated nonelectrolytes

As discussed in Chap. 8.3.1.1, in a series such as the 1-alkanols, the K_d values for highly crosslinked gels increase with increasing length of the hydrocarbon chain of the solute (Fig. 8.16). Fig. 8.17 shows that this phenomenon, which becomes more marked with increasing matrix concentration, is limited to the most highly cross-

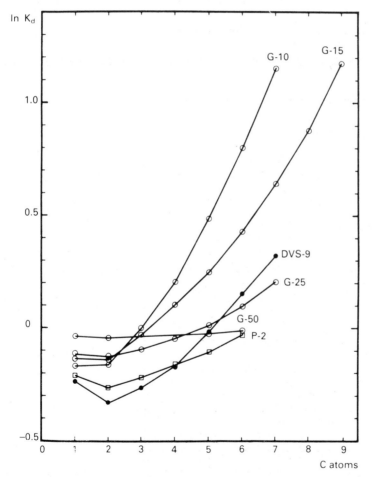

Fig. 8.17. The logarithm of the distribution coefficients of 1-alkanols in relation to the number of carbon atoms in the molecule for different water-swollen gels. G=Sephadex gels (open circles), DVS-9= divinylsulfone crosslinked dextran gel (W_r =0.85, filled circles), and P-2=Bio-Gel polyacrylamide (W_r = 1.7, unfilled squares). W_r =water regain.

linked gels [197]. Thus, in G-50 there is only a very slight tendency for, the K_d values of the 1-alkanol series to increase with hydrocarbon chain length and in G-100 (not shown) even less. This behavior is not confined to epichlorohydrin-crosslinked dextran gels but is also observed with the DVS-crosslinked dextran gel DVS-9 and the polyacrylamide Bio-Gel P-2 (Fig. 8.17).

The two lowest members of the alkanols, methanol and ethanol, are relatively polar, and the K_d values of both decrease slightly as the water regain of the gel is reduced (Fig. 8.18). This phenomenon can also be seen clearly in the curves for DVS-9 and P-2 in Fig. 8.17. However, from 1-propanol upwards a definite tendency for K_d to increase with decreasing water regain is evident for the Sephadex gels from G-25 to G-10. An increase of K_d with decreasing water regain is not confined to compounds of this type. As shown in Fig. 8.16, both urea and thiourea have the same tendency. As discussed in Sec. 8.3.1.4, a polar group, in this case NH_2, associated with a double-bonded carbon (not necessarily $C=C$) seems to promote affinity for these gels [36].

It is evident that the affinity for higher alcohols is not related linearly to the gel

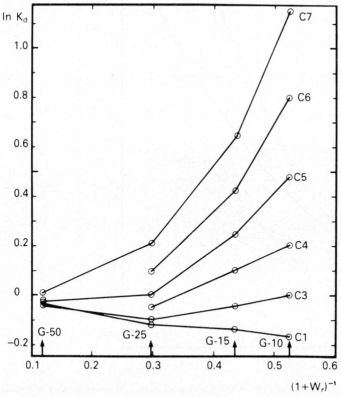

Fig. 8.18. The logarithm of the distribution coefficients of 1-alkanols in relation to the matrix concentration (kg dry matrix per kg water) in water-swollen Sephadex gels. C_i refers to the number of carbon atoms in the alcohol. The individual gels are indicated above the abscissa.

matrix concentration (Fig. 8.18) [197,198]. As shown in Fig. 8.19, this phenomenon is even more marked with aromatic solutes. There appears to be a point, at a matrix weight fraction of about 0.35 [water regain $(W_r) = 1.9$], where the affinity begins to rise more steeply. This rise is correlated with a similar abrupt upswing in the crosslink ratio (Fig. 8.14). That the high nonpolar affinity of G-10 is not simply a consequence of a low water content is suggested by the much lower affinity of the closely related dextran gel DVS-9, which actually has a slightly higher matrix concentration than G-10. Thus, the affinity of DVS-9 ($X^R = 0.35$) is much nearer to that of G-25 ($X^R = 0.34$), a gel with a similar crosslink ratio (Fig. 8.14). These data point to the significance of the latter in modifying affinity and, as can be inferred from Figs. 8.14 and 8.18, the crosslink ratio is correlated with the affinity for the

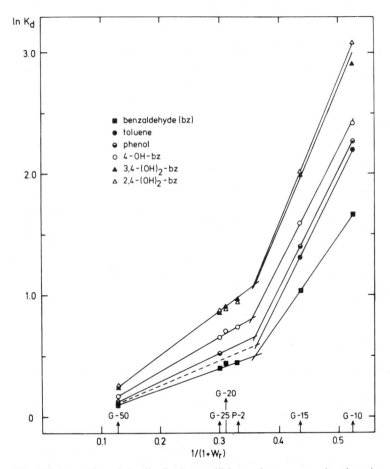

Fig. 8.19. Logarithm of the distribution coefficients of some aromatic solutes in relation to the matrix concentration in water-swollen Sephadex gels at 25°C. The individual gels are denoted by arrows. G = Sephadex, P-2 = Bio-Gel polyacrylamide. Some of the experimental points are omitted in the "less steep" region for reasons of clarity.

higher alcohols and also for aromatic compounds (Fig. 8.19). The aromatic affinity has been attributed to both the ether linkages [52] and the hydroxyls of the crosslinks [53,55], but there seem to be no good grounds for singling out these structures in preference to other ether oxygens or hydroxyls. Additionally, it may be noted that, as is evident from Fig. 8.19, an aromatic pattern of affinity, quantitatively and qualitatively very similar to that of G-25, was exhibited by the polyacrylamide gel Bio-Gel P-2, which lacks both ether oxygens and hydroxyl groups.

For the dextran gels there is also a correlation between the affinity and the ratio of ether oxygens to hydroxyls. With regard to the high concentration of ether oxygens in the most highly crosslinked gels and the reported dioxolane nature of the crosslinked matrix surface, the spectral behavior of a cycloheptaamylose complex is pertinent. Thus, the spectrum of the complex between the amylose and 4-t-butylphenol was practically superimposable on that of the phenol dissolved in dioxane [199], and this reflects the interaction of the aromatic included chromophore with the dioxane-like interior of the cycloamylose cavity [200]. By analogy, this suggests that nonpolar affinity for Sephadex may involve some type of inclusion process. As discussed below, this may provide a clue to the way in which crosslinks promote affinity without being adsorption sites themselves.

8.5. MECHANISMS OF SELECTIVITY

8.5.1. Steric exclusion

The selectivities of nonelectrolytes in natural and synthetic zeolites, which have a regular and rather rigid lattice structure, are primarily determined by steric hindrance [79,201]. Their very uniform pores create high selectivity [202]. The crosslinked gels that function as molecular sieves are, as far as is known, random networks with a selectivity cut-off that is not nearly as sharp as that of zeolites [79]. However, it is not only the random chains that we must consider. The system that is used for molecular sieving is the solvent-swollen gel, and the role played by the solvent is by no means unimportant.

8.5.2. Swelling pressure

A three-dimensional network, such as a covalently crosslinked polymer, is unable to disperse completely in a solvent, but it is capable of imbibing a certain quantity of any liquid which can solvate its meshes. A swollen gel bead thus forms an elastic, rather than a viscous solution [203]. Swelling continues until an equilibrium state is attained where the elastic contractive forces of the stretched matrix chains just balance the tendency to swell. This elastic force, which may be interpreted as a pressure acting on the gel, increases the chemical potential of the solvent within the gel to that of the external solvent. The network structure thus "performs the multiple role of solute, osmotic membrane, and pressure-generating device" [203]. However, Barkas [204] considered the swelling pressure to be fundamentally different from the osmotic pressure of a solution, since the latter has no rigidity.

The concept of swelling pressure was incorporated into Gregor's model of ion exchangers [205,206], which accounted successfully—at least qualitatively—for the selectivity sequence of alkali metal ions. This swelling pressure tends to squeeze solvent and solute molecules out of the gel. Ion exchangers of low water regain also exhibit steric exclusion to nonelectrolytes [38,207]. Like gels, they are random networks, lacking a well-defined regular lattice structure, and earlier explanations of their steric exclusion properties were not based on their mechanical sieve properties alone. Instead, attention was directed to the role of swelling pressure [79,208].

Thermodynamically, the distribution coefficient is related to the swelling pressure of the gel, Π, and the partial molar volume of the solute, $\overline{V}_2$, as follows [79]

$$\ln\left[(a_2)_g/(a_2)_o\right] = -\Pi\overline{V}_2/RT \tag{8.22}$$

where $(a_2)_g$ and $(a_2)_o$ are the activities of the solute inside and outside the gel, respectively. The larger the value of $\overline{V}_2$, the lower is the distribution coefficient. Swelling pressures for Sephadex G-200, G-100, G-75, and G-50, calculated from the data of Edmonds et al. [209], are given in Table 8.8. The table also gives the molecular weights of solutes which, if excluded only by the swelling pressure, would have distribution coefficients of 0.5 or 0.1. Since the gels actually exclude solutes which are over 30 times smaller, the swelling pressure alone cannot account for more than a very small part of the steric exclusion actually observed in these more loosely crosslinked gels. Pressure data on the more tightly crosslinked gels seem to be

TABLE 8.8

STERIC EXCLUSION DUE TO SWELLING PRESSURE OF GEL

Sephadex gels	Swelling pressures *, atm	K_{av}	Molecular weights, daltons **		
			calculated from swelling pressure ***	data from Pharmacia	observed/calculated †
G-200	0.013	0.5	$2.1 \cdot 10^6$	$5 \cdot 10^4$	0.024
		0.1	$7.0 \cdot 10^6$	$4 \cdot 10^5$	0.057
G-100	0.029	0.5	$9.4 \cdot 10^5$	$2.0 \cdot 10^4$	0.021
		0.1	$3.1 \cdot 10^6$	$9.0 \cdot 10^4$	0.029
G-75	0.075	0.5	$3.6 \cdot 10^5$	$1.0 \cdot 10^4$	0.028
		0.1	$1.2 \cdot 10^6$	$4.0 \cdot 10^4$	0.033
G-50	0.24	0.5	$1.1 \cdot 10^5$	$3.0 \cdot 10^3$	0.027
		0.1	$3.8 \cdot 10^5$	$1.3 \cdot 10^4$	0.034

* Calculated from ref. 209.

** These values are for solutes which, partitioning solely by steric exclusion, would have the given K_{av} values.

*** Calculated from eqn. 8.22.

† Ratio of molecular weights from the two previous columns.

References on p. A321

lacking. However, if it is assumed that monosaccharide partitioning is purely by steric exclusion, substitution of the K_d values of D-glucose [0.51 (G-10), 0.68 (G-15), and 0.82 (G-25)] into eqn. 8.22 gives very approximate values of the corresponding swelling pressures of 148, 85, and 44 atm, respectively. These values are by no means high compared with those for water-swollen ion exchangers (refs. 79, 210; cf. also refs. 137, 211).

Calculation for a sulfonic acid resin (Dowex-50 X8) has indicated that the pressure term actually has a larger influence on the K_d value than the interaction term [212]. Ginzburg and Cohen [213] compared the exclusion of some nonelectrolytes in a cation-exchange resin (Dowex 50), swollen to different degrees in Li^+ and Na^+ salts. In this ingenious experiment two resins of different water (and ion) content but otherwise identical in every respect were thus compared. There appeared to be a general trend for the K_d value to be lower in the more swollen Li^+ form, a result at variance with experience from Sephadex gels but predicted by eqn. 8.22, provided that pressure was the only significant factor. However, there is some doubt as to whether the states of water are comparable in the two forms [214]. Thus, although the imbibed water content of the Li^+ form is high because of the stronger hydration of this cation [215], it may actually contain less (free) water available for accommodating the partitioning nonelectrolyte [216].

8.5.3. Steric hindrance

Since the swelling pressure cannot account for more than a small part of nonelectrolyte exclusion in the Sephadex gels G-200 to G-50, steric hindrance must be the major factor, at least in these more loosely crosslinked gels. As discussed in Chap. 8.3.3.2, it seems well established that, in GPC with hydrophobic gels and solutes and θ solvents, the conformational or configurational entropy of the solute is a very important factor and may in some cases account for partitioning. However, these models were designed for rigid gels with a fixed pore-size distribution. Although this is essentially correct in the case of agarose, the most loosely crosslinked Sephadex gels have very mobile chains and therefore present a continually varying, dynamic network pattern. Thus, Hager [192], who attempted to derive a general calibration equation from a statistical model, visualized the penetrant molecules as being able to push aside the matrix chains when moving within the gel. Lecourtier et al. [217] regarded this process as akin to solubility and divided the standard free energy of transfer into the gel, ΔG_t^0, into three components

$$\Delta G_t^0 = \Delta G_s^0 + \Delta G_a^0 + \Delta G_d^0 \tag{8.23}$$

where ΔG_s^0 is the entropic (steric exclusion) term, ΔG_a^0 is the adsorptive term, and ΔG_d^0 is the dissolution term required in nonrigid gels. The last is described in the following way: In a nonrigid gel, the space accessible to solute molecules is no longer limited by the rigid walls of the pores, but the solute molecules can penetrate like the solvent molecules. The gel is, in a way, considered as a classical LLC stationary phase. Evaluation of this dissolution term proved very helpful for analyzing partitioning quantitatively in terms of the gel/solute interaction and the role of the solvent and gel structure in GPC. Unfortunately, however, it cannot be applied quantitatively to a strongly polar solvent, such as water.

The extent to which gel/solute interactions (ΔG_a^0) contribute depends on the concentration of the gel matrix and on the size and structure of the penetrant species. A good example of this is provided by the gel chromatography of proteins. A gel of high water regain, such as agarose or the most loosely crosslinked Sephadex, has sufficient porosity to admit proteins and exhibits satisfactory molecular sieving towards them, if they are "randomized". However, proteins contain residues of nonpolar and aromatic amino acids, which have an affinity for the tightly cross-linked Sephadex G-10 [60]. Sorption on G-200, on the other hand, is insignificant because of three factors:

(a) The matrix concentration is much lower in G-200 than in G-10, but the affinity is relatively even lower because of the anomalously high values in G-10 (Fig. 8.19).

(b) Most proteins contain a considerable fraction of polar, nonadsorbed residues [218].

(c) In the presence of a randomizing agent, such as guanidinium chloride, adsorption is weakened [219,220].

The reciprocal relationship between the matrix concentration and porosity underlines the pitfalls inherent in attempting to extend the use of these systems for determining the dimensions of solutes having low molecular weight [221]. As discussed in Chap. 8.3.1.2, in the latter case, molecular sieving seems to be mainly confined to polar saturated species, with which interactions are also very likely.

8.5.4. Solute/solute interactions

When two or more solutes are chromatographed together, misleading values of their elution volumes will be obtained if they interact chemically with each other. All the features of the transport behavior predicted by Gilbert [222,223] for chemically reacting species were observed for the elution of α-chymotrypsin, which underwent autolysis under the conditions used for elution [224]. Physical interaction between two species migrating so closely together that they overlap will also result in a concentration dependence, yielding spurious values for the elution volumes [225]. This can be corrected by using the reciprocals of the elution volumes in the Johnston–Ogston equation [226]. When albumin was eluted from Sephadex G-200 with an aqueous solution of a polymer (dextran, PEO, or polyvinyl alcohol), its K_{av} was increased [227]. This increase was attributed to steric exclusion of the protein from the polymer solution (cf. also refs. 228, 229).

It should be noted that the use of a nonpenetrant macromolecule as eluent causes osmotic shrinkage of the gel, a phenomenon that was exploited elegantly by Edmond et al. [209] to determine the swelling pressure in the more loosely crosslinked Sephadex gels. They also observed that, when dextran was used to elute albumin from Sephadex G-200, both albumin and the nonpenetrant void-volume indicator (Blue dextran) were retarded. Since the total gel volume was changed very little in the presence of the eluent, they concluded that the 15–20% reduction in the internal volume was balanced by a corresponding increase in the void volume.

8.5.5. Dynamic factors in gel behavior

If a polymer solution is used as the eluent for a very loosely crosslinked gel of very low rigidity, such as Sephadex G-200, a new factor may be of significance. Beads of Sephadex G-200 are watery domains which contain flexible dextran chains constrained by occasional crosslinks. The bead is, in fact, not very different from a 5% dextran solution.

8.5.5.1. Phase separation

Aqueous solutions of dextran and other polymers, such as PEO, are not always completely mutually miscible, but may separate into two phases. The partition coefficients of proteins between such phases are, in general, very dependent on the pH and electrolyte concentration [230]. It is thus very interesting that Brewer and Söderberg [231] have reported that the K_{av} values of several proteins were increased when they were eluted from Sephadex G-100 with 4% PEO. They were no longer a simple function of log MW and were also sensitive to the pH and ionic strength of the eluent. Their suggestion that a two-phase effect is responsible for these phenomena [232] is very plausible and, on the assumption that such effects require polymers to be in solution, this behavior indicates that the most loosely crosslinked Sephadex gels are essentially like dextran solutions. However, no phase separation should occur when a dextran solution is the eluent, since this should be compatible with Sephadex, unless the occasional crosslinks make the latter sufficiently different for phase separation to occur. As Hellsing [227] proposed, the effect of dextran of increasing the K_{av} in a Sephadex column should thus be mainly due to steric exclusion.

8.5.6. Gel/solute interactions

8.5.6.1. Ionic interactions

Many classes of biologically important molecules subjected to chromatography are electrolytes, possessing charged groups. Thus, if the sorbent contains charged groups, there will be strong interactions between the (poly)electrolyte sample molecules and the sorbent. In this case, any selectivity of the sorbent toward these solutes in terms of molecular size may be masked by the effects of these interactions. Hence, it is essential that the sorbent be as free from charged groups as possible.

Polysaccharides may develop charged (carbonyl) groups upon prolonged storage under oxidizing conditions. Gels based on agarose will contain charged groups if the selection of the starting material and its treatment prior to gel synthesis is not rigorously controlled so as to minimize the incorporation of the types of charged group that abound in the marine algal polysaccharides (i.e., pyruvate and sulfate).

Polyacrylamide and polyacrylic esters will also develop charged (carboxyl) groups upon storage under conditions of high or low pH, which lead to hydrolysis of the pendant amide or ester groups. Control of these effects is a major concern of the manufacturer in the first place, but the user should recognize that conditions of storage and regeneration should be governed by what these various materials will tolerate.

The potential energy of the interaction between two charged groups, U^C, is given by the well-known Coulomb expression

$$U^C = f\frac{q_R q_T}{\epsilon_0 r} \tag{8.24}$$

where q_R and q_T are the charges on the groups R and T, spaced a distance, r, apart. Included in the denominator of this expression is the dielectric constant, ϵ_0, of the solvent. This implies that, if undesirable ionic interactions between gel and solute are encountered in a chromatographic experiment, these can at least be minimized by increasing the ionic strength of the eluent. Ionic interactions between (poly)electrolytes in solution and a charged sorbent can be of interest in their own right, if the sorbent is chemically derivatized specifically to contain a large number of these groups. This creates a new type of selectivity that dictates how the separation will take place, based on the number and nature of charged groups on the matrix and solute. This is the principle of ion-exchange chromatography (cf. Chap. 7 and ref. 79).

8.5.6.2. Permanent multipoles

A covalently bonded molecule is, of course, not ionized, but this does not mean that the charge distribution is uniformly balanced over the entire surface of the molecule. Whenever heteroatoms are present in an organic molecule, differences in electronegativity between these atoms and carbon atoms will produce a certain degree of polarity. Such charge distributions will in the simplest cases consist of dipoles, but, since such molecules are complex, it is necessary to consider more complex arrangements, involving quadrupoles, octupoles, etc. Their contributions to the energy of interaction are by no means negligible. Indeed, for as simple a molecule as carbon dioxide, it has been shown that the quadrupole moment makes a decisive contribution to the lattice energy of dry ice [233]. Furthermore, these interactions are cumulative, and if the repeat distances between interacting groups are the same in the solute as in the matrix, allowing cooperative effects, the total interaction energy can be appreciable.

Permanent multipoles abound in biologically important molecules, and it would be very hard to conceive of a polymer suitable for use in a chromatographic sorbent that was devoid of such nonuniform charge distribution properties. Indeed, a sorbent for the gel chromatography of, e.g., proteins must be very hydrophilic in order to be maximally compatible with aqueous solutions and to minimize other, even more troublesome interactions (cf. Chap. 8.5.6.7). A prerequisite for this is the presence of a large number of polar groups, the most common being hydroxyl, hemiacetal, and—in crosslinked polysaccharides—ether groups. It would thus appear that some compromise between the requirement for hydrophilicity and the concomitant necessity to accept multipolar groups is desirable. As in the case of interactions between charged groups, multipolar interactions are of electrostatic (Coulombic) character:

$$U^C = f\left(\mu_R \mu_T \epsilon_0^{-1} r^{-3}\right) \tag{8.25a}$$

for dipole/dipole interactions, where μ_R and μ_T are the dipole moments of dipoles R and T, spaced r apart, and

$$U^C = f\left(Q_R Q_T \epsilon_0^{-1} r^{-5}\right) \tag{8.25b}$$

for quadrupole/quadrupole interactions, where Q_R and Q_T are the quadrupole moments of quadrupoles R and T, spaced r apart.

Hence, the dielectric constant is a useful experimental variable, if it is found to be necessary to reduce effects of this kind.

8.5.6.3. Permanent multipoles. Induced multipoles

In addition to the aforementioned interactions between permanent charges and multipoles, there will arise interactions due to induced redistribution of electrons in nearby groups. These are always attractive in character, since the induced polarity is of a sign opposite to that of the inducing group. The energy of the latter is thereby diminished, due to dissipation or redistribution of the polarity. Induction energies are expressed as follows:

$$U^I = f\left(q_R^2 \alpha_T r^{-4}\right) \qquad \text{for ion-induced dipole} \tag{8.26a}$$

$$U^I = f\left(\mu_R^2 \alpha_T r^{-6}\right) \qquad \text{for dipole-induced dipole} \tag{8.26b}$$

The polarizability, α, represents the readiness with which the electrons will redistribute themselves in response to the presence of a polar group with charge q_R, dipole moment μ_R, etc. Groups that typically have a high polarizability are those containing either conjugated electron systems or atoms such as sulfur, bromine, or iodine, in which outer atomic orbitals, well-shielded from the nucleus, readily respond to this type of perturbation.

8.5.6.4. Mutually induced multipoles

The types of interaction described in the previous sections owe their origin to permanent, i.e. time-independent, anisotropic distributions of electrons, arising from differences in the electronegativity of the constituent atoms in the molecule. But these atoms are also in motion relative to one another, in vibrational, bending, and torsional modes. Transitions between these states will give rise to transient dipoles which will, in turn, induce transient dipoles in nearby molecules. Such interactions, often referred to as dispersion or London interactions [234,235], are always attractive and can be of considerable energy. The interactions will be strongest when conjugated structures are encountered or when polarizable atoms, such as sulfur or iodine are involved, and they are, of course, cumulative in character. Large molecules that naturally "fit" well together, such as polymers having a regular repeat structure, will show particularly strong tendencies to aggregate due to such interactions. The interaction energy for mutually induced dipoles is

$$U^D = f\left(\alpha_R \alpha_T r^{-6} \right) \tag{8.27}$$

Corresponding expressions exist for more complex multipoles.

Induced polarity is not affected directly by the dielectric constant of the medium, and such interactions do not diminish at elevated temperatures. Thus, these interactions are likely to be of importance even under conditions where others are of little significance. Indeed, the first postulate of their existence [234,235] was due to observations of the failure of permanent polar interactions to account for Van der Waals effects in gases at higher temperatures [236,237].

8.5.6.5. Electron donor/acceptor interactions

The formation of an electron donor/acceptor complex involves overlap between an occupied orbital in one group and an empty ("antibonding") orbital in another. This can lead to very stable structures, held together by what is referred to as a dative covalent bond. Weaker complexes, which represent a partial formation of such a bond, are also very commonly encountered, e.g. in the context of chromatography. Invariably, these overlapping processes involve some degree of transfer of charge between the participating species, and in cases where this charge transfer is large, there will be appreciable changes in the electronic spectra upon complex formation, with the appearance of so-called charge transfer bands, usually in the visible region of the spectrum.

Typical interactions of this kind are the well-known $\pi-\pi$ interactions and metal complexes. Atoms containing empty d orbitals (e.g., S, Br, I) will readily act as electron acceptors. and this, combined with a pronounced polarizability, accounts for many adsorption phenomena associated with these atoms. Even the familiar case of hydrogen bonding involves an electron donor/acceptor-type of interaction, although it is now acknowledged that the stabilization of hydrogen bonds derives mainly from dipole and quadrupole effects [238] (see Chap. 8.5.6.6).

The hydroxyl, ether and acetal groups mentioned in Chap. 8.5.6.2 are nucleophilic in character by virtue of their nonbonded electrons, and they will thus tend to interact with solutes possessing electron-acceptor properties. Like the other so-called weaker interactions, these interactions are cumulative in character and can be amplified if regular arrays or clusters of groups possessing these propensities for interactions occur in the gel. Deliberate exploitation of these effects has led to a new type of chromatographic sorbents. Thus, Porath and Dahlgren Caldwell [239] and Egly and Porath [240] have shown that coupling of heteroatomic compounds to Sepharose can yield gels capable of separating compounds such as nucleotides or aromatic peptides. Since these separations are purported to be due to electron donor/acceptor interactions, the term charge-transfer chromatography has been adopted for this technique.

8.5.6.6. Hydrogen bonding

Of all the types of noncovalent interaction that can occur between hydrophilic species, hydrogen bonding probably is the most widely discussed. Hydrogen bonds are implicated as stabilizing factors in crystal strutures [241], the structure of ice and water [242], α- and β-structures in proteins [243], duplex DNA structures [244], and in countless other situations. Yet, although hydrogen bonding is relatively easy to identify by physico-chemical techniques, its exact nature is still in dispute. By definition, a hydrogen bond is said to occur when a covalently bound hydrogen atom forms a second bond to another atom. The hydrogen bond can be represented as A–H $\cdots$ B where A is an atom with electronegativity greater than hydrogen and B is any σ- or π-electron donor.

This definition gives a clue as to what type of interaction one might expect, since clearly both polar and electron donor/acceptor species are involved. Thus, hydrogen bond energies can be analyzed in terms of the following components [238]: electrostatic interactions (all charge and permanent-multipole interactions), induced multipoles (whether derived from permanent multipoles or mutually induced), exchange repulsion caused by exchange of electrons between A and B within occupied orbitals, and charge-transfer interactions involving overlap of occupied orbitals in A and unoccupied orbitals in B and vice versa. Calculations show [238] that for a typical hydrogen-bonded system, such as a water dimer, the magnitudes of the interactions are in the order: electrostatic > charge-transfer ≫ induced multipole; exchange repulsion ≈ charge-transfer interactions. Thus, it is evident that hydrogen bond energies are largely electrostatic in character, with quadrupoles and more complex multipoles making a considerable contribution. Next in importance come the repulsive exchange effects, which are somewhat offset by electron donor/acceptor interactions (charge-transfer). It may come as something of a surprise that Van der Waals (induced multipole) interactions are of relatively little significance here.

In the case of hydrophilic gels in aqueous media, hydrogen bonding between groups on the gel surface and water molecules will be prevalent, although thermal effects and the very high mass-action effect of water itself (its concentration being 55.6 M) will essentially prevent any stable structures from forming. Polar solutes will likewise be readily solvated by water through, inter alia, hydrogen bonds, but it is more probable that hydrogen bonding does not make a significant contribution to gel/solute interactions, even when only small quantities of water are present. Although information seems to be lacking about hydroxyl/hydroxyl interactions, this is true for amides. Thus, intermolecular hydrogen bonding between N-methyl acetamide molecules were not detected when the N-methyl acetamide:water molar ratio was less than about 1:1 [245,246]. In the interstices of the most tightly crosslinked dextran gels, which contain little water, gel/solute hydrogen bonding may become important. In this context, it is of interest that Kiehs et al. [247]

concluded from a study of the binding of 17 organic solutes to bovine hemoglobin in aqueous solution that hydrogen bonds were apparently negligible.

8.5.6.7. Hydrophobic interaction

It now seems to be generally recognized that the mutual attraction of nonpolar groups plays only a minor role in aqueous solution. Their hydrophobic interaction, i.e. their tendency to aggregate, as e.g. in micelles, arises primarily from the strong attractive forces between water molecules [43]. The cardinal role of water in hydrophobic interaction (HI) is underlined by the fact that in some cases the attraction of hydrocarbons for water is greater than their mutual attraction [248]. However, the latter is not negligible and, considering the pairwise approach of two nonpolar solutes in water, the free energy $\Delta G(R)$ can be separated into two terms [249].

$$\Delta G(R) = U_{SS}(R) + \delta G^{HI}(R) \tag{8.28}$$

where $U_{SS}(R)$ is the direct work required to bring the two solute molecules together in a vacuum, and $\delta G^{HI}(R)$ is the indirect part of the work associated with the solvent water. Some of the possible structural situations in solutions are illustrated in Fig. 8.20 and discussed in Chap. 8.6.

The properties of simple aqueous systems containing nonpolar molecules, such as alkanes, are difficult to study because of the very poor solubility of such molecules in water. However, this difficulty can be circumvented by use of some of the more soluble derivatives, which exhibit much the same properties as the unsubstituted hydrocarbons. These compounds, which possess one polar group capable of participating in a hydrogen bond with water, include alcohols, ketones, ethers, amides, etc. [250,251]. The polar group has only a short-range influence [41,42] and provides a more or less constant contribution to the properties of a homologous series. Thus, the difference between two members with consecutively longer chains is due almost entirely to the addition of a CH_2 group.

Butler [252] found that, although the aliphatic alcohols are very poorly soluble in water, they have negative enthalpies of hydration. He concluded that their aqueous solubility is limited by entropic factors. After similar studies were published about the same time [253–256], Eley [257,258] suggested that dissolved nonpolar gases create cavities, the formation of which is complicated by structural modifications in the water. In 1945, Frank and Evans [259] proposed their "iceberg" or "flickering cluster" model [260] in which nonpolar solutes are considered to promote the ordering of neighboring water molecules. Thus, HI is a measure of the partial reversal of a thermodynamically (entropically) unfavorable situation arising from the hydration of nonpolar groups (hydrophobic hydration). Hvidt [261] regards the HI as reflecting the incomplete hydration of nonpolar groups. However, entropy-driven processes are not unique to HI. Ion pairing, e.g., is also entropy-driven [42]. Ben-Naim [249] lucidly distinguishes hydrophobic hydration from HI, but his definition is not yet entirely accepted, and on some occasions both terms have been used for the same phenomenon. Ben-Naim thus defines hydrophobic hydration as the relative preference of a single, nonpolar molecule for water rather than for a nonpolar solvent, i.e. it refers to the solute/solvent interactions. HI, on the other hand, refers to the situation where two or more such solute molecules are present in water (see eqn. 8.28).

Some thermodynamic characteristics of hydrophobic hydration are given in Table 8.9 [42]. The ΔG_h^0 values are always positive, due to large negative entropies, whatever the sign of ΔH_h^0. On ascending a series, ΔG_h^0, ΔH_h^0, and ΔS_h^0 increase for each additional CH_2 group. The increase in heat capacity ($\Delta C_{P_h}^0$) per CH_2 group is roughly constant and is probably related to the area of hydrophobic surface exposed to water. Hence, it reflects the ordering of the latter [262–264]. If HI is due to a tendency to reduce the solute/water contact area, the aqueous solubility of a nonpolar solute should be correlated with the surface area rather than with the molar volume as actually seems to be the case [265–271]. However, in Shinoda's opinion [272], the solubility of nonpolar solutes in water is not entropy-dominated. Instead, he regards their poor solubility as a consequence of an excessively large positive enthalpy of mixing.

Since HI may be regarded as an entropy-conserving process, it should be suppressed by perturbants that disorder water structure and vice versa. Now, micelle formation by nonionic surfactants seems to be accepted as an example of HI [273–276], and this has been used as a model for protein denaturation [146]. Thus, water-structure perturbants, such as urea [277], or guanidinium thiocyanate or chloride [146] raise the critical micelle concentration, i.e. reduce HI. Similarly, urea has been reported to increase the aqueous solubility of alkanes [278]. However, in guanidinium sulfate the propensity of the sulfate anion to promote water structure (see below) dominates [279], so that micelle formation [43] is also promoted and the critical micelle concentration falls. Although urea and guanidinium salts clearly

TABLE 8.9

SOME THERMODYNAMIC PROPERTIES OF HYDROPHOBIC HYDRATION AND A COMPARISON WITH "NORMAL" SOLUTION BEHAVIOR [42]

ΔG_h^0, ΔH_h^0, and ΔS_h^0 are the changes in standard free energy, enthalpy, and entropy, respectively, which are associated with hydration; $\Delta C_{P_h}^0$ is the change in heat capacity and $\bar{V}_2$ is the partial molal volume of the solute; ΔS^E and ΔH^E are the excess properties.

	Essentially hydrophobic solutes	Polar solutes (and nonaqueous solution)
ΔG_h^0	>0	$\gtreqless 0$
ΔH_h^0	$\gtreqless 0$	$\gtreqless 0$
ΔS_h^0	<0	$\gtreqless 0$
	$T\lvert \Delta S^E\rvert > \lvert \Delta H^E\rvert$	$T\lvert \Delta S^E\rvert < \lvert \Delta H^E\rvert$
$\Delta C_{P_h}^0$	>0	$\leqslant 0$
$\bar{V}_2$	<0	$\gtrsim 0$

influence HI in proteins as well as in simple systems, their effect on the former is not only a matter of HI, since their interaction with amide and peptide groups is favored energetically [246].

In the same way, ions which exhibit marked effects on the solubility and conformations of proteins interact with amide groups [68,280–283], and this is modulated by vicinal nonpolar groups [280,284]. Notwithstanding the apparent complexity of their action, their effects in different systems follow a more or less constant pattern, paralleling their behavior in simpler systems, such as surfactant solutions. This is true for the effectiveness of various ions in stabilizing or destabilizing the native forms of collagen [285–287], ribonuclease [288], and DNA [289,290] and the conformation of a synthetic polymer, polyvinylmethyloxazolidinone [291], in aqueous solution. This pattern applies to all systems where there is a net transfer of nonpolar residues from an unhydrated to a hydrated environment [292]. Thus, ions which effectively stabilize macromolecular conformations are those which increase the energy barrier for the transfer of residues from the inside to the (hydrated) outside of the molecule. Such ions, e.g. sulfate, thus "salt out" the nonpolar group and promote the HI. At the other end of the scale are the highly polarizable anions, such as I^-, SCN^-, and ClO_4^-, which have the opposite effect and promote the hydration or "salting in" of the nonpolar residue, thus decreasing the HI [293]. These effects are evident, as will be discussed below, in the sorption of small nonpolar species in tightly crosslinked gels.

As a postscript to this somewhat oversimplified account of the HI, it is perhaps timely to add a cautionary word about the interpretation of processes as HI—at least in more complex systems—and in this context, the comments of Ben-Naim and Wilf [294] are apt. They remarked that, in explaining processes occurring in more complex systems, it has become fashionable to invoke the concept of HI. Thus " … it is very common to find statements referring to the HI as the most important factor that determines the driving force for various biological processes. To the best of the authors' knowledge, the validity of such statements has never been verified. It is well known that several factors, such as charge/charge interactions, Van der Waals interactions, and HI do combine to the overall driving force…it is still unclear which of these factors is the more (or most) important…". This caution is by no means misplaced. Even though considerable progress has been made in understanding the HI, its origin is still very far from clear. Evidently, it must be intimately related to the peculiar ability of water to associate [41].

8.6. HYDRATION OF GELS

Of the many books dealing with the properties of water and the consequences of its peculiar associative ability, the most comprehensive treatments are in refs. 295 and 296. In particular, the meaning of the term structure, as applied to liquid water, is discussed lucidly in ref. 295. Hydrophobic hydration and HI are illustrated schematically in Fig. 8.20. It shows: (a) structured water surrounding a nonpolar "hard sphere", (b) a HI where the amount of structured water bound to two

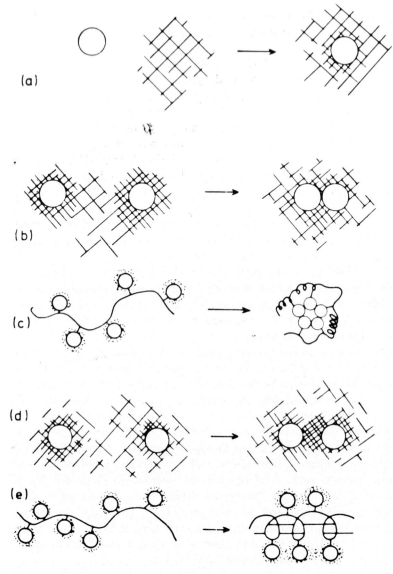

Fig. 8.20. Diagramatic representation of (a) hydrophobic hydration and (b–e) hydrophobic interactions; (b) Kauzmann–Nemethy–Scheraga contact interaction, (c) globular protein folding, (d) proposed long-range interaction (see text), (e) possible stabilization of helix interaction as in (d). (Reproduced from *Water. A Comprehensive Treatise, Vol. 4, Aqueous Solutions of Amphiphiles and Macromolecules*, Plenum, New York, 1975, Chap. 1, p. 1, with permission [295].)

nonpolar species in contact is less than that surrounding them when apart, (c) hydrophobic moieties of a globular protein associated to reduce contact with water, (d) a proposed longer-range HI, (e) the possible stabilization of a helix by long-range interactions. In the interpretation of (c) and (d) it was proposed that water molecules link together the hydration cages of two nonpolar groups [297].

The forces determining the structure of water are most probably short-range and, in a gel with a high water content and large internal voids, it is only the vicinal water [298], perturbed by the surface, which may have a structure different from that in the bulk. X-ray diffraction studies of water [299] suggest that local ordering may extend over about 0.8 nm at 25°C. The water spaces in the gel probably have, therefore, a sandwich structure, the layers of surface-perturbed water being separated by water with a more or less normal bulk structure [298,300]. However, there is another effect which modifies the structure of the water in narrow spaces. The normal structure of bulk water requires the participation of a certain minimum number of molecules. Thus, it is impossible, e.g., for the two water molecules in the cyclohexaamylose cavity (see Chap. 8.8) to be as fully coordinated as they might be in bulk. This phenomenon does not depend on interactions with a surface, but is merely an expression of confinement into too small a space. This is illustrated diagrammatically in Fig. 8.21.

Estimates of the average cluster size for normal water have varied between 6 and 10^4 molecules, involving distances of between 0.6 and 6 nm; more recent studies favor the lower values [301]. If the extent of surface-perturbed vicinal water and the minimum dimensions of a mass of normal bulk water are taken into account, it does not seem unreasonable to suppose that, in a space less than about 3 nm in diameter, most, if not all, of the water will not be normally structured [302]. Calculations [175] indicate that the average center-to-center distance between the chains is less than this in the most tightly crosslinked Sephadex gels. It is thus likely that solutes partitioning in these gels enter into confined spaces with an abnormal water structure and, indeed, the spaces may be so narrow as to prevent water from surrounding the solutes entirely, so that contact with the matrix becomes inevitable.

The state of the vicinally perturbed water will depend on the nature of the matrix surface. As discussed in Chap. 8.4.1, the substitution of diether-linked glyceryl crosslinks should, if anything, slightly increase the polarity of the surface [174]. There is also evidence (see Chap. 8.4.2) that the crosslinks are oligomeric and form dioxolane rings, but, although dioxane has a very low dielectric constant, its thermodynamic properties indicate that in aqueous solution it behaves more like a hydrophilic than a hydrophobic solute [303].

Although the hydration of polysaccharides is, in general, probably dominated by hydrophilic interactions, the influence of the hydrophobic groups cannot be entirely neglected [153]. The AGR contains CH as well as OH groups, and in the $^4C_1$ (C_1, chair) conformation, which is the most stable and probable form [304], there are essentially hydrophobic areas, capable of complexing nonpolar molecules [153]. Even in disaccharides, hydrophobicity may contribute to the mutual orientations of the residues. Thus, maltose appears to have a folded conformation, involving an inter-residue (intramolecular) [305] hydrophobic interaction. This reduces the contact area between the nonpolar regions and water [305,306] in a way analogous to that first suggested by Kauzmann [307] for proteins.

Nuclear magnetic relaxation studies of the orientation of the solvation shell water

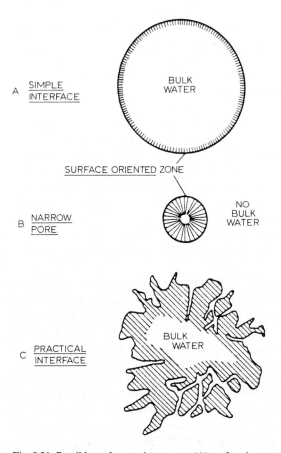

Fig. 8.21. Possible surface environments: (A) surface in contact with bulk water, (B) thin films and narrow pores, (C) practical surface. (Reproduced from *Water. A Comprehensive Treatise, Vol. 5, Water in Disperse Systems*, Plenum, New York, 1975, Chap. 1, p. 75, with permission [301].)

around nonpolar groups are also consistent with structuring in the form of clathrate-like preferences [308,309]. However, other NMR findings are ambiguous [310]. Computer simulation studies have provided considerable insight into the structure and molecular dynamics of pure water [311,312]. Such calculations also suggest a complex solvation shell structure around nonpolar species. Thus, the conclusion from a molecular dynamics simulation study of two Lennard-Jones (noble gas-like) particles and 214 water molecules [310] was that there are definite orientational preferences for the first solvation layer around the particles, reminiscent of clathrate-like structures [313,314] although no rigid arrangement comparable to a hydrate structure or ice crystal lattice could be recognized. It was also found, as previously suggested [297], that two adjacent hydration cages could be stabilized by a persistent bridging hydrogen bond, which thus functions as a longer-distance HI (see Fig. 8.20d). The translational and rotational motions of solvent-sheath water molecules are reduced by about 20% compared with those in bulk water. However, despite the ordering tendency, there is also substantial local disorder.

Ramiah and Goring [300] believe that, in the case of polysaccharides, the surface-perturbed vicinal water in the gel would be disordered. However, the hydroxyl and ether groups of the matrix should have a strong orienting influence in addition to that of the nonpolar groups. On these grounds, the structure of the internal water would thus seem more likely to be ordered, although, if there are two different types of order, there may be a disordered transitional zone between them, as postulated in the Frank–Wen model [249]. However, the combination of methylene groups and ether oxygens may have a net structure-breaking effect, since both dioxane and oligo(ethyleneoxide)s behave as water-structure breakers [146,220,315]. Finally, it should be mentioned that if the void is only two or three water molecules in diameter, hydrogen bonding between the latter may create new aqueous cross-links, which will further immobilize the gel chains [316].

8.7. HYDROPHOBIC INTERACTIONS IN GELS

8.7.1. Hydrophobic-interaction chromatography

Many of the adsorption phenomena found to occur in gel chromatography can be utilized for specific separation purposes. Mention has already been made of ion-exchange chromatography (Chap. 8.5.6.1) and charge-transfer chromatography (Chap. 8.5.6.5). Hydrophobic-interaction chromatography (HIC) is yet another example of this. Many gels, especially the most tightly crosslinked ones, possess HI properties and thus, in principle, lend themselves to use as sorbents for HIC. However, other adsorption effects, mainly of ionic and aromatic character, are often also present and complicate the situation.

More useful from the point of view of the experimenter is a system purposely designed to show well-defined HI. HIC is, in essence, a special case of reversed-phase chromatography. A discussion of HIC is appropriate here, because the technique, in a sense, grew out of gel chromatography. The distinguishing feature of HIC is that it is designed to fractionate macromolecular solutes, proteins in particular, which are predominantly hydrophilic in character, but which possess regions of pronounced hydrophobicity, allowing them to interact with a hydrophobic surface.

The hydrophobic residues of proteins are mostly located in the interior of the molecule and serve to stabilize the tertiary structure by hydrophobic interactions, but some of the hydrophobic residues are located on the surface [317]. The extent to which these hydrophobic patches appear on the surface differs from protein to protein, and it is these differences that are considered to be the basis of selectivity in HIC [318]. By choosing a matrix that is normally hydrophilic and as free as possible from other types of adsorption sites, e.g., charged groups, it is possible to introduce centers for HI to an extent that just matches the surface hydrophobicity of proteins and maximally exploits the selective differences in such hydrophobicity. One caveat here is that uncoiling of the protein will expose hydrophobic groups and dramatically increase the tendency to HI. Thus, it would perhaps be more correct to say that HIC depends upon the surface hydrophobicity of proteins and/or their tendency to unravel. Chothia [319] listed the distributions of different amino acid residues between the surfaces and interiors of a number of proteins. If the uncoiling is too extensive, denaturation will occur. HIC gels should be designed to avoid this. Conventional reversed-phase chromatography gels are too hydrophobic for denaturation to be avoided.

Accordingly, HIC gels have been almost exclusively based on agarose, where the matrix is both hydrophilic and of a concentration low enough to allow considerable porosity. Aliphatic side-groups can be introduced by different coupling methods, including CNBr [320–323], epoxidation [324], and direct coupling through an ether linkage [325]. However, the CNBr method is not recommended, since a positive charge, generated as a result of the coupling, will complicate or mask hydrophobic interactions. Likewise, the introduction of ω-aminoalkyl chains will give rise to separations which, although possibly of value experimentally, are hard to interpret. The simplest and most practical method is the direct coupling, through an ether linkage, of an aliphatic residue [325] to Sepharose. In most experimental work to-date the aliphatic chain has been between five and twelve carbon atoms in length, with eight as a convenient compromise. In a similar way, phenyl residues have been coupled to Sepharose, the separation mechanism being due not only to HI but also depending to a considerable degree on electron donor/acceptor interaction (see Chap. 8.5.6.5).

8.7.2. Hydrophobic interactions in tightly crosslinked dextran gels

Tightly crosslinked, but otherwise unsubstituted Sephadex gels clearly exhibit HI [36,44,198]. Indeed, it is probably ubiquitous, playing some role in the partitioning of all except perhaps the most polar solutes. It was first observed in a DVS crosslinked dextran gel [44] and later noted in Sephadex LH-20 [326]. That this property escaped general attention for so long is presumably due to the relatively restricted use of tightly crosslinked gels in the chromatography of low-molecular-weight, weakly polar solutes. In the gels of high water content, required for macromolecular chromatography, the matrix concentrations of the unsubstituted gels are too low to exhibit significant hydrophobic interactions.

According to Morris [327,328], three criteria must be met if chromatographic behavior is to be ascribed mainly to HI:

(a) A hydrophobic site should be identified.

(b) The K_d values should be higher at higher temperatures.

(c) High salt concentrations should increase the K_d value.

In a gel specially designed for HIC the first criterion is self-evident, but otherwise it is ambiguous; it is not clear whether it refers to nonpolar domains or to a condition where HI can occur. For example, the interior of a cycloamylose is by no means nonpolar, but it can accommodate nonpolar groups, and in some cases this is mainly due to HI (see Chap. 8.8). The third criterion, although valid for many salts, is not a general property, since chaotropic anions, such as I^- or SCN^-, reduce the affinity of aliphatic alcohols (see Fig. 8.22).

The selectivity of the more highly crosslinked Sephadex gels for nonpolar and weakly polar solutes, as represented by the 1-alkanols, has the following features, which suggest that the gel may be able to reduce hydrophobic hydration.

(a) The affinity increases as the series is ascended, and both the standard enthalpy of transfer (ΔH^0) and entropy (ΔS^0) become more positive. Further, $|T\Delta S^0| > |\Delta H^0|$ [36,44,220], and thus sorption appears to be an entropy-dominated process. The changes in the thermodynamic transfer functions in ascending the series, $\Delta(\Delta G^0) < 0$, $\Delta(\Delta H^0) > 0$ and $\Delta(\Delta S^0) > 0$, are therefore qualitatively the same as those occurring when a nonpolar solute is transferred from an aqueous to a nonpolar environment, i.e. the opposite of hydrophobic hydration. In Sephadex G-15 $\Delta(\Delta G^0)$ is about -0.6 kJ mol^{-1} per CH_2 group [36], and in G-10 about -1.3 kJ mol^{-1} [198]. Since the value of $\Delta(\Delta G^0)$ for transfer of a CH_2 group from water to a pure

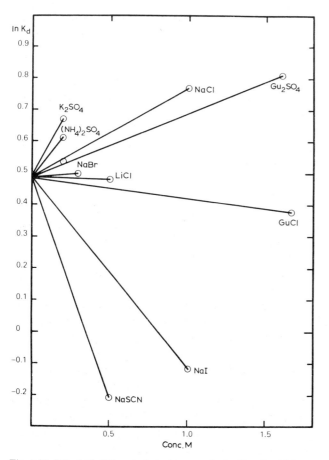

Fig. 8.22. Effect of different electrolytes on the ln K_d value of 1-pentanol in Sephadex G-10 at 25°C.

nonpolar phase is about -3.7 kJ mol^{-1} [43], Sephadex G-15 is about one-sixth and G-10 about one-third as "nonpolar" as a pure hydrocarbon.

(b) For the series of alcohols, there is an approximately linear relation between ΔH^0 and ΔS^0, i.e. enthalpy/entropy compensation [255], with a compensation temperature of about 240°K [220]. According to Lumry and Rajender [329], compensation temperatures in the approximate range 250–350°K are a consequence of the properties of liquid water.

(c) Water seems to be necessary for the affinity of the gels. In formamide, this is apparently abolished ($K_d < 1$) and the order of alkanol elution is reversed [330]. Further, in line with a loss of affinity, ΔH^0 is decreased to about zero [331].

(d) The addition of so-called water-structure perturbants to the eluent changes the K_d value in the same direction as it affects the tendency of a nonionic surfactant to form micelles [146,332]. The magnitude of this effect appears to increase with the number of CH$_2$ groups, at least up to 1-hexanol.

(e) Electrolytes also perturb the nonpolar affinity, as shown in Fig. 8.22, and the pattern reflects the different effects of the ions. Thus, the less polarizable or highly charged anions which stabilize water structure [260,333] increase the nonpolar affinity of Sephadex G-10; the more highly polarizable "chaotropic" anions decrease it. The same order of effectiveness of the various anions in these salting-out and salting-in effects has been found for a large number of nonpolar model nonelectrolytes in aqueous solution, as described in Chap. 8.5.6.7. It may be noted also that, in Sephadex G-10, the order of the K_d values of 1-pentanol in the presence of different anions is the opposite of that of the K_d values of the anions themselves (cf. Table 8.5).

(f) There is a high negative correlation between the affinity of the gel for, and the aqueous solubility of, the less polar solutes [334].

8.7.3. Driving forces for interactions in dextran gels

Although HI appears to play an important, if not dominant, role in the partition of nonpolar groups, it is clear that affinity may also be due to other factors. Thus, the lower enthalpy associated with the presence of double bonds (Table 8.2) suggests that another, energetically favorable interaction occurs. These data indicate that the aromatic ring does not behave in the same way as a saturated hydrocarbon and is not, as so often assumed, a valid representative of nonpolar behavior. However, Sephadex also exhibits affinity for polar solutes containing double bonds, such as urea and thiourea. It seems reasonable to ascribe the effect of the "double bond" in both types of solute to London dispersion interactions. As discussed in Chap. 8.5.6.6, gel/solute hydrogen bonding probably plays an insignificant role in aqueous systems, and this is probably true even in the relatively water-poor Sephadex G-10.

It is likely that ion/dipole interactions are responsible for the high affinity of certain anions for Sephadex. Thus, Moulik and Khan [335] reported that D-glucose associates with electrolytes, the anion apparently guiding the process. Other research workers have reported the association of sugars and salts [336–339]. Although Rendleman found no evidence that sugars combine with univalent anions, he thought it very probable that the anions were involved in carbohydrate/ion-pair interactions [337].

8.7.4. Site of the hydrophobic interaction

In no case does the affinity of a solute for the gel provide evidence of actual binding to a site, as opposed to an increase in concentration in the water in the neighborhood of the matrix, i.e. to a decreased activity coefficient [67]. The difficult question of the site(s) at which nonpolar solutes are located within the gel is complicated by our ignorance of the hydrated structure of the gel. A tentative suggestion [332] of association with the nonpolar faces of the AGR was questioned by Yano and Janado [198], who concluded that the high affinity of Sephadex G-10 could not be due to the AGR unless the latter were arranged in a stable array. They therefore suggested that the affinity was due to the accommodation of the nonpolar groups in abnormally highly structured water in the interstices of the network. This would constitute an escape of the nonpolar groups from bulk water and is analogous to the accumulation of hydrocarbons at a water/air interface, described long ago by Traube [340].

Recent NMR studies have clearly indicated that both matrix chains and cross-links in Sephadex G-10 are rigid and immobile. Further, calculation of the average center-to-center distance of the dextran chains in a hydrated state indicates that the molecular sieve characteristics of these most highly crosslinked Sephadex gels can only be accounted for if solutes are distributed in spaces considerably larger than the average distances. The observation in transmission electron microscopy of "membrane walls" and clustering [192], described in Chap. 8.4.3, indicates that the gels may not consist of random crosslinked networks, as depicted in Fig. 8.1a. The concept of such a heterogeneous structure with regions of condensed matrix alternating with more open domains can reconcile the discrepancy between the sieve properties and the size of the average mesh. Since the average center-to-center distances calculated for random packing are impossibly small, i.e. less than the Van der Waals diameter of the AGR, packing must therefore be, at least partially, nonrandom. The concept of a gel containing matrix-dense water-poor domains adjacent to more open, water-filled spaces is the sort of model structure envisaged by Flodin [16] in his original description. It thus seems quite likely that some sort of stable array—albeit not regular or crystalline in nature—may exist.

In view of the small average center-to-center distance of the matrix chains in the most tightly crosslinked Sephadex gels, most of the water is vicinal and, thus, unlike bulk water. However, nothing is known about the dimensions of the spaces accessible to solutes and, in view of this uncertainty, it seems rather futile to speculate on the internal solute/water interactions without further information. What is needed is a model system that exhibits the characteristic properties of the tightly crosslinked Sephadex gels: they are apparently hydrophilic and swell in water and other polar solvents, but they accommodate both polar and nonpolar species. In this, they are by no means unique: the water-soluble bacterial Schardinger dextrins or cycloamyloses (CA) also exhibit similar, but more marked complexing properties.

8.8. SCHARDINGER CYCLOAMYLOSES

8.8.1. Structure and properties

These remarkable macrocyclic, nonreducing D-glucosyl oligomers, discovered about the turn of the century, contain six or more α-D-$(1 \rightarrow 4)$-linked AGR. The more recent literature on this subject has been reviewed extensively [200,341–343], as has the older work [156,344,345]. As French [156] remarked, " ... it is surprising that a water-soluble carbohydrate would form complexes with hydrocarbons, halogenated hydrocarbons and the like ...". This discussion is mainly concerned with cyclo-hexaamylose (C6A) and cycloheptaamylose (C7A). The CA molecules are toroid, and the dimensions of the central cavities are given in Table 8.10. The AGR are in the $^4C_1$ conformation in both the crystalline state [346] and in aqueous solution [347–349].

The CA cavity has the shape of a truncated cone with the primary OH(6) groups lining the narrow end and the secondary OH(2) and OH(3) groups at the wider end [350]. The interior of the cavity is lined with regularly spaced glycosidic oxygens, each surrounded by a square array of four CH groups belonging to C(3) and C(5) of adjacent AGR [341]. The CH(1), CH(2), and CH(4) protons are located on the exterior. The lone orbitals of the glycosidic oxygens are orthogonal to the cylindrical CA axis, and this suggests an internal region of high electron density. The interior of the cavity is thus not pure hydrocarbon, as it would be if the AGR were in a boat conformation [351,352]. Although the interior is not pure hydrocarbon, it seems reasonable to regard it as less polar than water [353–356], especially with regard to its affinity for hydrocarbons. Further, as mentioned in Chap. 8.4.4.2, the spectrum of the C6A- 4-t-butylphenol complex is superposable on the spectrum of the phenol in dioxane [199]. This supports the notion that the interior of the CA is ether-like, as may be the case for tightly crosslinked Sephadex.

As far as is known, only the three lower CA form inclusion complexes [341,357]. However, the variety of solutes that can complex with CA is great, ranging from the nonpolar noble gases [358], open-chain and cyclic paraffins, and aromatic com-

TABLE 8.10

MOLECULAR DIMENSIONS OF CYCLOAMYLOSE CAVITIES AND THE NUMBER OF WATER MOLECULES THEY COULD CONTAIN

Cycloamylose	Diameter, nm	Length, nm	Volume[*], nm^3	Number of water molecules [*]
C6A	0.45 [**]	0.67 [**]	0.176	6
C7A	~ 0.7 [***]	~ 0.7 [***]	0.346	11
C8A	~ 0.85 [***]	~ 0.7 [***]	0.510	17

[*] Ref. 365.
[**] Ref. 359.
[***] Ref. 341.

pounds [346,359], to highly polar organic solutes [346,360]. Their ability to complex polar compounds also is evidenced by their affinity for some nucleotide bases [361–364]. Proof that the complexed aromatic solute is, as suspected, actually situated within the cavity was first obtained for C7A in solution by ^{1}H-NMR. The CH(3) and CH(5) protons were shielded by the magnetic field of the π-electron cloud of the aromatic ring, indicating that the latter is within the cavity [354]. However, in the case of C6A, only the CH(3) protons were shielded, suggesting that substrate penetration is limited [365]. Water is not, as has been thought [366] essential for complex formation; complexes—albeit much weaker than in water—can form in polar solvents, such as DMSO or dimethylformamide [367].

The behavior of the CA in aqueous solution is also consistent with the formation of inclusion compounds. Thus, the solubilities of aliphatic acids (C_6–C_{10}) were increased when CA was also present in the aqueous solution. The same applies to benzoic and o-, m-, and p-iodobenzoic acids, whereas species such as 2,3,5,6-tetra-methylbenzoic acid are not significantly affected, suggesting that they are too bulky to enter the CA. Further, a cyclic structure appears necessary for solubility enhance-ment, as neither glucose, methyl α-D-glucoside nor maltose influence the solubilities of organic acids [360]. Since the latter sugars, like CA, are in the $^4C_1$ (chair) conformation in aqueous solution, their lack of influence suggests that the surface of the ˜AGR alone does not determine complexing, but that an enclosed cavity is also necessary. This strongly suggests that the solvent, i.e. water, must play a cardinal role, and that the tendencies to complex should fall off with increasing diameter of the cavity [365]. The importance of the cavity is underlined by the apparent failure of the external methine hydrogens [CH(2) and CH(4)] to participate in complexing with nonpolar species [354].

8.8.2. Criteria and driving forces for inclusion

Both in the crystalline state and in aqueous solution, the C6A cavity contains two water molecules which probably play an important role in complexing. In contrast to other included molecules, these are in fixed positions, because the 0.5-nm wide C6A cavity is narrowed due to rotation of one AGR out of the original toroid arrange-ment, resulting in considerable steric strain [368]. When C6A forms an inclusion compound with another solute, the water molecules may be displaced and the ring strain relieved. Since the two internal water molecules have an incomplete comple-ment of hydrogen bonds, they are at a higher potential than in bulk water and have been referred to as high-energy or "enthalpy-rich" [353].

How well a solute fills a CA cavity seems to be an important factor in promoting complexing stability. Thus, a tight fit is more energetically favored than a loose one [350]. The relation between complexing and solute structure is not always stated as explicitly as is desirable. Thus, although inclusion complexes are formed with both nonpolar and polar molecules, this statement should not be taken at its face value. The important question is as to whether the whole or only part of a molecule is included in the cavity, and in the latter case, which part. In general, it can be concluded that substrates which fill the cavity tightly and have large hydrophobic areas that can interact with the ether-like interior of the cavity form the most stable complexes [199]. Thus, the observation that there is an approximately linear relation between the free energy of complex formation and the parachor, a measure of molecular volume, is not unexpected [369]. Polar substrates, on the other hand, may interact by intermolecular hydrogen bonding from outside the CA [200].

The driving forces which have been proposed for intracavitary complex formation are:

(a) relief of the conformational strain (C6A) due to the two internal water molecules [370,371],

(b) release of enthalpy-rich water [200],

(c) hydrophobic interactions,

(d) Van der Waals/London dispersion forces,

(e) hydrogen bonding.

Although there is a conformational change associated with complexing [370,371], Bergeron and his coworkers [365,372] concluded that relief of conformational strain did not contribute significantly to the binding of 4-nitrophenol or related compounds.

With respect to factors (b), (c), and (d) above, it is useful to consider the thermodynamic model of Tabushi et al. [373] for C6A. The model is basically similar to that of Cramer and Hettler [353]. The process of inclusion is conceived of as being divided into the following steps:

(a) Release of the two intracavitary water molecules, i.e. $H_2O_{CA} \rightleftharpoons H_2O_{gas}$. This is accompanied by positive enthalpy changes due to the loss of Van der Waals interactions and the breaking of the hydrogen bonds. There is also a gain of entropy due to the increased translational and rotational freedom outside the CA.

(b) Incorporation of the extruded molecules into the liquid phase. There are thus negative enthalpy and entropy changes due to condensation.

(c) The entering nonpolar guest is transferred from its "partial structured water cage" [374] outside the CA to the ideal gaseous state, and the cage then collapses. The work required for this process is equal to the number of hydrogen bonds which must be broken in the collapsing cage (cluster).

(d) The binding of the guest molecule to the CA cavity is associated with a negative enthalpy change due to the Van der Waals energy of the interaction and a loss of entropy due to the lost translational and reduced rotational freedom.

A word of caution is warranted here. Much of the data on CA concern the inclusion of aromatic rings, which seem to be widely regarded as nonpolar moieties. However, as discussed in Chap. 8.3.1.3, although cyclohexane and benzene have similar transfer free energies in Sephadex G-15, the enthalpy of benzene is considerably lower (see Table 8.2), indicating that other types of interaction (Van der Waals and electron donor/acceptor) are also involved.

Matsui and Mochida [375] studied the association of linear, branched, and cyclic saturated alcohols in C6A and C7A. The salient features of their results were:

(a) Linear alcohols have larger K_a values in C6A than C7A, whereas the converse is true for both the branched and cyclic alcohols. This suggests that association is promoted by a good fit, which should increase the Van der Waals interactions. Thus, the linear alcohols fit more tightly in C6A and associate more strongly than in C7A. The cyclic and branched members, on the other hand, are too bulky to be accommodated completely in C6A but fit better in C7A, with the exception of the smallest cyclanol, cyclobutanol, which has an higher affinity for C6A.

(b) There is a high positive correlation between the association constant (log K_a) for all alcohols in both C6A and C7A and the logarithm of the partition coefficient between diethyl ether and water. As might be expected, this is even better if the correlation is confined to a particular type, such as the linear primary alcohols.

The thermodynamic values obtained by Matsui and Mochida [375] are very interesting (Table 8.11). Whereas association with C6A is enthalpy-dominated, the behavior of the linear alcohols in C7A is entropy-dominated. However, in C7A the bulky alcohols behave in much the same way as do the linear alcohols in C6A. Thus, in C7A, 2,2-dimethyl-1-propanol and cyclohexanol have enthalpies which are negative and have absolute values greater than those of $T\Delta S^0$.

The thermodynamic data for the association of aliphatic alcohols with both C6A and C7A [375] are consistent with the hypothesis that the inclusion of hydrocarbon chains in CA involves an entropy-dominated HI. This is due to the transfer to an environment less polar than water with a gain of entropy owing to the consequent collapse of the ordered water cage [375,376]. Other interactions, which tend to drive both the enthalpy and entropy in a negative direction, also occur: (a) The displacement of enthalpy-rich water molecules from the cavity, especially in C6A, with possibly (b) a contribution due to the relief of conformational strain energy, and (c) Van der Waals/London interactions, which will be greater the closer the steric fit between guest and host [372]. In addition, the location of the guest within the cavity reduces both its translational and rotational entropy. Like the interstices of a gel, the toroid cavities of the CA are open to the solvent at both ends. Included compounds are thus less immobilized than in a hole with a blind end. The binding of substances, such as adamantane carboxylate [377] or 1-anilino-8-naphthalene sulfonate [378] is

TABLE 8.11

THERMODYNAMIC VALUES FOR ASSOCIATION OF CYCLOAMYLOSES AND ALCOHOLS AT 25°C [375]

	kJ mole^{-1}							
	C6A *				C7A *			
	K_d	ΔG^0	ΔH^0	$T\Delta S^0$	K_d	ΔG^0	ΔH^0	$T\Delta S^0$
1-Butanol	88.1	−11.1	−12	−0.9	16.8	−7.0	2.9	9.9
1-Pentanol	320	−14.3	−16	−1.7	63.8	−10.3	4.6	15.9
1-Hexanol	878	−16.8	−19	−2.2	214	−13.3	0.4	13.7
2,2-Dimethyl-1-propanol	29.6	−8.4	−12	−3.6	520	−15.5	−8.8	6.7
Cyclohexanol	63.8	−10.3	−14	−3.7	479	−15.3	−10.0	5.3

* C6A and C7A are the hexa- and heptacycloamyloses, respectively.

References on p. A321

markedly increased when the bottom (narrow end) of C7A is "capped" by attaching nonpolar groups. This does not, of course, prove that a hydrophobic interaction operates in unmodified C7A, although it is suggestive of this.

It would be of great interest to know more about the state of the water in C7A and higher CA. Since the radius of even C12A is not more than about 0.6 nm, all the water in the cavity will be influenced by the inner surface. The contribution of the molecules displaced by the entering guest will then depend on their state within the cavity. However, it may be assumed that the larger the CA cavity, the more bulk-like will the water be. Thus, the entropy changes due to shifts in water structure associated with the inclusion of saturated nonpolar species should decrease with increasing cavity size, at least in the larger CA. Since there are only two water molecules in the C6A cavity, it is unlikely that negative enthalpy changes resulting from their displacement would be correlated with the length of the hydrocarbon chain of the included alcohol. Therefore, the fact that in C6A there is a correlation between ΔH^0 and the chain length of a linear alcohol (Table 8.11) strongly suggests a contribution from a Van der Waals interaction in addition to any enthalpy change due to water extrusion.

Special attention has been paid to the interactions of CA with one type of polar compound, nucleotide bases [361–364], and both C6A and C7A have been used as sorbents [361,379] for the chromatography of a number of solutes, including nucleotides [361]. The selectivity for some of the latter was fairly good, and it was suggested that the CA might find a more general application in chromatography.

8.8.3. Cycloamyloses as models for nonpolar and aromatic affinity in tightly cross-linked dextran gels

The structure of the lower CA, which has been studied extensively [380], is in some respects comparable with that of tightly crosslinked Sephadex gels. Comparison of the thermodynamic characteristics of their affinity for nonpolar and aromatic solutes with those observed with such Sephadex gels should facilitate the interpretation of partitioning mechanisms in the gels. The observation that the solubilities of organic acids were not increased by the presence of maltose indicates that the nonpolar regions of this sugar [360] did not form association complexes in aqueous solution; this has been confirmed by NMR studies. It appears, therefore, that the affinity of the tightly crosslinked gels for nonpolar groups is not, as suggested previously [329], due simply to association with the matrix surface, but that a cavitary structure may be necessary.

On the other hand, the effect of D-glucose in decreasing critical micelle concentration [220] and the solubility in aqueous glucose solutions of a compound serving as a model for hydrophobic groups in proteins [381] point to a probable effect of the sugar on water structure. Structurally, CA differs from Sephadex in having a regular array of AGR and a well-defined cavity. Although the AGR are possibly not packed randomly in the most tightly crosslinked Sephadex gels, their structure cannot have the complete regularity of the CA. However, with high degrees of crosslinking the ether oxygen/hydroxyl ratio is high (Table 8.7) and, as in the CA, the interior is probably essentially ether-like. The sizes of the cavities in Sephadex presumably vary, but it seems likely that they may approximate those of the CA in some cases.

In view of the apparent rigidity of Sephadex G-10 and the small center-to-center interchain distance, it is highly probable that the mutual orientations of the chains are stable and time-independent. In this sense, they constitute an array presumably less regular than that in the CA. As suggested by Yano and Janado [198], this sort of structure might be capable of engaging in HI with nonpolar solutes. However, in view of the lack of reports of inclusion properties of the higher CA, it seems likely that a small cavity may be a requirement, and this is, of course, suggestive of an important role of water.

The evidence suggests that HI play an important role in the association of nonpolar and aromatic groups with both CA and Sephadex. The main difference is that association with CA may be accompanied by a favorable enthalpy change, which appears to be related to the closeness of fit of the ligand in the cavity. Since there are presumably cavities of different sizes in Sephadex, it is not surprising that G-15 is not thermodynamically equivalent to C6A (Tables 8.2 and 8.11). Table 8.12 shows a comparison of the number of water molecules in Ca and dextran gels [175], calculated per cavitary glycosidic oxygen in the CA and per oxygen atom in Sephadex. The CA data are calculated from the right-hand column in Table 8.10. The numbers in Table 8.12 should be a measure of the average cavity size. G-10, the most tightly crosslinked Sephadex gel, is in this respect equivalent to something between C7A and C8A. If this reasoning is correct, the enthalpy values might be expected to decline in G-10 or G-15 for more bulky nonpolar solutes which, fitting the cavities more tightly, would exhibit increased Van der Waals interactions.

There may be a profound difference between macroporous and microporous

TABLE 8.12

NUMBER OF WATER MOLECULES PER CAVITARY GLYCOSIDIC OXYGEN IN CYCLO-DEXTRINS * AND PER OXYGEN ATOM IN DEXTRAN GELS

Gel	No.
C6A	1
C7A	1.57
C8A	2.13
G-10	1.87
G-15	2.66
G-25	4.50
G-50	14.0
G-100	25.4
DVS-10 **	1.96
DVS-9	1.62

* Calculated from the number of water molecules that the cavity could contain (cf. Table 8.10).
** DVS-10 and DVS-9 are DVS-crosslinked dextran gels with water regain values of 0.98 and 0.85, respectively.

References on p. A321

cavities in that the surface properties of the latter are inevitably complicated by the fact that the cavities are too small to provide the minimal space required for a normal bulk water structure (Fig. 8.21). If the cavities are not much larger than the included solutes, it is evident that the transfer of the latter into the gel will, apart from other possible interactions, involve only the collapse of a vacated water cage in the bulk external aqueous phase. Within the gel, it will not be possible to form a new cage, since there is not enough space. Thus, the entropy change due to water structure changes should be positive. Such a mechanism was postulated for Sephadex [198,382] and polyacrylamide [383–385].

Under such circumstances, any water molecules displaced from occupied cavities in the most highly corsslinked Sephadex gels may be expected to be unimportant, since they should reduce the enthalpy less than water displaced from the smaller C7A cavities, and displacement from the latter is generally regarded as of little thermodynamic significance. Finally, it is perhaps worthy of note that, although, as Fig. 8.17 shows, the DVS-crosslinked dextran gel (DVS-9) has a much lower nonpolar affinity than Sephadex G-10, it has an even lower water content than the latter (Table 8.12). This suggests that the surface of this gel is more polar than G-10, a difference which may be due to the lower degree of crosslinking and/or the influence of the sulfone group.

8.8.4. Complexing properties of crown ethers

The complexing properties of crown ethers have considerable potential usefulness, not only as model systems for the study of affinity, but also in practical chromatography in view of the ether (dioxolane)-like matrix surface in Sephadex [386–388]. Crown ethers exhibit high complexing ability, e.g., with Group Ia salts [389,390]. They are also of interest because, being amphiphilic, they can form micelles and function as ionophoric transducers in membrane systems [391]. A cyclic structure is not necessary for complexing [392]. Even ethanediol can form complexes with Group IIa salts [393] and longer linear polyethers can wrap around cations [394] in different ways [395]. Nonelectrolytes have apparently been neglected, but stable 1:1 adducts between noncyclic crown-type polyethers and thiourea and urea have been reported [396].

8.9. AFFINITY CHROMATOGRAPHY

Affinity chromatography grew out of gel chromatography through modification by the CNBr [397], epoxy [322], thiol [398], hydroxysuccinimide [399], triazine [400,401], carbonyl imidazole [402], azido [403], sulfonyl [404], and bromine oxidative/reductive amination [405,406] methods. These methods allow the experimenter to couple an almost unlimited variety of specific ligands to chromatographic gels, which thus become centers of specific adsorption for the purification of biologically important molecules. The field is vast and covers the entire gamut of separation problems in the life sciences, from small metabolites to whole living cells. For a detailed and informed discussion the reader is referred to the monographs on this topic [407–410]. Here it is appropriate to discuss briefly the mechanism of the adsorption process.

Basically, any or all of the adsorptive phenomena discussed in Chap. 8.5.6 may be involved in the interaction between a sample molecule and a ligand that binds it specifically. Thus, e.g., proteins carry on their surface or in parts of their interior that can be made accessible to small ligands, groups having charge or multipole properties, aromatic residues that give rise to π–π interactions, and centers for HI or any other interactions mentioned in Chap. 8.5.6. These will bind to an appropriate ligand, coupled to a gel. Hydrogen bonding, discussed in Chap. 8.5, will probably not be important in aqueous systems, except in cases where multiple repeated arrays of hydrogen bonding groups exist, e.g., in nucleic acids. What is characteristic about this kind of process is not the kind of interactions that occur, but the way in which they are combined so that only molecules which sterically match each other with respect to the interactions and their juxtaposition will recognize one another and form a complex. By immobilizing one of the partners in such a complex one obtains an affinity chromatography gel, designed for extracting and purifying the other. The background matrix should ideally contain as few competing adsorption sites as possible. Hence, as in the case of HIC where low background adsorption is mandatory (cf. Chap. 8.7.1), Sepharose is the natural choice. An interesting extension of this development is the preparation, by using chiral templates, of sorbents with chiral cavities capable of racemic resolution [411]. Chiral recognition by pure crown ethers has also been reported [412].

8.10. ACKNOWLEDGEMENT

We wish to thank Drs. Björn Ingelman, Per Flodin, and John Sandblom for helpful comments.

REFERENCES

1 H. Determann, *Angew. Chem. Int. Ed. Engl.*, 3 (1964) 608.
2 H. Determann and J.E. Brewer, in E. Heftmann (Editor), *Chromatography*, 3rd Edn., Van Nostrand-Reinhold, New York, 1975, Chap. 14, p. 362.
3 H. Determann, *Gelchromatographie*, Springer, Berlin, 1967.
4 L. Fischer, *An Introduction to Gel Chromatography*, North Holland, Amsterdam, 1967.
5 T. Kremmer and L. Boross, *Gel Chromatography*, Akadémiai Kiadó, Budapest, 1979.
6 W.W. Yau, J.J. Kirkland and D.D. Bly, *Modern Size Exclusion Chromatography: Practice of Gel Permeation and Gel Filtration Chromatography*, Wiley, New York, 1979.
7 R.L.M. Synge, *Rapp. Discuss. 9e Conseil de Chimie, Bruxelles, 1953*, p. 152.
8 B. Ingelman, A. Grönwall, L.E. Gelin and R. Eliasson, *Acta Reg. Sci. Upsaliens.*, 12 (1969) 9.
9 D.L. Mould and R.L.M. Synge, *Analyst (London)*, 77 (1952) 964.
10 D.L. Mould and R.L.M. Synge, *Biochem. J.*, 58 (1954) 571.
11 D. Deuel and H. Neukom, *Adv. Chem.*, 11 (1954) 51.
12 B. Lindqvist and T. Storgårds, *Nature (London)*, 175 (1955) 511.

13 G.H. Lathe and C.R.J. Ruthven, *Biochem. J.*, 60 (1955) xxxiv.
14 G.H. Lathe and C.R.J. Ruthven, *Biochem. J.*, 62 (1956) 665.
15 J. Porath and P. Flodin, *Nature (London)*, 183 (1959) 1657.
16 P. Flodin, *Dextran Gels and Their Applications in Gel Filtration*, Pharmacia, Uppsala, 1962.
17 S. Hjertén and J. Porath, in *Uppsala University, 500 Years, 9, Chemistry, Acta Univ. Upsaliens.*, 1976.
18 J. Porath, *Biochem. Soc. Trans.*, 7 (1979) 1197.
19 S. Hjertén, *Biochim. Biophys. Acta*, 79 (1964) 393.
20 A. Polson, *Biochim. Biophys. Acta*, 50 (1961) 565.
21 R.L. Steere and G.K. Ackers, *Nature (London)*, 194 (1962) 114.
22 S. Hjertén, *Biochim. Biophys. Acta*, 62 (1962) 445.
23 J. Porath, J.-C. Janson and T. Låås, *J. Chromatogr.*, 60 (1971) 167.
24 P.J. Flory, *Principles of Polymer Chemistry*, Cornell Univ. Press, Ithaca, NY, 1953, Chap. 9, p. 357.
25 L. Sweetman and W.L. Nyhan, *J. Chromatogr.*, 32 (1968) 662.
26 W. Haller, *Nature (London)*, 206 (1965) 693.
27 W. Haller, *J. Chromatogr.*, 32 (1968) 676.
28 J.C. Giddings, *Anal. Chem.*, 40 (1968) 2143; *Dynamics of Chromatography*, Dekker, New York, 1965.
29 W.W. Yau and C.P. Malone, *Polym. Repr. Amer. Chem. Soc. Div. Polym. Chem.*, 12 (1971) 797.
30 A.W.J. Brough, R. Epton, G. Marr, A.T. Shackley and G.A. Sniezko-Blocki, in R. Epton (Editor), *Chromatography of Synthetic and Biopolymers, Vol. 1, Column Packings, G.P.C., G.F. and Gradient Elution*, Ellis Horwood, Chichester, 1978, Chap. 4, p. 70.
31 J. Borak, I. Cadersky, F. Kiss, M. Smrz and J. Viska, in R. Epton (Editor), *Chromatography of Synthetic and Biopolymers, Vol. 2, Hydrophobic, Ion Exchange and Affinity Methods*, Ellis Horwood, Chichester, 1978, Chap. 5, p. 91.
32 D.A. Rees, *Chem. Ind.*, 72 (1972) 630.
33 A. Amsterdam, Z. Er-El and S. Shaltiel, *Arch. Biochem. Biophys.*, 171 (1975) 673.
34 T. Låås, *Acta Univ. Upsaliens. (Science Dissertation)*, 1975.
35 M. Monsigny, M. Cornet, R. Tixier, M. Corgier and P. Girot, in R. Epton (Editor), *Chromatography of Synthetic and Biopolymers, Vol. 1, Column Packings, G.P.C., G.F. and Gradient Elution*, Ellis Horwood, Chichester, 1978, Chap. 3, p. 57.
36 Å.Ch. Haglund and N.V.B. Marsden, *J. Polym. Sci. Polym. Lett. Ed.*, 18 (1980) 271.
37 T.C. Laurent and J. Killander, *J. Chromatogr.*, 14 (1964) 317.
38 R.M. Wheaton and W.C. Bauman, *Ann. N.Y. Acad. Sci.*, 57 (1953) 159.
39 L.P. Hammett, *Physical Organic Chemistry*, McGraw-Hill, New York, 1940, Chap. 3, p. 82.
40 F. Franks and D.J.G. Ives, *J. Chem. Soc.*, (1960) 741.
41 J. Konicek and I. Wadsö, *Acta Chem. Scand.*, 24 (1971) 1571.
42 F. Franks, in F. Franks (Editor), *Water. A Comprehensive Treatise, Vol. 4, Aqueous Solutions of Amphiphiles and Macromolecules*, Plenum, New York, 1975, Chap. 1, p. 1.
43 C. Tanford, *The Hydrophobic Effect*, Wiley, New York, 1973, Chap. 2, p. 4.
44 N.V.B. Marsden, *Ann. N.Y. Acad. Sci.*, 125 (1965) 428.
45 A.J.P. Martin, *Biochem. Soc. Symp.*, 3 (1951) 4.
46 J.A. Thoma, *Talanta*, 8 (1961) 829.
47 F. Schmidt and B. Enevoldsen, *Carlsberg Res. Commun.*, 41 (1970) 91.
48 K.M. Chitumbo, *Acta Univ. Upsaliens. (Science Dissertation)*, 10 (1975) 20.
49 J.N. Brønsted, *Z. Phys. Chem., Abt. A (Bodenstein-Festband)*, (1931) 257.
50 S.J. Gill, N.F. Nichols and I. Wadsö, *J. Chem. Thermodyn.*, 8 (1976) 445.
51 B. Gelotte, *Chromatogr.*, 3 (1960) 330.
52 H. Determann and I. Walter, *Nature (London)*, 219 (1968) 604.
53 A.J.W. Brook and S. Housley, *J. Chromatogr.*, 41 (1969) 200.
54 A.J.W. Brook and S. Housley, *J. Chromatogr.*, 42 (1969) 112.
55 A.J.W. Brook and K.C. Munday, *J. Chromatogr.*, 47 (1970) 1.
56 A.J.W. Brook, *J. Chromatogr.*, 47 (1970) 100.
57 A.J.W. Brook and K.C. Munday, *J. Chromatogr.*, 51 (1970) 307.
58 Å.C. Haglund, *J. Chromatogr.*, 156 (1978) 317.
59 C.L. de Ligny, *J. Chromatogr.*, 172 (1979) 397.

60 D. Eaker and J. Porath, *Separ. Sci.*, 2 (1967) 507.

61 J. Porath, *Biochem. Soc. Trans.*, 7 (1979) 1197.

62 C. Streuli, *J. Chromatogr.*, 47 (1970) 355.

63 N. Yoza, *J. Chromatogr.*, 86 (1973) 325.

64 P.A. Neddermeyer and L.B. Rogers, *Anal. Chem.*, 40 (1968) 757.

65 G. Roth, *Acta Univ. Upsaliens. (Science Dissertation)*, 1975.

66 D. Saunders and R.L. Pecsok, *Anal. Chem.*, 40 (1968) 44.

67 T.St. Pierre and W.P. Jencks, *Arch. Biochem. Biophys.*, 133 (1969) 102.

68 P.H. von Hippel, V. Peticolas, L. Schack and L. Karlsson, *Biochemistry*, 12 (1973) 1256.

69 R. Epton, C. Holloway and J.V. McLaren, *J. Chromatogr.*, 117 (1976) 245.

70 J. Borák, *J. Chromatogr.*, 155 (1978) 69.

71 Y. Ueno, N. Yoza and S. Ohashi, *J. Chromatogr.*, 52 (1970) 321.

72 E.R. Nightingale, *J. Phys. Chem.*, 63 (1959) 1381.

73 G. Eisenman, *Biophys. J.*, Suppl. 2 (1962) 259.

74 T. Ogata, N. Yoza and S. Ohashi, *J. Chromatogr.*, 58 (1971) 267.

75 N.V.B. Marsden, *Naturwissenschaften*, 60 (1973) 257.

76 G. Kura, A. Koyama and T. Tarutani, *J. Chromatogr.*, 144 (1977) 245.

77 T. Deguchi, *J. Chromatogr.*, 108 (1975) 409.

78 T. Deguchi, A. Hisanaga and H. Nagai, *J. Chromatogr.*, 133 (1977) 173.

79 F. Helfferich, *Ion Exchange*, McGraw-Hill, New York, 1962, Chap. 5, p. 95.

80 H. Ortner and H. Spitzy, *Z. Anal. Chem.*, 221 (1966) 119.

81 H. Ortner and H. Spitzy, *Z. Anal. Chem.*, 238 (1968) 167.

82 H. Ortner and H. Spitzy, *Z. Anal. Chem.*, 238 (1968) 251.

83 N.V.B. Marsden, *J. Chromatogr.*, 105 (1975) 1.

84 N.V.B. Marsden and Å.C. Haglund, *J. Chromatogr.*, in press.

85 J.C. Moore, *J. Polym. Sci. Part A*, 2 (1964) 835.

86 W.B. Smith and A. Kollmansberger, *J. Phys. Chem.*, 69 (1965) 4157.

87 M.F. Vaughan, *Nature (London)*, 188 (1960) 55.

88 P.S. Brewer, *Nature (London)*, 188 (1960) 935.

89 B. Curtis-Jones, *Nature (London)*, 191 (1961) 272.

90 J.C. Moore and J.H. Hendrickson, *J. Polym. Sci. Part C*, 8 (1965) 233.

91 D.J. Harmon, *J. Polym. Sci. Part C*, 8 (1965) 243.

92 W. Billmeyer, *Textbook of Polymer Science*, Wiley, New York, 1973, Chap. 3, p. 62.

93 A.C. Ouano, *Advan. Chromatogr.*, 15 (1979) 233.

94 J.C. Giddings, E. Kucera, C.P. Russell and M.N. Myers, *J. Phys. Chem.*, 72 (1968) 4397.

95 H. Benoit, Z. Grubisic, P. Rempp, D. Decker and J.-G. Zilliox, *J. Chim. Phys.*, 63 (1967) 1507.

96 E.F. Casassa, *Polym. Lett.*, 5 (1967) 773.

97 E.F. Casassa and Y. Tagami, *Macromolecules*, 2 (1969) 14.

98 E.F. Casassa, *Macromolecules*, 9 (1976) 182.

99 E.F. Casassa, *Separ. Sci.*, 6 (1971) 305.

100 E.E. Brumbaugh and G.K. Ackers, *J. Biol. Chem.*, 243 (1968) 6315.

101 G. Ackers, *Biochemistry*, 3 (1964) 723.

102 W.W. Yau and C.P. Malone, *Polym. Lett.*, 5 (1967) 663.

103 W.W. Yau, C.P. Malone and S.W. Fleming, *Polym. Lett.*, 6 (1968) 803.

104 W.W. Yau, *J. Polym. Sci. Part A-2*, 7 (1969) 483.

105 K.O. Pedersen, *Arch. Biochem. Biophys.*, Suppl., 1 (1962) 157.

106 H. Small, *J. Colloid Interface Sci.*, 48 (1974) 147.

107 E.A. DiMarzio and C.M. Guttman, *J. Polym. Sci. Part B*, 7 (1969) 267.

108 E.A. DiMarzio and C.M. Guttman, *Macromolecules*, 3 (1970) 131.

109 D. Bernouilli, *Hydrodynamica*, Argentorati, 1738.

110 R.F. Stoisits, G.W. Poehlein and J.W. Vanderhoff, *J. Colloid Interface Sci.*, 57 (1976) 337.

111 C.M. Guttman and E.A. DiMarzio, *Macromolecules*, 3 (1970) 681.

112 J.J. Hermans, *J. Polym. Sci. Part A-2*, 6 (1968) 1217.

113 F.H. Verhoff and N.D. Sylvester, *J. Macromol. Sci. Chem.*, 4 (1970) 979.

114 E.F. Casassa, *J. Phys. Chem.*, 75 (1971) 3929.
115 Z. Grubisic, P. Rempp and H. Benoit, *J. Polym. Sci. Part B*, 5 (1967) 753.
116 J. Porath, *Pure Appl. Chem.*, 6 (1963) 233.
117 P. Squire, *Arch. Biochem. Biophys.*, 107 (1964) 471.
118 H. Waldmann-Meyer, in R. Epton (Editor), *Chromatography of Synthetic and Biological Polymers, Vol. 1, Column Packings, G.P.C., G.F. and Gradient Elution*, Ellis Horwood, Chichester, 1978, Chap. 19, p. 289.
119 A.G. Ogston, *Trans. Faraday Soc.*, 54 (1958) 1754.
120 D.M.W. Anderson and J.F. Stoddart, *Lab. Pract.*, 16 (1967) 841.
121 M.E. van Kreveld, *J. Polym. Sci. Polym. Phys. Ed.*, 13 (1975) 2253.
122 H. Kuhn, *Helv. Chim. Acta*, 31 (1948) 1677.
123 J.J. Weidmann, H. Kuhn and W. Kuhn, *J. Chim. Phys. Phys.-Chim. Biol.*, 50 (1956) 226.
124 K.A. Boni, F.A. Sliemers and P.B. Stickney, *J. Polym. Sci. Part A-2*, 6 (1968) 1579.
125 J.V. Dawkins and M. Hemming, *Makromol. Chem.*, 176 (1975) 1777.
126 J.V. Dawkins and M. Hemming, *Makromol. Chem.*, 176 (1975) 1795.
127 J.V. Dawkins and M. Hemming, *Makromol. Chem.*, 176 (1975) 1815.
128 F.R. Dintzis and R. Tobin, *J. Chromatogr.*, 88 (1974) 77.
129 B.G. Belenky, E.S. Gankina, M.B. Tennikov and L.Z. Vilenchik, *J. Chromatogr.*, 147 (1978) 99.
130 M.A. Lauffer, *J. Amer. Chem. Soc.*, 66 (1944) 1188.
131 A.J. de Vries, M. Le Page, R. Beau and C.L. Guillemin, *Anal. Chem.*, 39 (1967) 935.
132 D.J. Meier, *J. Phys. Chem.*, 71 (1967) 1861.
133 P. Flodin and K. Granath, *Markomol. Chem.*, 48 (1961) 160.
134 K.A. Granath and B.E. Kvist, *J. Chromatogr.*, 28 (1967) 69.
135 M. John, G. Trénel and H. Dellweg, *J. Chromatogr.*, 42 (1969) 476.
136 F. Schmidt and B. Enevoldsen, *Carbohydr. Res.*, 61 (1978) 197.
137 K.M. Chitumbo and W. Brown, *J. Polym. Sci. Part C*, 36 (1971) 279.
138 L.M. Siegel and K.J. Monty, *Biochim. Biophys. Acta*, 112 (1966) 346.
139 P.E. Davison, *Science*, 161 (1968) 906.
140 C. Tanford, K. Kawahara and S. Lapanje, *J. Biol. Chem.*, 241 (1966) 1921.
141 C. Tanford, K. Kawahara and S. Lapanje, *J. Amer. Chem. Soc.*, 89 (1967) 729.
142 Y. Nozaki and C. Tanford, *J. Amer. Chem. Soc.*, 89 (1967) 742.
143 W.W. Fish, K.G. Mann and C. Tanford, *J. Biol. Chem.*, 244 (1969) 4989.
144 W.W. Fish, J.A. Reynolds and C. Tanford, *J. Biol. Chem.*, 245 (1970) 5166.
145 Y. Nozaki, N.M. Schecter, J.A. Reynolds and C. Tanford, *Biochemistry*, 15 (1976) 3884.
146 W.B. Gratzer and G.H. Beaven, *J. Phys. Chem.*, 73 (1960) 2270.
147 W. Brown, *J. Chromatogr.*, 52 (1970) 273.
148 W. Brown, *J. Chromatogr.*, 59 (1971) 335.
149 W. Brown, *Chem. Scripta*, 2 (1972) 25.
150 W. Brown and Ö. Andersson, *J. Chromatogr.*, 57 (1971) 255.
151 W. Brown and K. Chitumbo, *Chem. Scripta*, 2 (1972) 88.
152 K. Chitumbo and W. Brown, *J. Chromatogr.*, 80 (1973) 187.
153 A. Suggett, in F. Franks (Editor), *Water. A Comprehensive Treatise, Vol. 4, Aqueous Solutions of Amphiphiles and Macromolecules*, Plenum, New York, 1975, Chap. 6, p. 519.
154 D.A. Rees and W.E. Scott, *J. Chem. Soc.*, (1971) 469.
155 A. Heyraud and M. Rinaudo, *J. Chromatogr.*, 166 (1978) 149.
156 D. French, *Advan. Carbohydr. Chem.*, 12 (1957) 189.
157 T.C. Laurent and K. Granath, *Biochim. Biophys. Acta*, 136 (1967) 191.
158 E. Grellert and C.E. Ballou, *Carbohydr. Res.*, 30 (1973) 218.
159 O. Hassell and B. Ottar, *Acta Chem. Scand.*, 1 (1947) 927.
160 R.E. Reeves, *Advan. Carbohydr. Chem.*, 6 (1951) 107.
161 R.B. Kelly, *Can. J. Chem.*, 35 (1957) 149.
162 E. Eliel, N. Allinger, S.J. Angyal and G.A. Morrison, *Conformational Analysis*, Wiley, New York, 1967, Chap. 7, p. 351.
163 J.B. Taylor, *Trans. Faraday Soc.*, 53 (1957) 1198.

164 L.F. Martin, N.R. Bertoniere and S.P. Rowland, *J. Chromatogr.*, 64 (1972) 263.
165 J.H. Carter and E.Y.C. Lee, *Anal. Biochem.*, 39 (1971) 521.
166 S.B. Horowitz and I.R. Fenichel, *J. Phys. Chem.*, 68 (1964) 3378.
167 M.L. White and G.H. Dorion, *J. Polym. Sci.*, 55 (1961) 731.
168 W. Brown and R.M. Johnsen, *Polymer*, 22 (1981) 185.
169 J.H. Bradbury and J.G. Collins, *Carbohydr. Res.*, 71 (1979) 15.
170 F. Bove, M. Daoud, M. Nierlich, C. Williams, J.P. Colton, B. Farnoux and G. Jannink, in *Symposium on Neutron Inelastic Scattering*, 1971, IAEA-SM 219/99, p. 563.
171 M. Daoud, J.P. Colton, B. Farnoux, G. Jannink, G. Sharma, H. Benoit, R. Duplessix, G. Picot and P.G. de Gennes, *Macromolecules*, 8 (1975) 804.
172 J.D. Aplin and L.D. Hall, *Carbohydr. Res.*, 75 (1979) 17.
173 E. Brynda, P. Štrop, F. Mikeš and J. Kálal, *J. Chromatogr.*, 196 (1980) 39.
174 C. Hansch and A.J. Leo, *Substituent Constants for Correlation Analysis in Chemistry and Biology*, Wiley, New York, 1979.
175 N.V.B. Marsden, unpublished data.
176 R.P. Bell, *The Proton in Chemistry*, Cornell University Press, Ithaca, N.Y., 1959, Chap. 11, p. 145.
177 S.W. Englander, N.W. Downer and H. Teitelbaum, *Ann. Rev. Biochem.*, 41 (1972) 903.
178 K.F. Bonhoeffer, *Z. Electrochem.*, 40 (1934) 469.
179 V.J. Frilette, J. Hanle and H. Mark, *J. Amer. Chem. Soc.*, 70 (1948) 1107.
180 J. Mann and H.J. Marrinan, *Trans. Faraday Soc.*, 52 (1956) 481.
181 J. Mann and H.J. Marrinan, *Trans. Faraday Soc.*, 52 (1956) 487.
182 J. Mann and H.J. Marrinan, *Trans. Faraday Soc.*, 52 (1956) 492.
183 K.E. Almin, *Sven. Papperstidn.*, 55 (1952) 767.
184 N.W. Taylor, H.F. Zobel, M. White and F.R. Senti, *J. Phys. Chem.*, 65 (1961) 1816.
185 N.W. Taylor, H.F. Zobel, N.N. Hellman and F.R. Senti, *J. Phys. Chem.*, 63 (1959) 599.
186 N.W. Taylor, J.E. Cluskey and F.R. Senti, *J. Phys. Chem.*, 65 (1961) 181.
187 N.V.B. Marsden, *J. Chromatogr.*, 58 (1971) 304.
188 M. Cohn and H.C. Urey, *J. Amer. Chem. Soc.*, 60 (1938) 679.
189 L. Kuniak and R.H. Marchessault, *Stärke*, 24 (1971) 110.
190 R. Rüchel, R.L. Steere and E.F. Erbe, *J. Chromatogr.*, 166 (1978) 563.
191 R. Rüchel and M.D. Brager, *Anal. Biochem.*, 68 (1975) 415.
192 D. Hager, *J. Chromatogr.*, 187 (1980) 285.
193 N.V.B. Marsden and B. Wieselblad, *Jeol. News*, 13 (1976) 11.
194 J. Kocoń, S. Muszyński and M. Gromadka, *Bull. Acad. Pol. Sci., Ser. Sci. Biol.*, 25 (1977) 761.
195 L.C. Hansen and R.E. Sievers, *J. Chromatogr.*, 99 (1974) 123.
196 N.E. Eriksson, N.V.B. Marsden and D.Z. Popov, *Experientia*, 30 (1974) 572.
197 N.V.B. Marsden, *Symposium on Water and Ions in Biological Systems, Bucharest, 1980*.
198 Y. Yano and M. Janado, *J. Chromatogr.*, 200 (1980) 125.
199 R.L. van Ettan, J.F. Sebastian, G.A. Clowes and M.L. Bender, *J. Amer. Chem. Soc.*, 89 (1967) 3242.
200 D.W. Griffiths and M.L. Bender, *Advan. Catal.*, 23 (1973) 209.
201 R.M. Barrer and J.D. Falconer, *Proc. R. Soc. London Ser. A*, 236 (1956) 227.
202 C.K. Hersch, *Molecular Sieves*, Reinhold, New York, 1961.
203 P.J. Flory, *Principles of Polymer Chemistry*, Cornell Univ. Press, Ithaca, NY, 1953, Chap. 13, p. 577.
204 W.W. Barkas, *Trans. Faraday Soc.*, 28 (1942) 194.
205 H.P. Gregor, *J. Amer. Chem. Soc.*, 70 (1948) 1923.
206 H.P. Gregor, *J. Amer. Chem. Soc.*, 73 (1951) 642.
207 R.M. Wheaton and W.C. Bauman, *Ind. Eng. Chem.*, 45 (1953) 228.
208 O. Samuelsson, *Ion Exchange Separations in Analytical Chemistry*, Wiley, New York, 1963, Chap. 2, p. 48.
209 E. Edmond, S. Farquhar, J.D. Dunstone and A.G. Ogston, *Biochem. J.*, 108 (1968) 755.
210 G.E. Boyd and B.A. Soldano, *Z. Elektrochem.*, 57 (1953) 162.
211 S. Hjertén, *J. Chromatogr.*, 50 (1970) 189.
212 M. Mattison and O. Samuelsson, *Acta Chem. Scand.*, 12 (1958) 1386.
213 B.Z. Ginzburg and D. Cohen, *Trans. Faraday Soc.*, 60 (1964) 185.

214 D. Reichenberg and W.F. Wall, *J. Chem. Soc.*, (1956) 3364.
215 E.G. Glueckauf and G.P. Kitt, *Proc. R. Soc. London Ser. A*, 228 (1955) 322.
216 W. Buser, P. Graf and W.F. Grütter, *Chimia*, 9 (1955) 73.
217 J. Lecourtier, R. Audebert and C. Quivoron, *J. Chromatogr.*, 121 (1976) 173.
218 I.M. Klotz, *Arch. Biochem. Biophys.*, 138 (1970) 704.
219 N.V.B. Marsden, *Naturwissenschaften*, 58 (1971) 415.
220 N.V.B. Marsden, *Acta Univ. Upsaliensis (Dissertation)*, 123 (1972).
221 J.M. Goodson, V. Distefano and J.C. Smith, *J. Chromatogr.*, 54 (1971) 43.
222 G.A. Gilbert, *Disc. Faraday Soc.*, 20 (1955) 68..
223 G.A. Gilbert, *Proc. R. Soc. London Ser. A*, 250 (1959) 377.
224 D.J. Winzor and H.A. Scheraga, *Biochemistry*, 2 (1963) 1263.
225 D.J. Winzor and L.W. Nichol, *Biochim. Biophys. Acta*, 104 (1965) 1.
226 J.P. Johnston and A.G. Ogston, *Trans. Faraday Soc.*, 42 (1946) 789.
227 K. Hellsing, *J. Chromatogr.*, 36 (1968) 170.
228 A.G. Ogston, *Br. Med. Bull.*, 22 (1966) 105.
229 A.G. Ogston and C.F. Phelps, *Biochem. J.*, 78 (1961) 727.
230 P.A. Albertsson, *Partition of Cell Particles and Macromolecules*, 2nd Edn., Almqvist & Wicksell, Stockholm, 1971.
231 J. Brewer and L. Söderberg, in R. Epton (Editor), *Chromatography of Synthetic and Biological Polymers, Vol. 1, Column Packings, G.P.C., G.F. and Gradient Elution*, Ellis Horwood, Chichester, 1978, Chap. 18, p. 286.
232 V.P. Shanbag and G.G. Axelsson, *Eur. J. Biochem.*, 60 (1975) 17.
233 A.D. Buckingham, *Q. Rev. Chem. Soc.*, 13 (1959) 183.
234 F. London, *Z. Phys.*, 63 (1930) 245.
235 F. London, *Z. Phys. Chem. Abt. B*, 11 (1930) 222.
236 P. Debye, *Z. Phys.*, 21 (1920) 178.
237 P. Debye, *Z. Phys.*, 22 (1921) 302.
238 H. Umeyama and K. Morokuma, *J. Amer. Chem. Soc.*, 99 (1977) 1316.
239 J. Porath and K. Dahlgren Caldwell, *J. Chromatogr.*, 133 (1977) 180.
240 J.-M. Egly and J. Porath, *J. Chromatogr.*, 168 (1979) 35.
241 M. Maurin, *Bull. Soc. Chim. Fr.*, (1962) 1497.
242 C.A. Coulson and D. Eisenberg, *Proc. R. Soc. London Ser. A*, 291 (1966) 445.
243 L. Pauling, R.B. Corey and H.R. Branson, *Proc. Nat. Acad. Sci. U.S.*, 37 (1951) 205.
244 J.D. Watson and F.H.C. Crick, *Nature (London)*, 171 (1951) 205.
245 I.M. Klotz and J.S. Franzen, *J. Amer. Chem. Soc.*, 84 (1962) 3461.
246 W.P. Jencks, *Catalysis in Chemistry and Enzymology*, McGraw-Hill, New York, 1969, Chap. 6, p. 323.
247 K. Kiehs, C. Hansch and L. Moore, *Biochemistry*, 5 (1966) 2602.
248 C. Tanford, *Proc. Nat. Acad. Sci. U.S.*, 76 (1979) 4175.
249 A. Ben-Naim, *Hydrophobic Interactions*, Plenum, New York, 1980, Chap. 1.
250 F. Franks, in A.K. Covington and P. Jones (Editors), *Hydrogen-Bonded Solvent Systems*, Taylor & Francis, London, 1968, p. 31.
251 G.C. Pimentel and A.L. McClellan, *The Hydrogen Bond*, W.H. Freeman, San Francisco, CA, 1960, Chap. 8.
252 J.A.V. Butler, *Trans. Faraday Soc.*, 33 (1937) 229.
253 J. Horiuti, *Sci. Pap. Inst. Phys. Chem. Res. (Tokyo)*, 17 (1931) 126.
254 I.M. Barclay and J.A.V. Butler, *Trans. Faraday Soc.*, 34 (1938) 1445.
255 R.P. Bell, *Trans. Faraday Soc.*, 33 (1937) 496.
256 J.A.V. Butler, D.W. Thomson and W.H. Maclennan, *J. Chem. Soc.*, (1933) 674.
257 D.D. Eley, *Trans. Faraday Soc.*, 35 (1939) 1281.
258 D.D. Eley, *Trans. Faraday Soc.*, 35 (1939) 1421.
259 H.S. Frank and M.W. Evans, *J. Chem. Phys.*, 13 (1945) 507.
260 H.S. Frank and W.Y. Wen, *Disc. Faraday Soc.*, 24 (1957) 133.
261 A. Hvidt, *Biochim. Biophys. Acta*, 537 (1978) 153.
262 S. Cabani, G. Conti and L. Lepori, *Trans. Faraday Soc.*, 67 (1971) 1933.

263 S. Cabani, G. Conti and L. Lepori, *Trans. Faraday Soc.*, 67 (1971) 1943.

264 S. Cabani, G. Conti and L. Lepori, *J. Phys. Chem.*, 76 (1972) 1343.

265 R.B. Hermann, *J. Phys. Chem.*, 76 (1972) 2754.

266 R.B. Hermann, *J. Phys. Chem.*, 79 (1975) 163.

267 R.B. Hermann, *Proc. Nat. Acad. Sci. U.S.*, 74 (1977) 4144.

268 R. Smith and C. Tanford, *Proc. Nat. Acad. Sci. U.S.*, 70 (1973) 289.

269 J.A. Reynolds, D.B. Gilbert and C. Tanford, *Proc. Nat. Acad. Sci. U.S.*, 71 (1974) 2925.

270 G.L. Amidon, S.H. Yalkowsky, S.T. Anik and S.C. Valvani, *J. Phys. Chem.*, 79 (1975) 2239.

271 G.L. Amidon, S.H. Yalkowsky and S. Leung, *J. Pharm. Sci.*, 63 (1974) 1858.

272 K. Shinoda, *J. Phys. Chem.*, 81 (1977) 1300.

273 D.C. Poland and H.A. Scheraga, *J. Phys. Chem.*, 69 (1965) 2431.

274 P. Mukerjee, *Advan. Colloid Interface Sci.*, 1 (1967) 241.

275 G. Némethy and H.A. Scheraga, *J. Phys. Chem.*, 66 (1962) 1773.

276 G. Némethy and H.A. Scheraga, *J. Phys. Chem.*, 67 (1963) 2888.

277 H.S. Frank and F. Franks, *J. Chem. Phys.*, 48 (1968) 4748.

278 D.B. Wetlaufer, S.K. Malik, L. Stoller and R.L. Coffin, *J. Amer. Chem. Soc.*, 86 (1964) 508.

279 P.H. von Hippel and K.-Y. Wong, *J. Biol. Chem.*, 240 (1965) 3909.

280 A. Hamabata and P.H. von Hippel, *Biochemistry*, 12 (1973) 1264.

281 A. Hamabata, S. Chang and P.H. von Hippel, *Biochemistry*, 12 (1973) 1271.

282 A. Hamabata, S. Chang and P.H. von Hippel, *Biochemistry*, 12 (1973) 1278.

283 D.R. Robinson and W.D. Jencks, *J. Amer. Chem. Soc.*, 87 (1965) 2470.

284 P.H. von Hippel and A. Hamabata, *J. Mechanochem. Cell Motility*, 2 (1973) 127.

285 P.H. von Hippel and K.-Y. Wong, *Biochemistry*, 1 (1962) 664.

286 J. Bello, *Biochim. Biophys. Acta*, 109 (1965) 250.

287 J. Bello, H.C.A. Riese and J.R. Vinograd, *J. Phys. Chem.*, 60 (1965) 1299.

288 P.H. von Hippel and K.-Y. Wong, *J. Biol. Chem.*, 240 (1965) 3909.

289 K. Hamaguchi and E.P. Geiduschek, *J. Amer. Chem. Soc.*, 84 (1962) 1329.

290 D.R. Robinson and M.E. Grant, *J. Biol. Chem.*, 241 (1966) 4030.

291 I.M. Klotz, *Fed. Proc., Fed. Amer. Soc. Exp. Biol.*, 24 (1965) 524.

292 P.H. von Hippel and T. Schleich, in S. Timascheff and G. Fasman (Editors), *Biological Macromolecules*, Dekker, New York, Vol. 2, 1969, p. 417.

293 P.H. von Hippel and T. Schleich, *Acc. Chem. Res.*, 2 (1969) 257.

294 A. Ben-Naim and J. Wilf, *J. Chem. Phys.*, 70 (1979) 771.

295 D. Eisenberg and W. Kauzmann, *The Structure and Properties of Water*, Oxford Univ. Press, Oxford, 1969.

296 F. Franks (Editor), *Water. A Comprehensive Treatise*, Plenum, New York, Vols. 1–3, 1973, Vols. 4–5, 1975.

297 A.H. Clarke, F. Franks, M.D. Pedley and D.S. Reid, *J. Chem. Soc. Faraday Trans. 1*, 73 (1978) 290.

298 W. Drost-Hansen, in H.D. Brown (Editor), *Chemistry of the Cell Surface*, Part B, Academic Press, New York, 1971, Chap. 6.

299 A.H. Narten, M.D. Darford and H.A. Levy, *Disc. Faraday Soc.*, 43 (1967) 97.

300 M.V. Ramiah and D.A.I. Goring, *J. Polym. Sci. Part C*, 11 (1965) 27.

301 J. Clifford, in F. Franks (Editor), *Water. A Comprehensive Treatise, Vol. 5, Water in Disperse Systems*, Plenum, New York, 1975, Chap. 2, p. 75.

302 J. Clifford, J. Oakes and G.J. Tiddy, *Spec. Disc. Faraday Soc.*, 1 (1970) 175.

303 F. Franks and D.S. Reid, in F. Franks (Editor), *Water. A Comprehensive Treatise, Vol. 2, Water in Crystalline Hydrates; Aqueous Solutions of Simple Nonelectrolytes*, Plenum, New York, Vol. 2, 1975, p. 323.

304 D.E. Dormar and J.D. Roberts, *J. Amer. Chem. Soc.*, 93 (1970) 4463.

305 J.L. Neal and D.A.I. Goring, *Can. J. Chem.*, 48 (1970) 3745.

306 D. Thom, *Ph.D. Thesis*, University of Edinburgh, 1973.

307 W. Kauzmann, *Advan. Protein Chem.*, 14 (1959) 1.

308 R. Pottel and C. Rädle, *Ber. Bunsenges. Phys. Chem.*, 77 (1973) 521.

309 H.G. Hertz and W.-Y. Wen, *Z. Phys. Chem.*, 93 (1973) 313.

310 A. Geiger, A. Rahman and F.H. Stillinger, *J. Chem. Phys.*, 70 (1979) 263.

311 A. Rahman and F.H. Stillinger, *J. Chem. Phys.*, 55 (1971) 3336.

312 F.H. Stillinger and A. Rahman, *J. Chem. Phys.*, 60 (1974) 1545.

313 D.N. Glew, *J. Phys. Chem.*, 66 (1962) 605.

314 D.N. Glew, H.D. Mak and N.S. Rath, in A.K. Covington and P. Jones (Editors), *Hydrogen-Bonded Solvent Systems*, Taylor & Francis, London, 1968, p. 197.

315 H.J. Sage and S.J. Singer, *Biochemistry*, 1 (1962) 305.

316 E. Forslind, *NMR — Principles and Progress*, 4 (1971) 145.

317 I.M. Klotz, *Arch. Biochem. Biophys.*, 138 (1970) 704.

318 C. Chothia and J. Janin, *Nature (London)*, 256 (1975) 705.

319 C. Chothia, *Nature (London)*, 254 (1975) 304.

320 H.J. Hofstee, in N. Catsimpoolas (Editor), *Methods of Protein Separation*, Vol. 2, Plenum, New York, 1976, p. 245.

321 P. O'Carra, in B. Spencer (Editor), *FEBS Symposium in Industrial Aspects of Biochemistry*, North-Holland, Amsterdam, 1974, p. 321.

322 H.P. Jennissen, *Protides Biol. Fluids, Proc. Colloq.*, 23 (1976) 754.

323 S. Shaltiel and Z. Er-El, *Proc. Nat. Acad. Sci. U.S.*, 70 (1973) 778.

324 L. Sundberg and J. Porath, *J. Chromatogr.*, 90 (1974) 87.

325 S. Hjertén, J. Rosengren and S. Påhlman, *J. Chromatogr.*, 101 (1974) 281.

326 H. Determann and K. Lampert, *J. Chromatogr.*, 69 (1972) 123.

327 C.J.O.R. Morris, *Trends Biochem. Sci.*, 2 (1977) N16.

328 C.J.O.R. Morris, *Trends Biochem. Sci.*, 1 (1976) N207.

329 R. Lumry and S. Rajender, *Biopolymers*, 9 (1970) 1125.

330 N.V.B. Marsden, in A.K. Covington and P. Jones (Editors), *Hydrogen-Bonded Solvent Systems*, Taylor & Francis, London, 1968, p. 227.

331 N.V.B. Marsden, in E. Broda, A. Locker and H. Springer-Lederer (Editors), *Proc. 1st Eur. Biophys. Congr.*, Vol. 3, Med. Acad., Vienna, 1971, p. 453.

332 N.V.B. Marsden, *Naturwissenschaften*, 64 (1977) 148.

333 R.W. Gurney, *Ionic Processes in Solution*, McGraw-Hill, New York, 1953.

334 Å.C. Haglund and N.V.B. Marsden, in F. Franks (Editor), *Biophysics of Water*, Wiley, New York, 1982.

335 S.P. Moulik and D.P. Khan, *Carbohydr. Res.*, 36 (1974) 147.

336 O. Wiklund, *Zucker*, 8 (1955) 6.

337 J.A. Rendleman, *J. Org. Chem.*, 31 (1966) 1839.

338 N. Roy and A.K. Mitra, *Carbohydr. Res.*, 24 (1972) 180.

339 S.P. Moulik and A.K. Mitra, *Carbohydr. Res.*, 29 (1973) 509.

340 J. Traube, *Justus Liebigs Ann. Chem.*, 265 (1891) 27.

341 J.A. Thoma and L. Stewart, in R.L. Whistler and E.F. Paschall (Editors), *Starch Chemistry and Technology*, Vol. 1, Academic Press, New York, 1965, p. 209.

342 M.L. Bender and M. Komiyama, in E.E. von Tamelen (Editor), *Bioorganic Chemistry*, Academic Press, New York, 1977, Chap. 2, p. 25.

343 M.L. Bender and K. Komiyama, *Cyclodextrin Chemistry, Reactivity and Structure Concepts in Organic Chemistry*, Vol. 6, Springer, Berlin, 1978.

344 H. Pringsheim, *Chemistry of the Saccharides*, McGraw-Hill, New York, 1932, Chap. 4, p. 180.

345 M. Samec, *Die neuere Entwicklung der Kolloidchemie der Stärke*, Steinkopf, Dresden, 1941, p. 239.

346 A. Hybl, R.E. Rundle and D.E. Williams, *J. Amer. Chem. Soc.*, 87 (1965) 2779.

347 V.S.R. Rao and J.F. Foster, *J. Phys. Chem.*, 67 (1963) 951.

348 C.A. Glass, *Can. J. Chem.*, 43 (1965) 2652.

349 B. Casa, M. Reggiani, C.G. Gallo and A. Vigevani, *Tetrahedron*, 24 (1968) 803.

350 R.J. Bergeron, *J. Chem. Educ.*, 54 (1977) 204.

351 K. Freudenberg, E. Schaaf, G. Dumpert and T. Ploetz, *Naturwissenschaften*, 27 (1939) 850.

352 K. Freudenberg, *J. Polym. Sci.*, 23 (1957) 791.

353 F. Cramer and H. Hettler, *Naturwissenschaften*, 54 (1967) 625.

354 D.V. Demarco and A.L. Thakkar, *J. Chem. Soc. Chem. Commun.*, (1970) 2.

355 C. van Hooidonk and J.C.A.E. Breebaart-Hansen, *Rec. Trav. Chim. Pays Bas*, 91 (1972) 958.

356 K. Harata, *Bull. Chem. Soc. Jap.*, 49 (1976) 2066.

357 F. Cramer, *Einschlussverbindung*, Springer, Berlin, 1954, p. 49.

358 F. Cramer and F.M. Hengelein, *Chem. Ber.*, 90 (1957) 2570.

359 W.J. James, D. French and R.E. Rundle, *Acta Crystallogr. Sect. B*, 12 (1959) 385.

360 H. Schlenk and D.M. Sand, *J. Amer. Chem. Soc.*, 83 (1961) 2313.

361 J.L. Hoffman, *Anal. Biochem.*, 33 (1970) 209.

362 J.L. Hoffman and R.M. Bock, *Biochemistry*, 9 (1970) 3542.

363 C. Formoso, *Biochem. Biophys. Res. Commun.*, 50 (1973) 999.

364 C. Formoso, *Biopolymers*, 13 (1974) 909.

365 R.J. Bergeron and M.P. Meeley, *Bioorg. Chem.*, 5 (1976) 197.

366 H. Schlenk, D.M. Sand and J.A. Tillotson, *J. Amer. Chem. Soc.*, 77 (1955) 3587.

367 B. Siegel and R. Breslow, *J. Amer. Chem. Soc.*, 97 (1975) 6869.

368 W. Saenger, M. Noltmeyer, P.C. Manor, B. Hingerty, and B. Klar, *Bioorg. Chem.*, 5 (1976) 187.

369 O.R. Quayle, *Chem. Rev.*, 53 (1953) 439.

370 P.C. Manor and W. Saenger, *J. Amer. Chem. Soc.*, 96 (1974) 3630.

371 D.A. Rees, *J. Chem. Soc. B*, (1970) 877.

372 R.J. Bergeron, D.M. Pillor, G. Gibeily and W.P. Roberts, *Bioorg. Chem.*, 7 (1978) 263.

373 I. Tabushi, Y. Kiyosuke, T. Sugimoto and K. Yamamura, *J. Amer. Chem. Soc.*, 100 (1978) 916.

374 G. Némethy and H.A. Scheraga, *J. Chem. Phys.*, 36 (1962) 3401.

375 Y. Matsui and K. Mochida, *Bull. Chem. Soc. Jap.*, 52 (1979) 2808.

376 H.A. Scheraga, *Ann. N.Y. Acad. Sci.*, 125 (1965) 253.

377 J. Emert and R. Breslow, *J. Amer. Chem. Soc.*, 97 (1975) 670.

378 I. Tabushi, K. Shimokawa, N. Shimuzu, H.S. Skirakata and K. Fujita, *J. Amer. Chem. Soc.*, 98 (1976) 7855.

379 J. Solms and R.H. Egli, *Helv. Chim. Acta*, 48 (1965) 1225.

380 D. French, A.O. Pulley, J.A. Elfenberger, M.A. Rougvir and M. Abdullah, *Arch. Biochem. Biophys.*, 111 (1965) 153.

381 T.S. Lakshmi and P.K. Nandi, *J. Chromatogr.*, 116 (1976) 177.

382 M. Janado, Y. Yano, H. Nakamori and T. Nishida, *J. Chromatogr.*, 193 (1980) 345.

383 M. Janado, K. Shimada and T. Nishida, *J. Biochem.*, 79 (1976) 513.

384 M. Janado, K. Shimada, N. Horie and T. Nishida, *J. Biochem.*, 80 (1976) 69.

385 M. Janado, R. Nakayama, Y. Yano and H. Nakamori, *J. Biochem.*, 86 (1979) 795.

386 C.J. Pederson, *J. Amer. Chem. Soc.*, 89 (1967) 2495.

387 G.W. Gokel and H.D. Durst, *Synthesis*, (1976) 168.

388 D.J. Cram, *Pure Appl. Chem.*, 43 (1976) 327.

389 D.G. Parsons, *J. Chem. Soc. Perkin I*, (1978) 451.

390 I.R. Hanson, D.G. Parsons and M.R. Truter, *J. Chem. Soc. Chem. Commun.*, (1979) 486.

391 Y. Moroi, E. Pramauvo, M. Grätzel, E. Pelizetti and P. Tundo, *J. Colloid Interface Sci.*, 69 (1979) 341.

392 F. Weber and F. Vögtle, *Tetrahedron Lett.*, (1975) 2415.

393 H. Sieger and F. Vögtle, *Tetrahedron Lett.*, (1978) 2709.

394 G. Weber, W. Saenger, F. Vögtle and H. Sieger, *Angew. Chem. Int. Ed. Engl.*, 18 (1979) 226.

395 G. Weber and W. Saenger, *Angew. Chem. Int. Ed. Engl.*, 18 (1979) 227.

396 W. Rasshofer and F. Vögtle, *Tetrahedron Lett.*, (1978) 309.

397 R. Axén, J. Porath and S. Ernbach, *Nature (London)*, 214 (1967) 1302.

398 K. Brocklehurst, J. Carlsson and M.P. Kierstan, *Biochem. J.*, 133 (1973) 573.

399 P. Cuatrecasas and I. Parikh, *Biochemistry*, 11 (1972) 2291.

400 G. Kay and M. Lilly, *Biochim. Biophys. Acta*, 198 (1970) 276.

401 T. Finlay, V. Troll, M. Levy, A. Johnson and L. Hodgins, *Anal. Biochem.*, 87 (1978) 77.

402 G.S. Bethell, J.S. Ayers, W.S. Hancock and M.T.W. Hearn, *J. Biol. Chem.*, 254 (1979) 2572.

403 M. Jagub and P. Guire, *J. Biomed. Mater. Res.*, 8 (1974) 291.

404 K. Nilsson and K. Mosbach, *Eur. J. Biochem.*, 112 (1980) 397.

405 O. Larm and E. Scholander, *Carbohydr. Res.*, 58 (1972) 249.

406 M. Einarsson, B. Forsberg, O. Larm, M.E. Riquelme and E. Scholander, *J. Chromatogr.*, 215 (1981) 45.
407 C.R. Lowe and P.D.G. Dean, *Affinity Chromatography*, Wiley, New York, 1974.
408 W. Jacoby and M. Wilchek (Editors), *Methods in Enzymology, Vol. 34, Affinity Techniques, Enzyme Purification*, Part B, Academic Press, New York, 1974.
409 J. Porath and T. Kristianson, in H. Neurath and R. Hill (Editors), *The Proteins*, 3rd edn., Vol. 1, Academic Press, New York, 1975.
410 J. Turkova, *Affinity Chromatography*, Elsevier, Amsterdam, 1978.
411 G. Wulff and W. Vesper, *J. Chromatogr.*, 167 (1978) 171.
412 E.P. Kyba, M.G. Siegel, L.R. Sousa, G.D.Y. Sogah and D.J. Cram, *J. Amer. Chem. Soc.*, 95 (1973) 2691.

Chapter 9

Electrophoresis

F.M. EVERAERTS, F.E.P. MIKKERS, Th.P.E.M. VERHEGGEN and J. VACÍK

CONTENTS

9.1. THE PHYSICAL BASIS OF ELECTROPHORESIS

Electrophoretic separation processes are generally based on the differential migration of electrically charged particles in an electric field. An electrophoretic system consists of:

(a) a liquid phase (the basic electrolyte system, including the compounds to be separated), in which separation takes place;

(b) a solid phase, which is in contact with the liquid phase (e.g., wall of the separation column, stabilizing porous medium);

(c) a gaseous phase, which is in equilibrium with the liquid phase (in methods in which a porous carrier of the liquid phase is placed in a so-called wet chamber, or the gaseous phase resulting from electrode reactions).

The term separation medium will be applied to electrophoretic systems that do not yet contain substances to be separated. Generally the separation medium should be in thermodynamic equilibrium prior to the experiment. This condition is fulfilled when all components have the same chemical potential at all sites in the system, the same electrical potential, or the same temperature; mechanical forces also have to be equilibrated. These conditions are first changed by adding the sample to a certain location in the separation medium. The equilibrium is further upset by the application of an electric field to the system and the subsequent flow of electric current. During the gradual separation of individual components of the sample, this imbalance further increases. Thus, simultaneous with the separation induced by the external force (electric field), transport phenomena that tend to destroy emerging concentration, temperature, and other gradients also arise.

In electrophoretic separations, these spontaneous processes (disturbances) usually increase with time. Time is generally an important factor, and the proper choice of the time interval may optimize the result of a separation. In some electrophoretic methods a steady state is established, where no further changes occur as electrophoresis progresses. The result of such a separation is no longer time-dependent after a steady state is attained. The addition of a sample at a certain location in the separation medium also usually alters the equilibrium of the medium. Different values of the chemical potential at different locations in the system are then responsible for the diffusion of migrants. However, the main cause of imbalance is the electric field applied to the electrophoretic system, which causes the migration of charged particles in the solution. As the electric current passes across a phase boundary (e.g., the surface of electrodes), electrode reactions (i.e. electrolysis) proceed. In addition to the migration of charged particles by diffusion, convection also occurs, i.e., transport of components caused by mechanical forces and heat conduction among particles.

9.1.1. Transport processes in solutions of electrolytes

The transport of each component of a solution can be described by using the basic equation of transport phenomena, i.e., the continuity equation. For the ith component with charge z

$$\frac{\delta c_{i,z}}{\delta t} = -\operatorname{div} \vec{J}_{i,z} \tag{9.1}$$

where $\vec{J}_{i,z}$ is the substance flow of the ith component with charge z, which is determined by the product $c_{i,z} \cdot \vec{v}$ ($\vec{v}$ is the vector of the rate of movement of a component at a given location in the solution). The substance flow can also be represented by

$$\vec{J}_{i,z} = \left(\vec{J}_{i,z}\right)_{\text{diff}} + \left(\vec{J}_{i,z}\right)_{\text{mig}} + \left(\vec{J}_{i,z}\right)_{\text{conv}} + \left(\vec{J}_{i,z}\right)_{\text{therm}} \tag{9.2}$$

where the terms on the right-hand side of the equation stand for diffusion, migration, convection, and thermal components of the substance flow.

If $\vec{J}$ is a vector

$$\operatorname{div} \vec{J} = \frac{\partial J_x}{\partial x} + \frac{\partial J_y}{\partial y} + \frac{\partial J_z}{\partial z} \tag{9.3}$$

The divergence of the vector $\vec{J}$ ($\operatorname{div} \vec{J}$) is a scalar independent of the system axes. It indicates the flow of the vector field through unit volume. The divergence of the substance flow expresses a decrease in the substance in unit volume per unit time.

9.1.1.1. Diffusion

The diffusion term of the substance flow $(\vec{J}_{i,z})_{\text{diff}}$ must be considered if the chemical potential of the ith component with charge z is different at different locations in the solution. The diffusion term follows Fick's law

$$\left(\vec{J}_{i,z}\right)_{\text{diff}} = -c_{i,z} \cdot D_{i,z} \cdot (RT)^{-1} \cdot \operatorname{grad} \mu_{i,z} \tag{9.4}$$

where $D_{i,z}$ is the diffusion coefficient of the ith component with charge z and $\mu_{i,z}$ is its chemical potential. This expression is valid under the assumption that in the scalar function

$$\operatorname{grad} \mu = \frac{\partial \mu}{\partial x} \cdot i + \frac{\partial \mu}{\partial y} \cdot j + \frac{\partial \mu}{\partial z} \cdot k \tag{9.5}$$

where i, j, and k are unit vectors having directions of positive axes of coordinates and magnitude of 1. The gradient of the scalar function ($\operatorname{grad} \mu$) is a vector vertical at each point of the region with respect to the surface area of the scalar field. It has a direction of the highest rate of increase and its coordinates are partial derivatives according to x, y, and z. It is independent of the system of coordinates.

In dilute solutions the chemical potential can be expressed as

$$\mu_{i,z} = \mu_{i,z}^0 + RT \ln c_{i,z} \tag{9.6}$$

where $\mu_{i,z}^0$ is the standard chemical potential. Combination of eqn. 9.6 with eqn. 9.4 gives

$$\left(\vec{J}_{i,z}\right)_{\text{diff}} = -D_{i,z} \cdot \operatorname{grad} c_{i,z} \tag{9.7}$$

References on p. A367

The diffusion coefficient is directly proportional to temperature and inversely related to the viscosity, η, of the solution. For a spherical particle of radius $r_{i,z}$

$$D_{i,z} = RT \cdot (6 \pi N_A \eta r_{i,z})^{-1} \tag{9.8}$$

where N_A is Avogadro's constant and $r_{i,z}$ is the hydrodynamic radius of the particle (compared with the radius of ions, the latter includes the hydration envelope).

9.1.1.2. Migration

The migration term of the substance flow, $(\vec{J}_{i,z})_{\text{mig}}$, characterizes the movement induced by an external force, the intensity of the electric field, $E = -\text{grad } \phi$ (where ϕ is the electric potential). When the electric field acts on particles of the ith species with charge z, the particles move with a velocity proportional to $\vec{E}$. Then,

$$(\vec{v}_{i,z})_{\text{mig}} = \text{sgn } z \cdot U_{i,z} \cdot \vec{E} \tag{9.9}$$

The terms sgn z (which is defined in such a way that sgn $z = 1$ for $z > 0$, sgn $z = -1$ for $z < 0$, and sgn $z = 0$ for $z = 0$) reflects the fact that a positively charged particle moves in the direction of the vector $\vec{E}$ and a negatively charged particle in the opposite direction. $U_{i,z}$ is the mobility.

The physical significance of the mobility, $U_{i,z}$, follows from eqn. 9.9, as it is the velocity of a charged particle of the component i with charge z in the electric field of unit potential gradient in a given electrolyte system. The mobility and diffusion coefficients are related by

$$U_{i,z} = |z| \cdot D_{i,z} \cdot F \cdot (RT)^{-1} \tag{9.10}$$

where F is the Faraday constant. Combining eqns. 9.10 and 9.8 it follows that the mobility of a spherical particle with a radius $r_{i,z}$ is given by

$$U_{i,z} = |z| \cdot e \cdot (6 \pi \eta r_{i,z})^{-1} \tag{9.11}$$

For large (colloidal) particles, the electrokinetic potential (ζ) is defined as

$$\zeta = \sigma \cdot \delta \cdot \epsilon^{-1} \tag{9.12}$$

When the mobility of a colloidal particle is considered, its mobility, U_{col}, is

$$U_{\text{col}} = \epsilon \cdot \zeta \cdot (6 \pi \eta)^{-1} \tag{9.13}$$

If the colloidal particle is not spherical, a numerical factor is required in the denominator, which varies between 4 and 8 depending on the shape of the particle. The dependence of the mobility on the reciprocal of the coefficient of viscosity can be deduced from eqns. 9.11 and 9.13. This coefficient depends on temperature according to the Arrhenius equation $\eta^{-1} = B_1 \cdot \exp(-B_2 \cdot T^{-1})$, where B_1 and B_2 are constants. Mobilities depend on temperature in a similar way. However, square-root series are usually used for the temperature dependence of mobilities:

$$U_\tau = U_{18} \left[1 + k_1 (\tau - 18) + k_2 (\tau - 18)^2 \right] \tag{9.14}$$

where τ is temperature (°C) and k_1 and k_2 are constants for various ions, which are given in tables [1–6]. The mobility, $U_{i,z}$, of each component (also called the actual mobility) is not a constant, characteristic of a given component, but depends on the concentration of all kinds of ions present in the solution.

In order to explain the effect of intra-ionic forces on the mobility of a migrant, the assumption of an ionic atmosphere, decreasing its movement in the electric field, was introduced. The effect of intra-ionic forces decreases on dilution of the solution and disappears as the concentration of all dissolved components approaches zero. In such solutions, the distances between ions are so large that intra-ionic forces are negligible. The mobility in such solutions, the absolute or limiting mobility, $(U_{i,z})^0$, is independent of concentration and is a characteristic constant of a given migrant.

The best-known theory relating mobility with concentration is that of Debye, Hückel and Onsager. According to this theory

$$U_{i,z} = (U_{i,z})^0 - \left[B_3 (U_{i,z})^0 - B_4 \right] (I_c)^{1/2} \cdot \left[1 + r_{i,z} B_5 (I_c)^{1/2} \right]^{-1} \tag{9.15}$$

where B_3, B_4, and B_5 are terms that can be determined by calculation. Eqn. 9.15 holds for dilute solutions of univalent symmetrical electrolytes. A unified theory characterizing the effect of intra-ionic forces even in more concentrated mixtures of polyvalent nonsymmetrical strong electrolytes, formulated by Onsager and Fuoss [7], leads to more complex relations.

The mobilities, $U_{i,z}$ and $(U_{i,z})^0$, defined so far, relate only to individual components. For a substance composed of several components, a further characteristic must be introduced, the effective mobility of a substance, $(U_i)_{\text{eff}}$ [8]. The following conditions apply to this term:

(a) the substance is composed of several components that are in equilibrium,

(b) the components exhibit different actual mobilities,

(c) individual components cannot be separated electrophoretically and the substance moves as a whole in the electric field,

(d) individual components of the substance contribute to its resulting velocity. The contribution of each component is proportional to its relative concentration in the substance.

Thus, $(U_i)_{\text{eff}}$ is defined by

$$(U_i)_{\text{eff}} = \sum_z y_{i,z} \cdot U_{i,z} \tag{9.16}$$

where the molar fraction $y_{i,z}$ is expressed in terms of respective dissociation constants and the pH of the solution by

$$y_{i,z} = \frac{c_{i,z}}{c_i} = \frac{\left\{ \dfrac{\prod\limits_{l=B_6}^{B_7} K_{i,l}}{C_{H_3O^+}^{|z|}} \right\}^{-\text{sgn}\,z}}{1 + \sum\limits_{k=B_8}^{B_9} \left\{ \dfrac{\prod\limits_{l=B_{10}}^{B_{11}} K_{i,l}}{C_{H_3O^+}^{|z|}} \right\}^{-\text{sgn}\,z}} \tag{9.17}^\star$$

* Footnote on p. A336.

For $(U_i)_{eff}$ the following equation is obtained

$$(U_i)_{eff} = \frac{\sum_z U_{i,z} \left\{ \dfrac{\prod K_{i,l}}{c_{H_3O^+}^{|z|}} \right\}^{-sgn\,z}}{1 + \sum \left\{ \dfrac{\prod K_{i,l}}{c_{H_3O^+}^{|z|}} \right\}^{-sgn\,z}} \qquad (9.18)$$

To characterize the movement of substances in a porous medium, the macroscopic mobility of the substance, $(U_i)_{macro}$, and the relative mobility, $(U_i)_{rel}$, can be introduced (ref. 9, Chap. 3).

9.1.1.3. Conductivity of electrolytes

In addition to the mobility, $U_{i,z}$, ionic conductivities $\lambda_{i,z}$, defined by

$$\lambda_{i,z} = |z| \cdot F \cdot U_{i,z} \qquad (9.19)$$

can be used to characterize individual ions. Ionic conductivities are used particularly for the characterization of the conductivity of the electrolyte as a whole. By this means it is possible to define the molar conductivity of the electrolyte, Λ, and the specific conductivity, κ, based on eqns. 9.20 and 9.21:

$$\Lambda = \sum_i \sum_z |z| \cdot F \cdot U_{i,z} = \sum_i \sum_z \lambda_{i,z} \qquad (9.20)$$

and

$$\kappa = \sum_i \sum_z c_{i,z} \cdot |z| \cdot F \cdot U_{i,z} = \sum_i \sum_z c_{i,z} \cdot \lambda_{i,z} \qquad (9.21)$$

The units of molar and specific conductivity are $\Lambda = S \cdot m^2 \cdot mole^{-1}$ and $\kappa = S \cdot m^{-1}$; for practical purposes they are tabulated [1–6] in $S \cdot cm^2 \cdot mole^{-1}$ and $S \cdot cm^{-1}$, respectively.

9.1.1.4. Convection

The convection of the substance flow characterizes the movement of the solution at a given location:

$$(\vec{J}_{i,z})_{conv} = C_{i,z} \cdot \vec{v}_{conv} \qquad (9.22)$$

In electrophoretic systems, fluxes induced by pressure differences at both ends of the separation column, by capillary forces in the porous medium or by the electro-

---

* For $z < 0$ (when the molar fraction of anions in a weak acid is calculated), the limits $B_6 = z$, $B_7 = -1$, $B_8 = z_{min}$, $B_9 = -1$, $B_{10} = k$, and $B_{11} = -1$ are applicable; k is determined by the component present; z_{min} is the highest number of elementary charges of anions in the ith compound. This equation holds also for $z > 0$. The following limits are then applicable: $B_6 = 0$, $B_7 = z - 1$, $B_8 = 1$, $B_9 = z_{max}$, $B_{10} = 0$, $B_{11} = k - 1$; z_{max} is the highest number of positive elementary charges of cations in the ith substance.

List of symbols on p. A365

osmotic flux are involved. The hydrodynamic flow induced by pressure differences at the ends of the cylindrical column has a constant velocity along the whole column and can be calcuated from Poiseuille's equation. However, owing to internal resistance, a velocity gradient originates in the tube. The distribution of velocities is different in the case that the hydrodynamic flow is brought about by capillary forces in the stabilizing porous medium.

9.1.1.5. Electroosmotic flow

The electroosmotic flow originates when an electric field is applied to the system. Under the influence of the field the spatial charge of the diffusive part of the electric double layer moves to the oppositely charged electrode, and a one-sided flow of ions originates near the wall. The whole solution then moves together with these ions. Near the boundary (wall of the separation column), a velocity gradient of the liquid originates. The flow velocity is zero at the boundary, increases inside the solution and reaches a maximum at a certain, very small distance (where $\zeta = 0$). This velocity, $\vec{v}_{os}$, can be expressed as

$$\vec{v}_{os} = \vec{E} \cdot \epsilon \cdot \eta^{-1} \cdot \zeta \tag{9.23}$$

Also, the remainder of the liquid in the column moves with this velocity. In this way the electroosmotic flow differs from the hydrodynamic flow.

A different distribution occurs when the electrode spaces are closed. The one-sided flux of ions along the wall of the column then carries along a portion of the attached solution and moves, together with it, to the closed end of the column, where it turns around and flows in the opposite direction through the middle of the column.

9.1.1.6. Heat conduction and heat flow

It is a characteristic feature of all electromigration separation methods that the Joule heat originates during the passage of an electric current through the solution. The system is not isothermal; the distribution of the temperature, T, is a function of spatial coordinates and time and can be described by the continuity equation:

$$c_s \cdot \rho_s \cdot \frac{\partial T}{\partial t} = -\operatorname{div} \vec{\mathfrak{I}} + q^* \tag{9.24}$$

$\vec{\mathfrak{I}}$ is the heat flow determined by the equation $\vec{\mathfrak{I}} = k_s \cdot \operatorname{grad} T + \vec{v} \cdot T \cdot c_s \cdot \rho_s$, where k_s, c_s, and ρ_s are the heat conduction, specific heat capacity, and density of the solution, respectively, and $\vec{v}$ is the velocity of the liquid flow at a given location; q^* is generally the change of heat density in the solution. In electrophoretic systems this change is determined by both the generated Joule heat, q_j^*, and the dissipation of heat over the surface of the separation column, q_k^*; $q^* = q_j^* - q_k^*$. The Joule heat, q_j, generated when a current I passes through a resistance R for time t is given by

$$q_j = RI^2 t \tag{9.25}$$

When the resistance is expressed by means of specific conductivity, the equation

$q_j = LI^2t \cdot (\kappa S)^{-1}$ is obtained. For the temperature balance the heat flow generated by unit volume, q_j^*, is required:

$$q_j^* = q_j \cdot (t \cdot S \cdot L)^{-1} = I^2 \cdot (\kappa S^2)^{-1} \qquad (9.26)$$

Heat is usually dissipated from the liquid phase through the wall of the separation column. The amount of heat, q_k, passing during time t through an area P and thickness d is proportional to the heat conductivity, k_t, of the solid phase and to the difference between the temperature $(T - T_0)$ of the two surfaces of the plate; $q_k = k_t \cdot P \cdot t(T - T_0)d^{-1}$. For the heat flow, q_k^*, coming from the unit volume we obtain

$$q_k^* = q_k \cdot (t \cdot S \cdot L)^{-1} = k_t \cdot (T - T_0) \cdot (P^* \cdot d)^{-1} \qquad (9.27)$$

P^* is the fraction of the volume and surface area of the liquid phase. Thus, for a cylindrical separation column with an inner diameter r_0 and length L, the following approximate equation is obtained (when the inner and outer surface areas of the column are set identical):

$$P^* = L \cdot S \cdot (P)^{-1} = \pi r_0^2 L \cdot (2\pi r_0 L)^{-1} = 0.5 r_0$$

A temperature gradient is responsible for the origination of thermal flow. In the random thermal movement the flow towards a lower temperature prevails over the opposite flow, so that particles are transferred to sites of lower temperature. The velocity of the thermal flow is expressed by

$$(\vec{v}_{i,z})_{\text{therm}} = -D_{i,z}^* \, \text{grad} \, T \qquad (9.28)$$

where $D_{i,z}^*$ is the thermal diffusion coefficient of the i, zth component, so that for the thermal term of the substance flow eqn. 9.29 is obtained.

$$(\vec{J}_{i,z})_{\text{therm}} = -c_{i,z} \cdot D_{i,z}^* \cdot \text{grad} \, T \qquad (9.29)$$

9.1.2. Transport phenomena in stabilizing media

The undesirable effects of certain transport processes can be limited, e.g., by increasing the viscosity of the basic electrolytic system, by forming a density gradient in the electrolyte, by using some dynamic methods, or by performing the separation in a suitable stabilizing medium (carrier). Most gels, compact porous carriers with an inner capillary microstructure, and columns with suitable loose contents are examples of stabilizing media.

9.1.2.1. Spatial effects of the inner structure of capillary systems

The microstructure of the capillary systems is usually highly complex, the pores being irregular with different curvatures. A number of schemes have been formulated for the theoretical expression. According to the simplest assumption [10], pores in a solid carrier are curved and therefore the path followed by molecules

List of symbols on p. A365

during the migration is in fact longer than that which is measured macroscopically. The correction factor known as the tortuosity factory [10], γ, is defined by the ratio of length of the porous medium, L, and the real length of the pores, l:

$$\gamma = L \cdot l^{-1} \tag{9.30}$$

The factor γ can be determined experimentally, e.g., on the basis of conductivity measurements. It is also used to correct the free diameter of capillaries in a porous medium, s, with the free diameter of the porous medium, S, and with the total cross-section of the porous medium, S_t:

$$s = \gamma S = \gamma \bar{\epsilon} S_t$$

where $\bar{\epsilon}$ is the porosity of the medium, defined by $S = \bar{\epsilon} S_t$. Correction factors defined in a different way are described in the literature [11–15], viz., $\gamma' = (l \cdot L^{-1})^2$; $\gamma'' = (l \cdot L^{-1})^2 - 1$ or $\gamma''' = (l \cdot L^{-1})^2 \cdot \bar{\epsilon}^{-1}$.

Correction by means of the tortuosity factor is applicable only when the diameter of all capillaries is larger than the diameter of any of the moving particles. When the hydrodynamic diameters of migrating particles are comparable with those of the pores, or when in the porous medium the pores are distributed according to their radii, more complex schemes must be applied. These schemes are based on the fact that a migrating particle can travel only through pores with a radius greater than its own radius. Porous materials with particles of different sizes influence the path traveled by the moving particles to different extents.

9.1.2.2. Distribution function and the constant R_E

During their transport across a porous medium, a distribution of separated substances between the solid (stationary) and liquid phases occurs. As a result, the velocity of movement of individual substances in the porous medium decreases in comparison with that in the electrolytic system. This deceleration can be characterized by R_E, defined as the fraction of the velocity of migration of the ith substance in the porous medium ($\bar{v}_{c_i}$) relative to the velocity of migration (v_i)$_{mig}$ of the same substance in the electrolytic system. The velocity (v_i)$_{mig}$ can be expressed by the equation

$$(\vec{v}_i)_{mig} = \operatorname{sgn} z \cdot (U_i)_{eff} \cdot \vec{E} \tag{9.31}$$

on the basis of eqns. 9.9 and 9.16. The equation for ($\vec{v}_{c_i}$), derived in ref. 9, is given by

$$(\vec{v}_{c_i}) = \frac{\operatorname{sgn} z \cdot (U_i)_{eff} \cdot \vec{E}}{1 + \dfrac{\partial \Gamma_i^*}{\partial c_i}} \tag{9.32}$$

where Γ_i^* is the distribution function indicating the amount of the ith substance in a certain amount of the stationary phase, which is in equilibrium with the ith substance in the solution. The amount of the stationary phase is given in mass, surface area, or volume units. Γ_i^* in eqn. 9.32 is related to the amount of the solid phase with a unit volume of free pores. The term "distribution coefficient" is used for the fraction $\Gamma_i^* \cdot c_i^{-1}$.

By using eqns. 9.31 and 9.33, $(R_E)_i$ can be calculated, analogous to R_F in chromatographic separation methods.

$$(R_E)_i = (\vec{v}_{c_i}) \cdot (\vec{v}_i)_{\text{mig}}^{-1} = \left(1 + \frac{\delta \Gamma_i^*}{\delta c_i}\right)^{-1} \tag{9.33}$$

The distribution function Γ_i^* can be determined on the basis of experimental electrophoretic results. By substituting $\vec{E} = -U \cdot \gamma \cdot L^{-1}$ and $x = X \gamma^{-1}$ (where U is the total voltage applied, L the length of the porous medium, γ the tortuosity factor, x the real and X the macroscopically measured distance to which the ith compound traveled during time t) in eqn. 9.32 we obtain the equation

$$(R_E)_i = \left(1 + \frac{\partial \Gamma_i^*}{\partial c_i}\right)^{-1} = -X \cdot L\left[\text{sgn } z \cdot (U_i)_{\text{eff}} \cdot U \cdot \gamma^2 \cdot t\right]^{-1} \tag{9.34}$$

It appears that for a porous medium containing pores with a diameter larger than that of any of the separated particles the distribution function determined in this way is identical with the adsorption isotherm obtained when static methods are used. For a porous medium with pores of various diameters, comparable with the size of the separated particles, the distribution function includes not only the effect of adsorption, but also the effect of the inner structure of the porous medium, determined by the elongation (or reduction) of the path of the ith compound through which a particle of the electrolytic system has to pass.

9.1.2.3. Electroosmosis in capillary systems

When a capillary system serves as the stabilizing medium, the contact area between the solid and liquid phases is large and electroosmosis takes place to a considerable extent. Eqn. 9.23 holds for the linear velocity of the osmotic flow through a column. When a porous system of length L contains a total of ν parallel capillaries with a cross-section of $S \cdot \nu^{-1}$, the total voltage, U, at the end of the capillaries may serve to express the intensity of the electric field according to $\vec{E} = -U \cdot L^{-1}$. For the linear velocity of flow through each capillary, the equation $\vec{v}_{os} = -\epsilon \cdot \zeta \cdot U \cdot (\eta L)^{-1}$ is then obtained. However, the volume velocity, $\vec{w}_{os}$, of the electroosmotic flow through all ν capillaries (i.e., the amount of solution transferred by electroosmosis per unit time) is often more interesting. Using Ohm's law in the form $U = R \cdot I = L \cdot I(\kappa S)^{-1}$, we have

$$\vec{w}_{os} = \vec{v}_{os} \cdot S = -\epsilon \zeta S U \cdot (\eta L)^{-1} = -\epsilon \zeta I \cdot (\eta \kappa)^{-1} \tag{9.35}$$

For curved capillaries (with length $l = L \cdot \gamma^{-1}$ and cross-section $s \cdot \nu^{-1} = = \gamma \cdot \bar{\epsilon} \cdot S_t \cdot \nu^{-1}$), the equation becomes

$$\vec{w}_{os} = -\epsilon \zeta \bar{\epsilon} S_t \gamma^2 U \cdot (\eta L)^{-1} = -\epsilon \zeta I \cdot (\eta \kappa)^{-1} \tag{9.36}$$

Obviously, the expression in which current and specific conductivity are used is most advantageous, as no parameters of the inner structure of the porous medium are involved.

9.1.2.4. Evaporation of the electrolyte and sucking flows

Certain experimental arrangements use real capillary carriers, e.g., paper, thin layers or foils, placed in the so-called wet chamber for stabilization. This is a space in which the gaseous phase is saturated with water vapor prior to the experiment. During separation, the electrolyte is heated by the generated Joule heat, and a temperature gradient, originating in the chamber, leads to the evaporation of water from the carrier and its condensation on the walls and cover of the chamber. When the evaporation is not too intensive, it occurs uniformly over the whole surface of the carrier, as was confirmed experimentally. The amount of water, m^*, evaporated from unit area of the carrier per unit time is proportional to the Joule heat: $m^* = kq_j$ (where k is a constant). Together with the evaporation of water from the surface of the carrier, water is removed from both electrode spaces due to capillary forces, and the electrolyte flows towards the middle of the carrier. The velocity of this flow, $\vec{v}_{suck}$, in a carrier of length L, thickness d and porosity $\bar{\epsilon}$, is determined by the equation

$$\vec{v}_{suck} = -m^*(X - 0.5L) \cdot (\rho_r d\bar{\epsilon})^{-1} \tag{9.37}$$

for $0 \leqslant X \leqslant L$, in which ρ_r is the solution density and X a positional coordinate. When the evaporation is intense (high production of Joule heat), the liquid cannot be removed sufficiently by capillary forces, and a moisture gradient is formed in the carrier. The carrier is dried most completely in the middle (for $X = 0.5L$). In an extreme case, even thermal destruction can occur in the middle of the carrier.

9.1.3. Electrode reactions and transport phenomena

When an electric current is to pass through the system, processes that facilitate its passage must occur on the electrodes. Electrode reactions, characterized by an immediate exchange of charged particles between the electrode and the solution, are involved. On the cathode, substances are reduced to a lower oxidation state. The reduced form remains in the solution or separates on the electrode, forming a gaseous or metal phase. Simultaneous with the reduction process on the cathode, oxidation processes proceed on the anode. Particles are oxidized to a higher soluble oxidation state or electrode material is oxidized, giving rise to soluble ions or complexes. The changes that take place on the electrodes and in the solution in which the electrodes are immersed are generally called electrolysis. Quantitatively, the conditions during electrolysis can be characterized by Faraday's law on the equivalence of the substance yield of the electrode reaction and the charge passed: the amount of substance m transformed by electrolysis is proportional to the charge passed, $Q = It$. Thus,

$$m = AQ = MIt \cdot (zF)^{-1} \tag{9.38}$$

The proportionality constant A is the so-called electrochemical equivalent, expressed by $A = M \cdot (zF)^{-1}$; M is the molar mass of the separated substance.

As a result of electrode reactions, concentration gradients originate near the electrodes, and cause diffusion and migration flows. If these flows are not eliminated, concentration gradients may increase to such an extent that the composition of the electrolytic system in the separation column is affected.

9.1.4. Mathematical description of the electrophoretic process

During an electrophoretic separation, individual components participate in dissociation and phase equilibria, in addition to transport processes. The behavior of the i, z th component is thus characterized either by the continuity equation (eqn. 9.1) or by an equation for the respective equilibria. In order to compare them with equations characterizing the chromatographic separation, these equations are sometimes combined, although this makes the calculations more difficult.

A detailed mathematical description of all electrophoretic techniques is beyond the scope of this chapter. Such information may be found in Chap. 1 of ref. 9 or in the textbooks listed in refs. 16–36.

9.2. CLASSIFICATION OF ELECTROMIGRATION METHODS

Electrophoretic separation techniques now form an integral part of protein chemistry and chromatography. However, the early advances in electrophoresis (kataphoresis, ionophoresis) were in connection with low-molecular-weight substances and colloids. The great importance of electrophoresis for protein chemistry was demonstrated by the pioneer work of Arne Tiselius. His moving-boundary equipment was described in detail in 1937 [37]. Tiselius himself was convinced of the general analytical applicability of electrophoresis, but it seem that soon after the extreme usefulness of electrophoresis in protein research was established its much wider applicability was lost sight of.

As discussed in Chap. 9.1.1, ionic species migrate under the influence of an applied electric field, and differences in effective mobilities cause differences in velocities. By utilizing this effect the ionic species can be separated. Separation techniques based on this principle (electrophoretic techniques) can be divided into three main types: zone electrophoresis, moving-boundary electrophoresis (MBE), and isotachophoresis. In isoelectric focusing, ionic species (ampholytes) are separated according to differences in pI values rather than differences in effective mobilities. Because the ionic species migrate until they attain a steady state, isoelectric focusing may also be regarded as an electrophoretic technique. Hence, four main types of electrophoresis may be distinguished.

In principle, all of these electrophoretic techniques can be carried out in any type of electrophoretic equipment. Such equipment generally consists of at least of five units: the anode and cathode compartments, the separation chamber, the injection

List of symbols on p. A365

system, and the detection devices (detectors used during the separation process or staining procedures used afterwards).

9.2.1. Zone electrophoresis

In zone electrophoresis experiments the separation column and electrode compartments are filled with a single electrolyte having a specific conductivity κ. The mixture of substances to be separated is applied at a certain location in the separation column. The width of the starting zone is much less than the length of the separation column. After application of an electric field to the system, individual substances migrate according to their effective mobilities towards the electrodes and form zones. For a velocity $\vec{v}_{c_i}$ of the ith substance at a concentration c_i, eqn. 9.39 is obtained by solving the continuity equation (eqn. 9.1) for all z components of the ith substance and by using the definition of the effective mobility (eqn. 9.16)

$$\left\{\frac{\partial x}{\partial t}\right\}_{c_i} = \vec{v}_{c_i} = \frac{\text{sgn}\, z \cdot (U_i)_{\text{eff}} \cdot E}{1 + \dfrac{\partial \Gamma_i^*}{\partial c_i}} = \frac{\text{sgn}\, z \cdot (U_i)_{\text{eff}} \cdot \dfrac{j}{\kappa}}{1 + \dfrac{\partial \Gamma_i^*}{\partial c_i}} \tag{9.39}$$

The shapes of individual zones are influenced both by the distribution of the potential gradient and by the shapes of the adsorption isotherms (this holds for separations on carriers). In zone electrophoresis, the distribution of the potential gradient can have two characteristic courses:

(a) The specific conductivity of the basic electrolyte is such that it is not influenced by the presence of the substance to be separated. The potential gradient will then be constant along the whole column. This is the most common type of zone electrophoresis.

(b) The specific conductivity of the solution at a location in the zone κ_c differs from that of the basic electrolyte. Two possibilities are: $\kappa_c > \kappa$ [usually if $(U_i)_{\text{eff}} > (U_{el})_{\text{eff}}$] and $\kappa_c < \kappa$ [usually if $(U_i)_{\text{eff}} < (U_{el})_{\text{eff}}$]. In the former instance the potential gradient is higher at the site of the zone than outside of it. This results in a situation where the rear boundary of the zone becomes sharper (ions that had been delayed enter a region of a higher potential gradient and catch up), whereas the front boundary becomes extended (ions that had outrun the zone move to a region of higher potential gradient and are even further removed). If $\kappa_c < \kappa$, the opposite situation occurs (the front boundary will become sharper and the rear boundary will trail).

Similar to the distribution of the potential, the participation of the ith substance in adsorption equilibria also influences the shape of the zones. A linear adsorption isotherm ($\partial^2 \Gamma_i / \partial c_i^2 = 0$), like a constant potential gradient, does not deform the zone, which will remain symmetrical throughout the entire migration. The same "spreading" of both boundaries of symmetrical zones is caused both by participation of z, i components of the ith substance in ionic equilibria and by diffusion. An adsorption isotherm concave with respect to the concentration axis ($\partial^2 \Gamma_i / \partial c_i^2 < 0$,

References on p. A367

TABLE 9.1

CHARACTERISTICS OF ZONE ELECTROPHORESIS

	Shape of zone		
	Symmetrical	Sharp front boundary	Sharp rear boundary
Cause of zone shape	$\kappa_c = \kappa$ and $$\frac{\partial^2 \Gamma_i}{\partial c_i^2} = 0$$ Ionic equilibria and diffusion	$\kappa_c < \kappa$ or $$\frac{\partial^2 \Gamma_i}{\partial c_i^2} < 0$$	$\kappa_c > \kappa$ or $$\frac{\partial^2 \Gamma_i}{\partial c_i^2} > 0$$
Maximal concentration in the zone	Decreases continuously during separation		
Zone width	Increases continuously during separation		

e.g., Langmuir's isotherm), will cause a sharpening of the front boundary, whereas an adsorption isotherm convex to the concentration axis ($\partial^2 \Gamma_i / \partial c_i^2 > 0$) will cause a sharpening of the rear boundary of the zone.

The time course of separation is also important. In symmetrical zones, the interzonal distances (determined on the basis of the position of maximal concentration in the zones) increase. However, the width of the zone increases with increasing time (the zone spreads) and the maximal concentration of a substance in the zone decreases. With dilute samples, a large portion of the sample will move to places where the concentration falls below the limit of the detection and the amount of sample will show on apparent decrease. Widening of asymmetric zones is even more pronounced, with the result that certain zones are incompletely separated. The characteristics of individual zones are presented in Table 9.1. Thus, zone electrophoresis is analogous to elution chromatography.

9.2.2. The moving-boundary method

The moving-boundary method resembles zone electrophoresis. It may be characterized by the following parameters. The separation column is divided into three compartments. Both side compartments are filled with the same electrolyte and the middle part contains, in addition to the same electrolyte, the mixture of substances to be separated. The length of the middle compartment is usually comparable to the length of the side compartments and, as a result, the mixture cannot be separated into individual zones. As the starting zone moves, only a gradual disengagement of substances from the front boundary occurs. The fastest moving substance is followed by a mixture of the two most mobile substances, then a mixture of the three most mobile substances, and so on. A converse arrangement of the slowest moving substances also occurs (see Fig. 1.1).

The solution of the equations for electrophoretic transport in the moving-boundary

List of symbols on p. A365

method leads to a general equation for the regulating function (also known as the Kohlrausch function) for each location in the separation column

$$\sum_i \sum_z \frac{|z| \cdot c_{i,z}}{U_{i,z}} = \text{constant} \tag{9.40}$$

which allows concentration profiles of individual substances in relation to time and positional coordinates to be drawn. The shape of the boundary is influenced by, among other factors, diffusion and convection flows. In addition, flows brought about by the radial temperature gradient will occur when electrolytes of higher ionic strength are used. The moving-boundary method is analogous to the frontal chromatographic method (Chap. 1.1). This analogy is particularly evident in arrangements of the electrophoretic experiment where only front or only rear boundaries are detected. MBE is not a separation method, but for a theoretical evaluation of isotachophoresis it is indispensible.

9.2.3. Isotachophoresis

A characteristic feature of isotachophoresis is that it cannot be used to separate simultaneously substances that carry both positive and negative charges. The separation of anions will be described here (analogous conditions are used for the separation of cations). The separation compartment is divided into three unequal parts. One part of the anode compartment and the separation column is filled with the leading electrolyte. A second part is formed by a compartment into which the mixture of substances to be separated is introduced. The third part represents the compartment filled with a terminating electrolyte (the cathode compartment, in this instance). The leading electrolyte contains anions with an effective mobility higher than that of any of the anions in the sample mixture (and cations, having a buffering capacity that can be utilized). The terminating electrolyte contains an anion with an effective mobility lower than that of any anion in the sample mixture. The cations of the terminating electrolyte are not important for the separation. On application of an electric field, migration proceeds until a steady state is established. This steady state is characterized by the fact that individual substances are separated, according to their effective mobilities, into independent, sharp, yet close zones. The so-called separated boundaries are located between the zones and a separated substance is located at only one side of the boundary. The steady state, during which all substances (zones, zone boundaries) move with the same velocity (hence the name of the method) is characteristic of isotachophoresis. Prior to the establishment of the steady state, individual zones are also separated from each other. However, in addition to zones that contain only one of the sample substances (pure zones), zones with several sample substances (mixed zones) are formed.

The solution of the equations for the electrophoretic separation in the steady isotachophoretic state leads to certain important conclusions:

(a) The potential gradient in the ith zone is determined by the effective mobility of anions in this zone, as

$$v = (U_1)_{\text{eff}} \cdot E_1 = (U_2)_{\text{eff}} \cdot E_2 = (U_i)_{\text{eff}} \cdot E_i = \text{constant} \tag{9.41}$$

References on p. A367

where v is the velocity of movement of zone boundaries.

(b) The concentration of any separated anion, B, with charge z_B is determined by the concentration of the leading anion, A (with charge z_A), by the mobilities of both anions and by the mobility of a common counterion C. This relationship is expressed by means of the Kohlrausch regulating function in the form

$$c_{B,z_B} = c_{A,z_A} \cdot (U_{A,z_A} + U_{C,z_C}) \cdot U_{B,z_B} \cdot |z_A| \cdot [(U_{B,z_B} + U_{C,z_C}) \cdot U_{A,z_A} \cdot |z_B|]^{-1} \quad (9.42)$$

This feature of isotachophoresis is particularly important for dilute solutions, where the concentration corresponds to eqn. 9.42, and distinguishes it from zone electrophoresis.

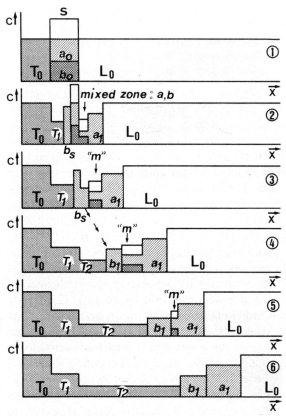

Fig. 9.1. Dynamics of isotachophoretic separation. Ordinate, c=increasing concentration; abscissa, x=position in the separatoin chamber; s=position of sample introduction. (1) The sample, a mixture of a+b (original concentrations a_0 and b_0), is introduced between the leading electrolyte L and the terminating electrolyte T (original concentrations L_0 and T_0) at s. In the end, three different regions, marking the terminator, are obtained (T_0, T_1 and T_2), in addition to the zones of the sample species separated as is shown in No. 6. (2) Zones adjusted to the concentration of the leading electrolyte (L_0), a_1 and mixed zone of a+b, and zones adjusted to the original sample concentration ($a_0 + b_0$): b_s and T_1. (3) Elongation of zones. (4) All zones in the separation compartment migrate adjusted to the leading zone L_0, a_1, "m", b_1, and T_2. (5) Further elongation of zones. (6) Steady state.

List of symbols on p. A365

The separation of two substances is illustrated schematically in Fig. 9.1. After establishment of the steady state, the distribution shows a characteristic, stepwise pattern. In isotachophoresis the self-sharpening effect of the electric field on all zone boundaries is of considerable importance. When an ion is delayed and therefore enters the succeeding zone with a higher potential gradient, its velocity will increase, and the ion will catch up until it reaches the zone of origin and enters again. On the other hand, when an ion outruns a zone, it will move to a zone with a lower potential gradient. Its velocity will therefore decrease, and the ion will be overrun by the zone of origin. The pH of a zone may play an important role [38]. Diffusion flows and flows brought about by pressure or temperature gradients counteract the self-sharpening effect. The shape of zone boundaries can also be influenced by phase equilibria. Isotachophoresis is analogous to displacement chromatography (see Chap. 1.2). Extensive mathematical treatments of isotachophoretic processes can be found in refs. 9 and 38–40.

9.2.4. Focusing methods

The methods discussed so far are based on the fact that in the substance flow every substance is characterized by a non-zero migration term, oriented in one direction throughout the entire separation. Also, the substance flow of all components in non-zero at any location in the separation column. In methods in which the substance flow of each substance decreases from a maximal positive value at one end of the separation column through a zero value to a maximal value at the other end of the column, the course and particularly the results of the separation are completely different.

A number of procedures have been described that allow this relationhsip between the substance flow and the positional coordinate to be demonstrated in practice. Two methods that differ in the way in which they bring about the required course of the substance flow, isoelectric focusing and electrorheophoresis, will be described here as examples.

9.2.4.1. Isoelectric focusing

Isoelectric focusing is used for the separation of mostly macromolecular ampholytes. The apparatus is divided into three parts: two electrode compartments and the separation column. A stable gradient of pH values, limited by minimal and maximal pH values in the anode and cathode spaces, respectively, is formed in the column. In this gradient, ampholytes with a pI intermediate between the minimal and maximal pH values can be focused. When a mixture of ampholytes, applied at an arbitrary location in the column, is subjected to an electric field, they will migrate towards either the cathode or the anode, according to their effective mobilities. The velocity of movement of all substances decreases during the separation. After a certain time, a dynamic equilibrium is established, which is characterized by the fact that each ampholyte has already moved to a position at which its effective mobility is zero, i.e., to a position where the pH is identical with the pI of a given ampholyte. Since

References on p. A367

TABLE 9.2

CHARACTERISTIC FEATURES OF BASIC ELECTROPHORETIC METHODS

Parameter	Method			
	Zone	Moving boundary	Isotachophoresis	Focusing methods
Analogous chromatographic method	Elution	Frontal	Displacement	
Simultaneous separation	Particles with charges of both signs	Basically particles with charges of both signs, but in practice particles with charges of one sign	Particles with charges of only one sign	Particles with charges of both signs
Zone composition	Zones of individual substances in the basic electrolyte	Only a zone of the fastest substance in the basic electrolyte; other zones are mixed	After establishment of the steady state, each zone contains only one separated substance	Each zone contains only a given substance
Concentration in the zone	Decreases permanently during separation	Remains constant during separation	May increase or decrease during separation; after establishment of the steady state, it is constant and is determined by a regulating function	Increases during focusing and remains constant after establishment of dynamic equilibrium
Zone boundary	One sharp and the other diffuse or both diffuse	One sharp and the other diffuse (second boundary need not occur)	All boundaries sharp	Both boundaries sharp
Zone width	Increases continuously during separation	Increases continuously during separation	Increases or decreases during separation; remains constant after establishment of the steady state	Decreases during focusing; remains constant after establishment of dynamic equilibrium
Velocity of zone movement	Different for different substances; may change during separation	Different for different substances; remains constant during separation	After establishment of the steady state, identical for all substances and constant with time	During focusing, it changes with distance (to a different extent for different substances); after establishment of dynamic equilibrium, the velocity of all separated substances is zero

certain complex substances are subject to a similar dependence of U_{eff} on pH, they are also separated.

A stable pH gradient in the column is essential for isoelectric focusing. It is usually produced as follows. The column is filled with a mixture of ampholytes, the so-called ampholyte carrier. Each of the ampholytes in this mixture must have a certain buffering capacity near its isoelectric point, as well as adequate conductivity and solubility. The mixture of ampholytes should be in such relative proportions as to cover the required pH range with its pI values. The pH gradient is first formed as a result of the different pH values in the anode compartment, the column, and the cathode compartment. As the electric current passes through the column, the substances in the ampholyte carrier, originally homogeneously distributed along the whole column, will move according to their pI values as a result of isoelectric focusing. With this distribution, the individual components of the ampholyte carrier have a buffering and stabilizing effect on the required pH gradient.

9.2.4.2. Electrorheophoresis

Because electrorheophoresis utilizes the dependence of the convection flow on the spatial coordinate, it can be used for any substance. A gradient of hydrodynamic flow of the electrolyte occurs as a result of sucking flow, caused by evaporation of the electrolyte from the surface of the stabilizing porous medium. The velocity of a substance at any location in the column or paper strip is determined by the sum of the migration velocity and the velocity of the electrolyte flow. In a given gradient of hydrodynamic flow, it is possible to focus substances having a migration velocity that is lower than the velocity of the electrolyte flow.

The formation of a stable velocity gradient, which is a necessary condition for this method, can be achieved by choosing a composition of the basic electrolyte system in which all substances have approximately the same volatility. Otherwise, volatile constituents (solvent) are preferentially evaporated, and the electrolyte concentrates in the porous carrier. The evaporation of the electrolyte from the entire surface and its replacement from the electrode spaces leads to concentration of the electrolyte in the direction of the point of zero hydrodynamic flow. The formation of a concentration gradient is also reflected in a nonuniform distribution of the potential gradient (a decrease in the middle and an increase at the sides of the porous carrier). The increase in the potential gradient at both ends of the carrier can cause an increase in migration velocity such that a substance which was focused at the beginning near one of the ends will move towards the end of the carrier and finally leave it completely.

Characteristic features of the electrophoretic methods discussed so far are listed and compared in Table 9.2.

9.2.5. Combined methods

Among the various combined methods, which have increased in importance in recent years, we will consider, as representative examples of the combination of two different methods, disc electrophoresis and immunoelectrophoresis. The combination of electrophoretic migration methods with other separation techniques, such as chromatography or gel permeation will not be discussed. Their application to proteins (Chap. 11) and peptides (Chap. 10) are examples of the great resolving power of such combiations.

9.2.5.1. Disc electrophoresis

In disc electrophoresis the experimental arrangement allows the consecutive application of isotachophoretic and zone electrophoretic principles. The separation column, packed with a suitable gel (usually polyacrylamide), consists of two parts: the stacking part and the separation part. In each of these parts, there is a different separation medium, and different electrophoretic arrangements apply. The stacking part of the column is shorter and is packed with dilute gel. Because the internal structure of this gel has virtually no effect on the mobilty of individual substances, their mobility is determined solely by the effective mobility of each substance. The separation part of the column is considerably longer and the gel density is higher. Because it was prepared by using a higher content of crosslinking agent, its internal structure does have an effect on the separation. The composition and pH of the electrolyte systems are also different in the separation and focusing parts. An appropriate choice of the electrolyte systems in the cathode and anode compartments and in the stacking and separation parts of the column can produce concentration and arrangement of individual substances in narrow, adjacent zones on the border between the dilute and dense gel by an isotachophoretic mechanism. In the separation part, the substances are segregated into zones according to the laws of zone electrophoresis in solid carriers (the sieving effect of the polyacrylamide gel occurs in this stage). After the separation is completed, substances are detected by staining. The advantage of this method is that optimal starting conditions for the zone electrophoretic separation are produced by the concentration in narrow bands, resulting from the preceding isotachophoresis step.

9.2.5.2. Immunoelectrophoresis

Immunoelectrophoresis is an electrophoretic procedure that exploits the highly sensitive and highly specific immunochemical precipitation of the antigen–antibody reaction for detection. If both parts of the complex, i.e. antigen and antibody, come into contact at optimal concentrations, characteristic precipitation lines are formed, but the complex is soluble in the excess of either antigen or antibody. The shape of the precipitation lines is also determined by the way in which both antigen and antibody come into contact. For this purpose, differences in orientation of diffusion and migration flows are exploited.

In the classical version of the method, the mixture of antigens (e.g., serum antigens) is first separated in agarose gel by the zone electrophoresis. Then, a suitable antibody (e.g., rabbit or horse polyspecific antiserum) is introduced into a channel, cut parallel to the direction of the separation in the gel plate, so that conditions for the occurrence of diffusion flows are fulfilled. Antigens diffuse radially from the locations they have reached during zone electrophoresis, while antibodies migrate laterally from the channel until they meet the antigens. After a period of time (usually a few days, because diffusion is slow), a series of radial precipitation lines form where antibodies and antigens have met.

In modifications of immunoelectrophoresis, the slow diffusion of antigens and antibodies is replaced by a much faster migrational flow. A method analogous to the original one is the so-called crossed electrophoresis. In the first stage (separation of antigens by zone electrophoresis on agarose gel), the method is identical with the classical version (a in Fig. 9.2). Then a new separation medium, another layer of agarose gel, is added to the strip of agarose gel containing the separated antigens. That layer contains, in addition to the electrolyte system, the polyspecific antiserum. The composition and pH of the electrolyte are chosen so as to make the effective mobility of antibodies zero. When an electric field is imposed on the system in a direction perpendicular to the original direction of separation, antigens will migrate into the antibody-containing medium. Again characteristic precipitation lines are formed in areas where antigens meet antibodies at optimal concentrations (b in Fig. 9.2).

The migration of antigens toward nonmigrating antibody also forms the basis of the Laurell "rocket" method, which is used in clinical biochemistry for the determination of a single antigen. In this instance an agarose gel plate is saturated with the basic electrolyte and the monospecific antibody, having an effective mobility of zero, but a narrow strip at the edge of the plate where the sample was applied is not treated. After a series of samples has been applied (usually at least three standards for calibration), the electric field is applied. While most substances in the samples pass through the agarose carrier, the antigens will form characteristic precipitation lines (see b in Fig. 9.2). The size (height) of the precipitation arcs is proportional to the antigen concentration in the sample.

A more generally applicable method is the "fused rocket" method. The basic electrolyte system that saturates the agarose gel plate — with the exception of a narrow strip at the edge where the samples are applied — also contains the polyspecific antiserum, the antibodies having an effective mobility of zero. A series of samples, obtained by chromatography, preparative electrophoresis, centrifugation, or isotachophoresis of some mixture, is applied to the plate. The precipitation lines obtained after an immunoelectrophoretic separation may be intensified by staining with dyes suitable for the particular type of substances separated. Sometimes two or more dyes are used to distinguish different species present in the sample.

Fig. 9.2 exemplifies the application of various electrophoretic techniques to serum proteins: (a) Zone electrophoresis, (b) immunoelectrophoresis, (c) isoelectric focusing.

9.3. ISOTACHOPHORESIS

This section is devoted mainly to the separation of low-molecular-weight substances in narrow-bore tubes of Teflon® (PTFE). Of course, isotachophoresis has

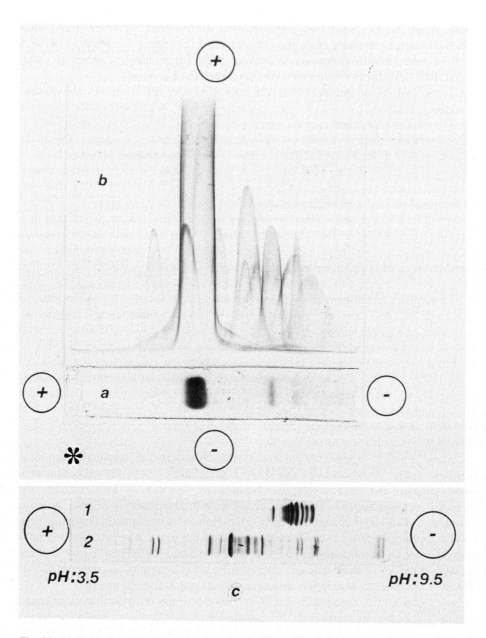

Fig. 9.2. (a) Separation of human serum proteins by zone electrophoresis on agarose gel. Stained with amido black after separation. (b) Separation of human serum proteins by zone electrophoresis, followed by immunoelectrophoresis. Staining with amido black shows the precipitated antigen–antibody complexes. (c) Separation of (1) hemoglobin and (2) L-amino acid oxidase by isoelectric focusing on polyacrylamide gel. Stained with amido black. (Reproduced by permission of LKB Produkter AB, Bromma, Sweden.)

List of symbols on p. A365

been successfully applied in the protein field, but this is covered in Chap. 11.

The characteristic features of isotachophoresis are discussed in Chap. 9.2.3. During migration in the steady state, the separated species may be detected by means of universal detectors [38] (thermocouples, thermistors, potential-gradient, conductivity, and high-frequency [41] detectors) or specific photometric detectors [38]. A combination of two detectors is always advantageous.

9.3.1. Qualitative characteristics

The basic qualitative characteristics of ionic species, separated in consecutive zones according to their effective mobilities, can be deduced from the signals of universal detectors. They are complex numerical values of their absolute mobilities, and a mathematical model can be used for a computer program to calculate their effective mobilities [38]. The calculated effective mobilities are then used to evaluate the signals obtained from universal detectors. In practice, a series of relative qualitative characteristics, in a well-defined operational system, must first be collected. These values are proportional to the effective mobilities (or proportional to values related to these effective mobilities). Commonly, the conductivity of zones (fig. 9.3) is measured as soon as they pass the sensing electrodes of the conductivity probe. Because of their step-wise character, we call these values step heights (h_i). Instead of the absolute step height, h_i, relative step heights, $(h_i)_{rel}$, are almost always used:

$$(h_i)_{rel} = (h_i - h_L)(h_s - h_L)^{-1} \tag{9.43}$$

The signals derived from specific photometric detectors can be handled analogously and transformed into photometric relative step heights, $(f_i)_{rel}$ (see Fig. 9.3) [42], according to the equation

$$(f_i)_{rel} = (f_i - f_L)(f_s - f_L)^{-1} \tag{9.44}$$

Analogous to the definition of $(h_i)_{rel}$, the values f_i, f_L, and f_s refer to signals obtained with a photometric device for zones of ionic species in the sample (i), leading ion (L), and reference species (s), passing the detector. As reference species a substance must almost always be chosen which strongly absorbs UV light, especially if the leading electrolyte shows no or only slight UV absorption. The main difference between $(h_i)_{rel}$ and $(f_i)_{rel}$ is that $(h_i)_{rel}$ is always positive, whereas $(f_i)_{rel}$ may have either a positive or a negative value; $(h_i)_{rel}$ will only have a negative value if, owing to a pH shift, an ionic species with a higher effective mobility cannot pass the ionic species in front of it, having a lower effective mobility. This is observed, e.g., when H^+ is used as a terminator (operational system for cationic separation at low pH). For the characterization of a complex mixture of UV-absorbing substances, migrating in a mixed zone (equal effective mobilities), it may be advantageous to use spectrophotometric detection [42]. Particularly when the zones are so long that the total spectrum of the substances in the mixed zone can be measured, the qualitative information will be much more reliable. Further information will be found in refs. 9 and 38.

References on p. A367

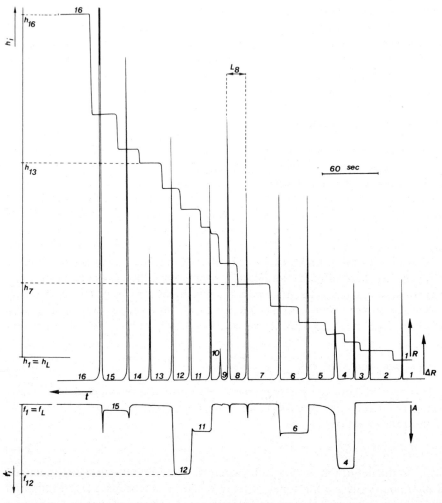

Fig. 9.3. Isotachophoretic separation of a mixture of anions in an operational system (cf. Table 9.3). Conductimetric [integral (R) and differential (ΔR) tracing] and UV absorption photometric (tracing A) detection. A = UV absorption; R = electric resistance; t = time. Qualitative information is derived by measuring step heights in R and A (h_i and f_i); quantitative information is obtained by measuring distances between peaks ΔR (e.g., L_8). Peaks: 1 = chloride; 2 = sulfate; 3 = chlorate; 4 = chromate; 5 = malonate; 6 = pyrazole-3,5-dicarboxylate; 7 = adipate; 8 = acetate; 9 = propionate; 10 = β-chloropropionate; 11 = benzoate; 12 = naphthalene-2-monosulfate; 13 = glutamate; 14 = enanthate; 15 = benzyl-DL-aspartate; 16 = morpholinoethanesulfonate.

9.3.2. Quantitative characteristics

Quantitative information relating to the sample species can be obtained when a steady state has been attained in the isotachophoretic analysis. This information is based on the measurement of the zone length (L_i). For a more precise determination

List of symbols on p. A365

of the zone length, the differential of the linear trace from the conductivity detector is generally used (Fig. 9.3). The length, L_i, can be used to calculate the real zone length, l_i, of a substance i in the separation compartment: $L_i = l_i v_r v^{-1}$, where v_r is the chart paper speed of the recorder and v is the velocity of the zones in the separation compartment for which the isotachophoretic condition (eqn. 9.41) is valid. Because the concentrations of the sample ionic species in their own zones are constant in the steady state, the following equation gives the amount of substance of this species (n_i) in the sample:

$$n_i = c_i L_i E_i (U_i)_{\text{eff}} S v_r^{-1} \tag{9.45}$$

where c_i is the concentration of the sample species (i) in the zone of i, and S is the cross-sectional area of the separation compartment in which the analysis is performed.

When the volume injected (V_0) is known, the concentration $(c_i)_0$ of a species in the injected sample may be calculated from the equation

$$(c_i)_0 = n_i (V_0)^{-1} = c_i E_i (U_i)_{\text{eff}} L_i S (V_0 v_r)^{-1} \tag{9.46}$$

The first three parameters on the right-hand side of eqn. 9.46 can be calculated; the others must be determined experimentally.

Using $f^* = (c_i)(c_L)^{-1}$, eqn. 9.45 can be written as

$$L_i = n_i v_r \kappa_L \left(I f^* (U_L)_{\text{eff}} c_L \right)^{-1} = A_{(i,L)} V_0 (c_i)_0 v_r I^{-1} \tag{9.47}$$

For reliable quantitative information, one can use either the method of absolute calibration ($A_{(i,L)}$ can be calculated or determined experimentally) or the internal standard method. In the latter, the zone length (L_i) is compared with that of a reference substance (internal standard) (L_s), which is added to the sample solution in a known concentration. For the ratio L_i/L_s, the applicable equation is

$$L_i (L_s)^{-1} = A_{(i,L)} (c_i)_0 \left[A_{(s,L)} (c_s)_0 \right]^{-1} = D_{i,s} (c_i)_0 (c_s)_0^{-1} \tag{9.48}$$

In eqn. 9.48, $D_{i,s}$ is the relative correction factor [43]. Using eqn. 9.45, the so-called calibration constant, K_{cal}, can be defined.

$$V_0 (c_i)_0 v_r (c_i L_i)^{-1} = \left[E_i (U_i)_{\text{eff}} S \right]^{-1} = w^{-1} = K_{\text{cal}} \tag{9.49}$$

K_{cal} will be constant for all sample species in a well-defined operational system, as can be seen from the isotachophoretic condition (eqn. 9.41), and because K_{cal} is equal to the reciprocal of the volume velocity of the zones (w) [38,44]. When K_{cal} is determined experimentally and c_i calculated by using eqn. 9.42 (c_L is known), one can calculate the concentration $(c_i)_0$ from the zone length (L_i) measured.

For obtaining reliable quantitative information from small zone lengths, measurement of the zone length alone is no longer reliable [42], especially if quantitative information is required for species present at levels below the detection limit. This limit is given by the amount of a species which still provides all the information required from a given detector. For instance, the information required from a conductivity detector is proportional to the effective mobility. The limits for qualitative evaluation may differ [38,45]. For the quantitative evaluation of zones below the detection limit, the determination of the relative photometric step height values [42] and the photometric "dilution" method [38,46] are especially useful.

9.3.3. Instrumentation

Isotachophoresis is a relatively recent electrophoretic separation technique, developed mainly during the last decade. Analytical isotachophoresis is generally performed in narrow-bore tubes of insulating material. Of course, the equipment developed for isotachophoresis can also be used for moving boundary electrophoresis [38] or zone electrophoresis [38] experiments. On the other hand, equipment

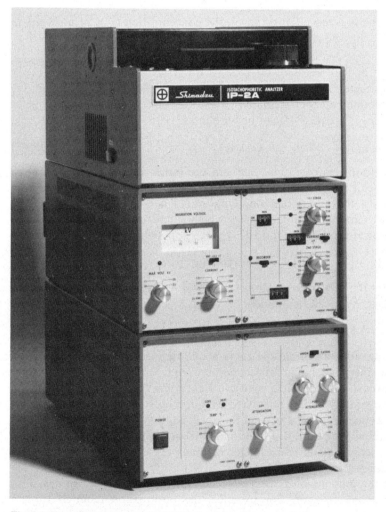

Fig. 9.4. Shimadzu (Kyoto, Japan) IP-2A Isotachophoretic Analyzer.

List of symbols on p. A365

developed for other electrophoretic techniques, in which use is made of stabilizing agents (e.g., columns filled with gels, thin layers of gels, paper, or cellulose poly-acetate) can also be used for isotachophoretic experiments.

At present, commercial equipment is produced by LKB Produkter (Bromma, Sweden) (Tachophor and the Tachofrac micropreparative unit) and Shimadzu Scientific (Columbia, MD, USA) (IP-1B and IP-2B capillary-type analyzers). The LKB apparatus includes a thermometric or a conductimetric and a photometric detector. The Shimadzu equipment includes a potentiometric and a photometric detector. Figs. 9.4 and 9.5 show the Shimadzu and LKB equipment, respectively. The conventional types of isotachophoretic equipment (Fig. 9.6) utilize mainly conducti-metric and photometric detectors [9,38] Fig. 9.6a is a block diagram of the conventional isotachophoretic equipment (without the micropreparative device), compared with equipment embodying coupled columns (Fig. 9.6b). Analytes often occur in solutions containing numerous substances at higher concentrations, requiring sample pretreatments, such as extraction, column chromatography, or salting-out procedures. The equipment described has a large load capacity and, therefore, no sample pretreatment is necessary when a column-coupling system is used. It may be combined with other separation techniques, such as CC or zone electrophoresis. Of course, different operational conditions may be provided in the preseparation and separation tube, to give optimal isotachophoretic separation.

Fig. 9.7 is a photograph of the coupled-column system. The apparatus consists essentially of three parts: (a) the preseparation compartment, (b) The bifurcation

Fig. 9.5. LKB (Bromma, Sweden) 2127 Tachophor, developed for isotachophoretic analysis.

References on p. A367

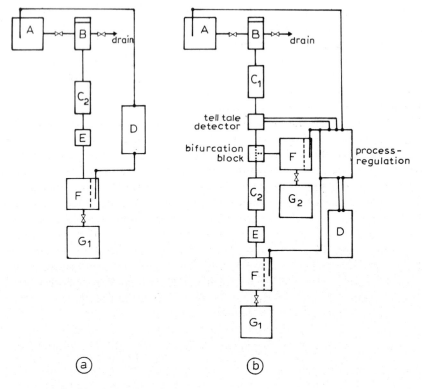

Fig. 9.6. Comparison between conventional isotachophoretic apparatus (a) and equipment with coupled columns (b). A=compartment for terminating electrolyte; B=injection block; C_1 =preseparation compartment; C_2 =separation compartment; D=current-stabilized (high-voltage) power supply; E=set of analytical detectors (conductivity or potential gradient and UV absorption); F=counter-electrode compartment with semipermeable membrane; G_1 =reservoir with leading electrolyte for the separation compartment; G_2 =reservoir with leading electrolyte for the preseparation compartment.

block with the "tell-tale" detector, and (c) the final separation compartment. Details of the construction and operation are discussed in ref. 38. The bifurcation block has three different channels: (a) a wide-bore channel (0.8 mm) in which the "tell-tale" detector is mounted and which is connected with a wide-bore PTFE preseparation tube; (b) a narrow-bore channel (0.2 mm) on which the narrow-bore PTFE separation tube is mounted and which is in line with the wide boring; (c) a flat channel (1 mm wide and 0.05 mm high), perpendicular to the borings of 0.8 mm and 0.2 mm, which forms the connection with the counterelectrode compartment, applied during the preseparation.

The dimensions of the flat channel are chosen to minimize diffusional effects and allow optimal trapping. Since the separation compartments are in line with each other, mixing of separated zones during trapping is minimal. It should be emphasized that the distance between the preseparation and separation compartment in

List of symbols on p. A365

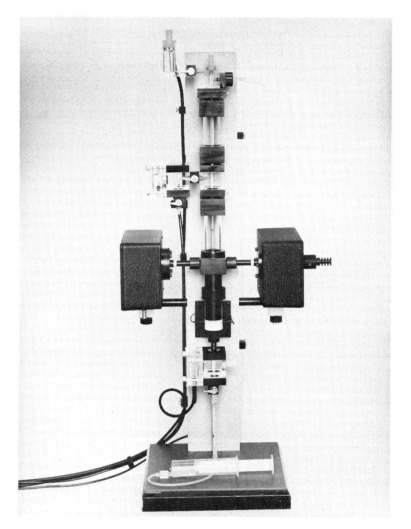

Fig. 9.7. Apparatus with coupled columns, developed by Verheggen and Mikkers, Eindhoven University of Technology, Eindhoven, The Netherlands.

the bifurcation block is only 0.05 mm. Because heat-transfer in this channel is excellent, high preseparation currents are permissible. The "tell-tale" detector monitors the preseparation. Under carefully chosen operational conditions all zones migrate with equal velocity and, therefore, the time needed for a zone boundary to cover the distance between the "tell-tale" detector and the bifurcation is constant. The delay time, t_1, is readily determined with the aid of dyes or by measuring the $d\phi(dt)^{-1}$ of the current-stabilized power supply in a leading electrolyte/terminating electrolyte experiment.

References on p. A367

Once the zones have been identified by the "tell-tale" detector, the moment at which they reach the bifurcation of the preseparation column and analytical column is known. Hence, the zones to be analyzed can easily be selected, even if they are not migrating consecutively. These zones are further analyzed and detected in the analytical column with the UV and conductivity detectors. The maximal load capacity can be increased by one order of magnitude without increasing the total analysis time. Handling of the equipment with coupled columns is fully automatic. It was compared with the conventional equipment. Straight calibration curves of injected amount versus zone length were obtained, and no loss of material attributable to the construction of the bifurcation block was detected. The equipment proved to be especially useful for the analysis of ionic material in urine and serum samples. Reproducibility was better than 2%.

9.3.4. Examples of applications

It is impossible to describe more than a few applications of analytical isotachophoresis here. To predict whether isotachophoresis as an analytical method is feasible, the ratio of molecular weight to effective charge may be used. In general, this ratio should not exceed 3000. Needless to say, the compound must have adequate solubility in the solvent chosen. Generally, ionic substances (even in complex mixtures) can be isolated quantitatively and determined at picomole levels. Under special conditions, even lower levels can be attained. By way of illustration, two applications will be reported.

9.3.4.1. Determination of valproate in serum

Sodium valproate is an anticonvulsant drug useful in primary generalized epilepsy. The determination of the anticonvulsant in serum is needed for correct treatment of epileptic patients. Optimal therapeutic serum concentrations should be around 60 μg/ml. Several GC procedures have been described, each having advantages and limitations. A disadvantage, common to all GC procedures, is the need

TABLE 9.3

CONDITIONS FOR THE SEPARATION OF URATE AND VALPROATE IN SERUM

	Leading electrolyte	Terminating electrolyte
Anion	Cl^-	MES^- *
Concentration	0.01 M	0.005 M
Counterion	EACA **	$Tris^+$
pH	5.0	6.5
Additive	0.25% HEC ***	none

   * Morpholinoethanesulfonic acid.
  ** ε-Aminocaproic acid.
*** Hydroxyethylcellulose.

List of symbols on p. A365

for pretreatment of the sample before it can be injected. The existing procedures call for solvent extraction, derivation, and evaporation. Isotachophoresis is capable of giving both qualitative and quantitative results on ionic solutes in a relatively short time. The method requires no sample pretreatment, and only minute amounts of sample are needed for an accurate determination. Valproate is such an ionic solute with a therapeutic concentration just below the millimolar range which can be determined directly by analytical isotachophoresis.

The coupled column system, developed by Everaerts et al. [47], was used at a leading ion concentration of 0.01 M with driving current of 377 μA in the preseparation compartment and 10 μA in the analytical column. The voltages varied between 1 and 15 kV. The electrolyte systems and other operational conditions are given in Table 9.3. Serum samples were injected directly, with a microliter syringe, and separated zones were detected by measuring the electrical conductance as well as the UV absorption at 254 nm. The concentration of the leading ion in the preseparation compartment was 0.01 M. At a high driving current, serum samples were separated in approximately 6 min. The swamping amount of chloride was allowed to pass the bifurcation with the analytical column. The valproate zone was trapped in the analytical column, which contained the leading ion at a concentration

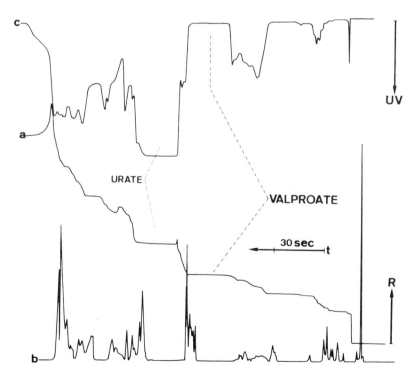

Fig. 9.8. Isotachophoretic separation of serum. UV = UV absorption at 254 nm; R = resistance; t = time. Injection: 3.0 μl of serum. Recordings: a = UV, b = differential conductimetric, c = integral conductimetric tracing.

References on p. A367

of 0.005 M. Fig. 9.8 shows a representative result on 3 µl of serum. The total time of analysis was less than 15 min. Since trapping was started two sec before the valproate zone reached the bifurcation point, some other solutes were included in the analysis. However the valproate zone can easily be located in both the UV and the conductimetric recordings (Fig. 9.8). The results in Fig. 9.8 show that uric acid could have been used as the terminating ion instead of morpholinoethanesulfonic acid. This would have resulted in a lower endvoltage and a further decrease in analysis time. For the quantitative analyses, the characteristics of the calibration line, i.e. zone length versus amount of valproic acid, were determined. A linear relation was found with a correlation coefficient of 0.99914 ($n = 26$). Reproducibility was better than 2%, and day-to-day variations were small. Other drugs did not interfere. The isotachophoretic results correlated well with the GC results.

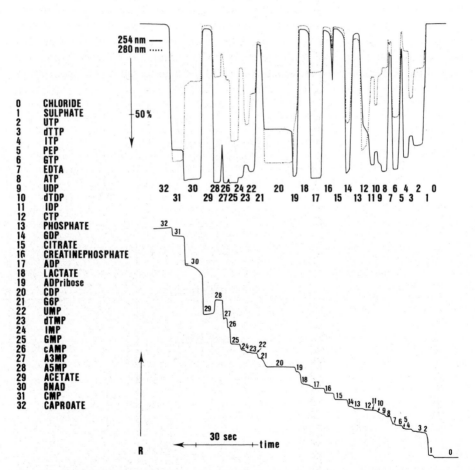

0	CHLORIDE
1	SULPHATE
2	UTP
3	dTTP
4	ITP
5	PEP
6	GTP
7	EDTA
8	ATP
9	UDP
10	dTDP
11	IDP
12	CTP
13	PHOSPHATE
14	GDP
15	CITRATE
16	CREATINEPHOSPHATE
17	ADP
18	LACTATE
19	ADPribose
20	CDP
21	G6P
22	UMP
23	dTMP
24	IMP
25	GMP
26	cAMP
27	A3MP
28	A5MP
29	ACETATE
30	BNAD
31	CMP
32	CAPROATE

Fig. 9.9. Isotachophoretic separation of nucleotides and other cell constituents. The analyses were performed under the operational conditions listed in Table 9.5. Conductimetric (bottom) and photometric (top) (at 254 and 280 nm) detectors were used.

List of symbols on p. A365

TABLE 9.4

UV ABSORBANCE RATIOS OF NUCLEOTIDES

The ratios were obtained in a PTFE (Teflon) capillary, 0.2 mm ID, under operational conditions listed in Table 9.5.

Compound	UV absorption ratios [*] 254 nm/280 nm
Uridine-MP, DP, TP	2.17, 2.52, 2.59
Desoxythymidine-MP, DP, TP	1.36, 1.40, 1.42
Inosine-MP, DP, TP	3.52, 3.88, 4.73
Adenosine-[5]MP, [3]MP, DP, TP	2.90, 2.98, 3.03, 3.23
Cytidine-MP, DP, TP	0.92, 0.77, 0.72
Guanosine-MP, DP, TP	1.34, 1.45, 1.50

[*] See also Fig. 9.3.

TABLE 9.5

OPERATIONAL CONDITIONS FOR ANIONIC SEPARATIONS AT pH 3.9

Parameter	Preseparation compartment	Separation compartment
Column diameter	0.8 mm	0.2 mm
Driving current	350 μA	20 μA
Leading constituent	0.01 M Cl$^-$	0.01 M Cl$^-$
Counter constituent	β-Alanine	β-alanine
Detection	Conductimetric	Conductimetric; UV absorption at 280 nm and 254 nm
Terminating constituent	Caproic acid	Caproic acid
Additive	0.2% HEC [*]	0.2% HEC [*]
Recorder	—	6 cm/min

[*] Hydroxyethylcellulose.

9.3.4.2. Separation of a mixture of nucleotides

Fig. 9.9 shows the separation of a mixture of nucleotides by isotachophoresis with conductimetric and photometric detection (at 254 and 280 nm). The UV-absorbance ratios are listed in Table 9.4. The operational conditions are summarized in Table 9.5.

9.3.5. Preparative isotachophoresis

Isotachoporesis has been applied both on a macro scale and on a micro scale, especially for the separation of proteins [9] (cf. Chap. 11). The isolation of proteins by isotachophoresis [48,49] has many advantages over conventional zone electro-phoresis. In zone electrophoresis, the sample must be applied in highly concentrated form in a thin, uniform zone. During electrophoresis, free diffusion will cause the band-width of the separated zones to increase, and the resolution may decrease drastically. Moreover, the sample molecules will pass through a gel matrix over a period of time that is inversely proportional to their mobility, i.e., slowly migrating molecules are eluted in considerably larger volumes than rapidly migrating molecules.

Ornstein [50] and Davies [51] introduced "steady-state stacking" as a method of concentrating the sample into a thin starting zone and, in a second step, they converted the system into conventional zone electrophoresis. When polyacrylamide gel is used as an anticonvection medium, the method is known as disc electrophoresis. Steady-state stacking and isotachophoresis are identical: the sample molecules are concentrated between a rapidly migrating ion (the leading ion), with a mobility higher than that of any of the sample molecules, and a slowly migrating ion (the terminating ion), with a mobility lower than that of any of the sample molecules. At equilibrium, the sample molecules are arranged in a series of consecutive zones in the order of decreasing mobility and in immediate contact with each other, and all migrate at the same velocity. The concentration of a constituent in a zone is constant and a function of the concentration of the leading ion and the mobilities of the leading ion, that constituent, and the counterion.

Svendsen and Rose [52] introduced the use of Ampholine carrier ampholytes as "spacers" in isotachophoresis. Ampholine is a mixture of polyamino and polycarboxylic acids, displaying a wide range of pI values and mobilities that coincide with and fall between those of, e.g., human serum proteins. When Ampholine is stacked, a smooth migrating pH gradient is formed, within which sample molecules migrate until they reach a region with a pH were they attain an actual mobility that matches the actual mobility of that region. In principle, this is very similar to isoelectric focusing, in which sample molecules are separated according to their pI or, in fact, to zero actual mobility. By employing the isotachophoretic principle for preparative purposes, the drawbacks and difficulties mentioned above are completely eliminated.

A laboratory-built apparatus [53], made of acrylic and polyvinylchloride, takes advantage of the electrode arrangement by Bergrahm [54] and Svendsen [55] and is an improvement over the LKB Uniphor preparative electrophoresis apparatus with respect to handling, versatility, and cooling. It also offers the possibility of inspecting all critical areas during an experiment. The elution system has been optimized according to the theory by Svendsen [56] by using another design of the elution stopper by Bergrahm and Harlestam [57]. More information may be found in ref. 9, Chap. 11.

In biochemistry and medicine there is increasing interest in the isolation of pure fractions from small amounts of samples. For this purpose, the analytical equipment (Fig. 9.6a) was adapted to a preparative use by introduction of the Tachofrac fraction collector. The advantage of such a system is that isotachophoresis may be combined with other separation techniques (e.g., immunoelectrophoresis) or other identification techniques (e.g., enzymatic, staining, or radiographic procedures). Detailed information may be found in ref. 9, Chap. 11.

List of symbols on p. A365

9.4. LIST OF SYMBOLS

A_r	Ionic species
$B, B_1, \ldots, B_{11}$	Constants
C	Common counterion
c	Concentration of all solutes (mole $\cdot$ m^{-3})
$C_{A_r,u}$	Concentration of ionic species A_r in zone u (mole $\cdot$ m^{-3})
c_i	Concentration of substance i (mole $\cdot$ m^{-3})
$c_{i,z}$	Concentration of substance i, z (mole $\cdot$ m^{-3})
$D, D_{i,z}$	Diffusion coefficient (m^2 $\cdot$ sec^{-1})
$D_{i,z}^*$	Thermal diffusion coefficient of component i, z (m $\cdot$ °K^{-1} $\cdot$ sec^{-1})
d	Wall thickness of the separation column, internal diameter of injector tube or initial thickness of injected streak (m)
$\vec{E}, E$	Electric field strength (V $\cdot$ m^{-1})
$\vec{E}_u$	Electric field strength in zone u (V $\cdot$ m^{-1})
e	Elemental charge (C)
F	Faradays's constant (C $\cdot$ mole^{-1})
f_i	Signal intensity (height) of the photometric recording (m)
$(f_i)_{rel}$	Relative signal intensity (height) of the photometric recording
G	Constant (including Faraday's constant)
h_i	Zone height of the ith substance on the isotachopherogram (m)
$(h_i)_{rel}$	Relative zone height of the ith substance
h_L	Zone height of the leading electrolyte (m)
h_s	Height of the standard ion species zone (m)
I	Electric current (A)
I_c	Ionic strength of the solution (mole $\cdot$ m^{-3})
I_0	Light intensity (W)
i	Unit vector
$\vec{J}_{i,z}$	Substance flow of component i, z (mole $\cdot$ m^{-2} $\cdot$ sec^{-1})
$(\vec{J}_{i,z})_{diff}$	Diffusion contribution of the substance flow of component i, z (mole $\cdot$ m^{-2} $\cdot$ sec^{-1})
$(\vec{J}_{i,z})_{mig}$	Migrational contribution of the substance flow of component i, z (mole $\cdot$ m^{-2} $\cdot$ sec^{-1})
$(\vec{J}_{i,z})_{conv}$	Convective contribution of the substance flow of component i, z (mole $\cdot$ m^{-2} $\cdot$ sec^{-1})
$(\vec{J}_{i,z})_{therm}$	Thermal contribution of the substance flow of component i, z (mole $\cdot$ m^{-2} $\cdot$ sec^{-1})
j	Current density ($A \cdot$ m^{-2})
$\vec{j}$	Unit vector
K	Apparent equilibrium constant
K_A	Dissociation constant of an acid (mole $\cdot$ dm^{-3})
K_B	Dissociation constant of a base (mole $\cdot$ dm^{-3})
k	Unit vector
k_t	Thermal conductivity of the solid phase (W $\cdot$ m^{-1} $\cdot$ °K^{-1})
L	Length of the separation column, length of the porous bed (m)

L_i	Length of the ith zone in an isotachopherogram (m)
ΔL	Length of the mixed zone on the start (m)
l	Actual pore length, actual distance migrated (m)
N_A	Avogadro's number (mole^{-1})
$n_{i,z}$	Amount of substances of component i, z (mole)
P	Surface area (m^2)
P^*	Constant
pI	Isoelectric point
pK	$-\log K$
Q	Total charge (C)
q_j	Joule's heat (J)
q_k	Heat removed (J)
q^*	Change of thermal flow in unit volume
q_j^*	Thermal flow generated by unit volume (W $\cdot$ m^{-3})
q_k^*	Thermal flow leaving unit volume (W $\cdot$ m^{-3})
R	Molar gas constant (J $\cdot$ $^\circ$K^{-1} $\cdot$ mole^{-1})
r	Radius of a spherical particle or Stokes radius (m)
r_0	Internal radius of the separation column (m)
S	Cross-section of a column or cross-section of a porous medium (m^2)
S_t	Total cross-section of a porous medium (m^2)
T	Absolute temperature ($^\circ$K)
T_0	Temperature of the external surface of the separation column ($^\circ$K)
t	Time (sec)
U	Total imposed voltage (V)
U_{A_L}	Mobility of ionic species A in the leading electrolyte (m^2 $\cdot$ sec^{-1} $\cdot$ V^{-1})
U_{col}	Actual mobility of a colloid particle (m^2 $\cdot$ sec^{-1} $\cdot$ V^{-1})
$(U_i)_{eff}$	Effective mobility of the ith substance (m^2 $\cdot$ sec^{-1} $\cdot$ V^{-1})
$U_{i,z}$	Actual mobility of the i, zth component (m^2 $\cdot$ sec^{-1} $\cdot$ V^{-1})
$(U_{i,z})^0$	Absolute (limit) mobility of the i, zth component (m^2 $\cdot$ sec^{-1} $\cdot$ V^{-1})
V	Volume (m^3)
V_0	Injected volume (m^3)
V_k	Volume of the separation compartment (m^3)
$\vec{v}, v$	Velocity (m $\cdot$ sec^{-1})
$\vec{v}_{c_i}$	Velocity of the ith substance at concentration c_i
$\vec{v}_{conv}$	Velocity of convective flow
$\vec{v}_L$	Velocity of the leading zone in isotachophoresis (m $\cdot$ sec^{-1})
$\vec{v}_{os}$	Linear velocity of the osmotic flow (m $\cdot$ sec^{-1})
v_r	chart speed (m $\cdot$ sec^{-1})
$\vec{v}_{suck}$	Velocity of the suction flow (m $\cdot$ sec^{-1})
$\vec{v}_u$	Velocity of zone u (m $\cdot$ sec^{-1})
w	Volume rate of flow of electrolytes through the chamber (m^3 $\cdot$ sec^{-1})

$\vec{w}_{os}$	(Volume) velocity of the osmotic flow ($m^3 \cdot sec^{-1}$)
$y_{i,z}$	Molar fraction of component i, z in the ith substance
$|z|$	Number of elementary charges of the component; the sign of z determines the polarity of the ion

sgn z	Polarity determination: sgn $z = 1$ for $z > 0$
	                             sgn $z = 0$ for $z = 0$
	                             sgn $z = -1$ for $z < 0$

$\alpha_{|z|}$	Degree of dissociation
Γ_i	Adsorption isotherm of the ith substance
$\Gamma_{i,z}$	Adsorption isotherm of the i, zth component
$(\Gamma_{i,z})_{max}$	Maximum amount of the i, zth component bound to the surface of solid phase of the unit mass
Γ_i^*	Distribution function of the ith substance
γ	Tortuosity factor
δ	Effective width of the double layer (m)
ϵ	Permittivity of the medium ($S \cdot m^{-1}$)
$\bar{\epsilon}$	Porosity
ζ	Electrokinetic potential
η	Coefficient of viscosity
κ	Specific conductivity of the solution ($S \cdot m^{-1}$)
κ_c	Specific conductivity of the solution in the zone area ($S \cdot m^{-1}$)
Λ	Molar conductivity of the solution ($S \cdot m^2 \cdot mole^{-1}$)
$\lambda_{i,z}$	Ionic conductivity of the i, zth components ($S \cdot m^2 \cdot mole^{-1}$)
$\mu_{i,z}$	Chemical potential of the i, zth component ($J \cdot mole^{-1}$)
$\mu_{i,z}^0$	Standard chemical potential of the i, zth component ($J \cdot mole^{-1}$)
Π	Symbol for multiplication
ρ_s	Density of the solution ($k \cdot m^{-3}$)
Σ	Symbol for summation
σ	Surface charge density on the surface of the phase ($C \cdot m^{-2}$)
τ	Temperature (°K)
ϕ	Potential (V)

REFERENCES

1 B.E. Conway, *Electrochemical Data*, Elsevier, Amsterdam, 1952.
2 J. D'Ans and E. Lax, *Taschenbuch für Chemiker und Physiker*, Springer, Berlin, 1964–1970.
3 N.A. Lange and G.M. Forker, *Handbook of Chemistry*, McGraw-Hill, New York, 1967.
4 R. Parson, *Handbook of Electrochemical Data*, Butterworths, London, 1959.
5 D.D. Perrin, *Dissociation Constants of Organic Bases in Aqueous Solution*, Suppl., Butterworths, London, 1972.
6 M.H. Rauen, *Biochemisches Taschenbuch*, Springer, Berlin, 1967.
7 N. Onsager and R.M. Fuoss, *J. Phys. Chem.*, 36 (1932) 2689.
8 A. Tiselius, *Nova Acta Regiae Soc. Sci. Ups., Ser. 4*, 4 (1930) 7.
9 Z. Deyl (Editor), *Electrophoresis, Part A: Techniques*, J. Chromatogr. Library Series Vol. 18, Elsevier, Amsterdam, 1979.
10 H.G. Kunkel and A. Tiselius, *J. Gen. Physiol.*, 35 (1951) 89.

11 J. Vaćik and J. Cabicar, *Collect. Czech. Chem. Commun.*, 25 (1960) 404.
12 J. Vacík, O. Grubner and J. Dvořák, *Collect. Czech. Chem. Commun.*, 25 (1960) 625.
13 H.G. Kunkel and R. Trauman, in M. Bur (Editor), *Electrophoresis*, Academic Press, New York, 1959, p. 225.
14 N. Striet, *Aust. J. Chem.*, (1958) 607.
15 M.R.I. Wyllic and A.R. Gregory, *Ind. Eng. Chem.*, 47 (1955) 1379.
16 N.K. Adam, *Physical Chemistry*, Oxford University Press, London, 1956.
17 G.M. Barrow, *Physical Chemistry*, McGraw-Hill, New York, 1973.
18 R.B. Bird, W.E. Steward and N.E. Lightfoot, *Transport Phenomena*, McGraw-Hill, New York, 1963.
19 R. Bridčka, *Grundlagen der physikalischen Chemie*, VEB Deutscher Verlag der Wissenschaften, Berlin, 1967.
20 R. Brdička and J. Dvořák, *Základy Fysikálni Chemie*, Academia, Prague, 1977.
21 G.W. Castellan, *Physical Chemistry*, Addison-Wesley, Reading, 1971.
22 J. Dvořák, J. Koryta and V. Boháčková, *Elektrochemie*, Academia, Prague, 1975.
23 J. Eggert, L. Hock and G.M. Schwab, *Lehrbuch der Physikalischen Chemie*, Hirzel, Stuttgart, 1968.
24 T. Erdey-Grúz, *Transport Phenomena in Aqueous Solutions*, Akadémiai Kiadó, Budapest, 1974.
25 A. Eucken, *Lehrbuch der Physikalischen Chemie*, Akademische Verlagsges., Leipzig, 1949.
26 H. Eyring, D. Henderson and W. Jost, *Physical Chemistry, An Advanced Treatise*, Academic Press, New York, 1967–1975.
27 H. Falkenhagen, *Elektrolyte*, Hirzel, Leipzig, 1953.
28 H.S. Harned and B.B.Owen, *The Physical Chemistry of Electrolyte Solutions*, Reinhold, New York, 1950.
29 D.A. McInnes, *The Principles of Electrochemistry*, Dover, New York, 1961.
30 K. Jellinek, *Lehrbuch der Physikalischen Chemie*, Enke, Stuttgart, 1928–1937.
31 G. Kortüm and J. O'M. Bockris, *Textbook of Electrochemistry*, Elsevier, Amsterdam, 1951.
32 W.J. Moore, *Physical Chemistry*, Prentice-Hall, Englewood Cliffs, NJ, 1972.
33 J.R. Partington, *An Advanced Treatise of Physical Chemistry*, Longmans Green, London, 1949–1954.
34 L. Pauling, *General Chemistry*, Freeman, San Francisco, CA, 1970.
35 R.A. Robinson and R.H. Stokes, *Electrolyte Solutions*, Butterworths, London, 1970.
36 K. Schwabe, *Physikalische Chemie*, Akademie-Verlag, Berlin, 1973–1974.
37 A. Tiselius, *Trans. Faraday Soc.*, 33 (1937) 524.
38 F.M. Everaerts, J.L. Beckers and Th.P.E.M. Verheggen, *Isotachophoresis*, J. Chromatogr. Library Series, Vol. 6, Elsevier, Amsterdam, 1976.
39 F.E.P. Mikkers, F.M. Everaerts and J.A.F. Peek, *J. Chromatogr.*, 168 (1979) 293.
40 F.E.P. Mikkers, F.M. Everaerts and J.A.F. Peek, *J. Chromatogr.*, 168 (1979) 317.
41 B. Gaš, M. Demjanĕnko and J. Vacík, *J. Chromatogr.*, 192 (1980) 253.
42 M. Svoboda and J. Vacík, *J. Chromatogr.*, 119 (1976) 539.
43 P. Boček, M. Deml and J. Janák, *J. Chromatogr.*, 91 (1974) 829.
44 J.L. Beckers, *Thesis*, Eindhoven University of Technology, Eindhoven, 1973.
45 L. Arlinger, *J. Chromatogr.*, 91 (1974) 785.
46 J.P.M. Wielders and F.M. Everaerts, in B.J. Radola and D. Graesslin (Editors), *Electrofocusing and Isotachophoresis*, De Gruyter, Berlin, New York, 1977, p. 527.
47 F.M. Everaerts, T.P.E.M. Verheggen ad F.E.P. Mikkers, *J. Chromatogr.*, 164 (1979) 21.
48 R. Routs, *Thesis*, Technical University of Eindhoven, Eindhoven, 1971.
49 T.M. Jovin, *Biochemistry*, 12 (1973) 871, 879, 890.
50 L. Ornstein, *Ann. N.Y. Acad. Sci.*, 121 (1964) 321.
51 B.J. Davies, *Ann. N.Y. Acad. Sci.*, 121 (1964) 404.
52 P.J. Svendsen and C. Rose, *Sci. Tools*, 17 (1970) 13.
53 P.J. Svendsen, unpublished work, 1970.
54 B. Bergrahm, *Sci. Tools*, 14 (1967) 34.
55 P.J. Svendsen, *Anal. Biochem.*, 25 (1968) 236.
56 P.J. Svendsen, *Sci. Tools*, 19 (1972) 21.
57 B. Bergrahm and R. Harlestam, *Sci. Tools*, 15 (1968) 26.

Subject Index

Page numbers referring to analyses of compounds are printed in italics.

A

Abate, *B446*
Abiatane, *B157*
Abscisic acid, *B156, B157*
Acebutolol, *B318, B319*
Acetaminophen, *B299, B315*
Acetanisidine, *B315*
Acetate, *B471*
Acetylene, *B496*
Acetylneuraminic acid, *see* Sialic acid
ACTH, *B21*
Actinides, *A245, A248*
Actinium, *A246, B474, B476*
Actinomycins, *B338*
Activity coefficients,
    A54, A55, A58–60, A65, A67, A68
Acylglycerols, neutral, *B111–118*
  argentation chromatography of, *B111–113*
  GLC of, *B113–117*
  HPLC of, *B117, B118*
  isolation of, *B80–87*
Adsorption, A60, A61, A63, A65, A66
Adsorption chromatography, A75–78
Aerogel, A260
Aesculin, *B423*
Affinity chromatography, A8, A320, A321
  of carbohydrates, B245–247
  of proteins, B57, B58
  of RNA, B356, B357
Agarose gels, A260, A263–265
Alanine, *B3, B6, B7, B9, B26, B27, B30, B32*
Aldadiene, *B206*
Aldosterone, *B206, B207*
Aldrin, *B440, B446, B447*
Alkali metals, *A273, A275*
Alkaline earths, *A248*
Alkaloids, steroidal, *B198, B199*
Alkyllead, *B501*
Allose, *B261*
Alprenolol, *B299, B306, B307*
Altrose, *B261*
Aluminum, *A246, B466*
Ametryn, *B438, B439*
Amides, *A268*
Amikacin, *B334*

Amino acid analyzers, B2
Amino acids, *B1–52*
  acyl esters, *B28–31*
  dansyl derivatives, *B11*
  DNP derivatives, *B11, B13*
  enantiomers of, *B13–16*
  fluorescamine derivatives of, *B11, B13*
  GC of, *B21–33*
  HPLC of, *A88, A89, B4–21*
  in biological samples, *B36–38*
  ion-exchange chromatography of, *B2–4*
  ligand-exchange resolution of, *A251, A252*
  MS of, *B35–38*
  MTH derivatives of, *B10*
  OPA derivatives of, *B3, B6, B7, B11*
  PTH derivatives of, *B6, B10–13*
  TMS derivatives of, *B24–28*
Aminobutyric acid, *B3, B26, B30*
Aminocarb, *B437*
Aminocyclitols, *B333, B334*
Aminoisobutyric acid, *B3, B26, B30*
Aminonitrazepam, *B302*
Aminopterin, *B309*
Amino sugars, *B227, B237, B238, B244, B251, B254–256, B258, B261–263, B266–268, B271, B273*
Amitriptyline, *B293, B294, B301, B314*
Ammonia, *B492, B498, B501*
Amorphene, *B155*
Amphetamines, *B317, B318*
Ampholine, *A364*
Amphotericins, *B337, B338*
Ampicillin, *B336*
Amylopectins, *B276*
ANB, *B296*
Androstadienedione, *B203*
Androstane derivatives, *B202–204*
Androstanedione, *B202, B203*
Androstenedione, *B203, B204*
Androstenol, *B203*
Androsterone, *B202–204*
Angiotensin, *B20, B21*
Anions, *A243, A274, A276*
Anorexicants, *B318*
Antazoline, *B311*

ELECTROPHORESIS

A Survey of Techniques and Applications

edited by Z. DEYL, Czechoslovak Academy of Sciences, Prague

JOURNAL OF CHROMATOGRAPHY LIBRARY, 18

PART A: TECHNIQUES

Z. DEYL *(editor)*

F. M. EVERAERTS, Z. PRUSÍK *and*
P. J. SVENDSEN *(co-editors)*

"... provides a sound, state-of-the-art survey of its subject".
— Chemistry in Britain

"... the editors have set out to bring everything together into a coherent whole... they have succeeded remarkably well... the book is bound to be well liked and appreciated by readers".
— Journal of Chromatography

This first part deals with the principles, theory and instrumentation of modern electromigration methods. Both standard procedures and newer developments are discussed and hints are included to help the reader overcome difficulties frequently arising from the lack of suitable equipment. Adequate theoretical background of the individual techniques is given and a theoretical approach to the deteriorative processes is presented to facilitate further development of a particular technique and its application to a special problem. In each chapter practical realisations of different techniques are described and examples are presented to demonstrate the limits of each method.

CONTENTS:
Introduction. Chapters: 1. Theory of electro-migration processes *(J. Vacík)*. 2. Classification of electromigration methods *(J. Vacík)*. 3. Evaluation of the results of electrophoretic separations *(J. Vacík)*. 4. Molecular size and shape in electrophoresis *(Z. Deyl)*. 5. Zone electrophoresis (except gel-type techniques and immunoelectrophoresis) *(W. Ostrowski)*. 6. Gel-type techniques *(Z. Hrkal)*. 7. Quantitative immunoelectrophoresis *(P.J. Svendsen)*. 8. Moving boundary electrophoresis in narrow-bore tubes *(F.M. Everaerts and J.L. Beckers)*. 9. Isoelectric focusing *(N. Catsimpoolas)*. 10. Analytical isotachophoresis *(J. Vacík and F.M. Everaerts)*. 11. Continuous flow-through electrophoresis *(Z. Prusík)*. 12. Continuous flow deviation electrophoresis *(A. Kolin)*. 13. Preparative electrophoresis in gel media *(Z. Hrkal)*. 14. Preparative electrophoresis in columns *(P.J. Svendsen)*. 15. Preparative isoelectric focusing *(P. Blanický)*. 16. Preparative isotacho-phoresis *(P.J. Svendsen)*. 17. Preparative isotacho-phoresis on the micro scale *(L. Arlinger)*. List of frequently occurring symbols. Subject Index.

1979   xvi + 390 pp.   US $72.25/Dfl. 170.00
ISBN 0-444-41721-4

PART B: APPLICATIONS

Z. DEYL *(editor)*

A. CHRAMBACH, F.M. EVERAERTS *and*
Z. PRUSÍK *(co-editors)*

Part B is an exhaustive survey of the present status of the application of electrophoretic techniques to many diverse compounds. Those categories of compounds most suited to these separations, such as proteins and peptides, are dealt with in detail, while the perspectives of the applications of these techniques to other categories of compounds less commonly electrophoresed are given. Special attention is paid to naturally occurring mixtures of compounds and their treatment. This is the first attempt to cover the field on such a broad scale and the book will be valuable to separation chemists, pharma-cologists, organic chemists and those involved in biomedical research.

CONTENTS: 1. Alcohols and phenolic compounds *(Z. Deyl)*. 2. Aldehydes and ketones *(Z. Deyl)*. 3. Carbohydrates *(Z. Deyl)*. 4. Carboxylic acids *(F.M. Everaerts)*. 5. Steroids and steroid conjugates *(Z. Deyl)*. 6. Amines *(Z. Deyl)*. 7. Amino acids and their derivatives *(Z. Deyl)*. 8. Peptides and structural analysis of proteins *(Z. Prusík)*. 9. Gel electro-phoresis and electrofocusing of proteins *(edited by A. Chrambach)*. Usefulness of second-generation gel electrophoretic tools in protein fractionation *(A. Chrambach)*. Membrane proteins, native *(L.M. Hjelmeland)*. Membrane proteins, denatured *(H. Baumann, D. Doyle)*. Protein membrane receptors *(U. Lang)*. Steroid receptors *(S. Ben-Or)*. Cell surface antigens *(R.A. Reisfeld, M.A. Pellegrino)*. Lysosomal glycosidases and sulphatases *(A.L. Fluharty)*. Heamocyanins *(M. Brenowitz et al.)*. Human haemoglobins *(A.B. Schneider, A.N. Schechter)*. Isoelectric focusing of immuno-globulins *(M.H. Freedman)*. Contractile and cytoskeletal proteins *(P. Rubenstein)*. Proteins of connective tissue *(Z. Deyl, M. Horáková)*. Micro-tubular proteins *(K.F. Sullivan, L. Wilson)*. Protein hormones *(A.D. Rogol)*. Electrophoresis of plasma proteins: a contemporary clinical approach *(M. Engliš)*. Allergens *(H. Baer, M.C. Anderson)*. 10. Glycoproteins and glycopeptides (affinity electrophoresis) *(T.C. Bøg-Hansen, J. Hau,)*. 11. Lipoproteins *(H. Peeters)*. 12. Lipopoly-saccharides *(P.F. Coleman, O. Gabriel)*. 13. Electro-phoretic examination of enzymes *(W. Ostrowski)*. 14. Nucleotides, nucleosides, nitrogenous constituents of nucleic acids *(S. Zadražil)*. 15. Nucleic acids *(S. Zadražil)*. 16. Alkaloids *(Z. Deyl)*. 17. Vitamins *(Z. Deyl)*. 18. Antibiotics *(V. Betina)*. 19. Dyes and pigments *(Z. Deyl)*. 20. Inorganic compounds *(F.M. Everaerts, Th. P.E.M. Verheggen)*. Contents of "Electrophoresis, Part A: Techniques". Subject Index. Index of compounds separated.

1982   xiii + 462 pp.   US $104.75/Dfl. 225.00
ISBN 0-444-42114-9

ELSEVIER
P.O. Box 211, Amsterdam
The Netherlands
52 Vanderbilt Avenue
New York, NY 10017, U.S.A.

7255